G000141087

PERGAMON SERIES OF MONOGRAPHS IN

FURNITURE AND TIMBER

GENERAL EDITOR: JACK KAPE, A.R.C.A., A.T.D., F.S.A.E.

VOLUME 11

METHOD STUDY AND THE FURNITURE INDUSTRY

PERGAMON SERIES OF MONOGRAPHS IN

FURNITURE AND TIMBER

Volume 1. BROWN—*An Introduction to the Seasoning of Timber*
Volume 2. PARKER—*Costing in the Furniture Industry*
Volume 3. CLARK—*Veneering and Wood Bending in the Furniture Industry*
Volume 4. AKERS—*Particle Board and Hardboard*
Volume 5. FINDLAY—*Timber Pests and Diseases*
Volume 6. COLLIER—*Woodfinishing*
Volume 7. OLIVER—*The Development and Structure of the Furniture Industry*
Volume 8. SILVESTER—*Mechanical Properties of Timber*
Volume 9. FARMER—*Chemistry in the Utilization of Wood*
Volume 10. ANDREWS—*An Introduction to Timber Engineering*

Method Study and the Furniture Industry

R. H. GLOSSOP

Principal Lecturer and Deputy Head of the Department of Management and Social Science, High Wycombe College of Technology and Art

PERGAMON PRESS

Oxford · New York · Toronto · Sydney · Braunschweig

Pergamon Press Ltd., Headington Hill Hall, Oxford
Pergamon Press Inc., Maxwell House, Fairview Park, Elmsford, New York 10523
Pergamon of Canada Ltd., 207 Queen's Quay West, Toronto 1
Pergamon Press (Aust.) Pty. Ltd., 19a Boundary Street, Rushcutters Bay, N.S.W. 2011, Australia
Vieweg & Sohn GmbH, Burgplatz 1, Braunschweig

First edition 1970

Library of Congress Catalog Card No. 75–112711

PRINTED IN GREAT BRITAIN BY A. WHEATON AND CO., EXETER

08 015653 3

Contents

List of Illustrations

Preface

METHOD study constitutes a procedure for the analysis of present or proposed methods of doing work in order to effect improvements. The techniques, which comprise this important division of work study, have been used by business and industry for many years as a means of providing solutions to production problems, whether they are of the office or the factory. The tools of method study were not developed by any one individual, but have been evolved over many years by the contributions of individuals who developed and applied these tools with their own particular problems in mind. The method study approach has produced remarkable results. It has been a means of satisfying the desire of management for cost reduction and for the introduction of more efficient methods of production.

The purpose of this volume is to provide the student with an introduction to this subject with a hope that its contents, based upon the author's experience of teaching and practical application of the subject over the past 20 years, will prove of assistance to those who wish to become more familiar with this procedure. It has not been the intention to present a detailed and comprehensive treatment of the subject as this would not be appropriate having regard to the limits of space and the fact that information about the various facets of the subject is easily available elsewhere in a more comprehensive and detailed form. Thus this volume is primarily concerned with the presentation of an overall explanation of the procedure and its techniques, as used by the furniture industry, and the conduct of investigations in the various areas of application. In order that the information presented may be supplemented by further reading, selected and authoritative references are given at the end of each chapter.

It should be realized that there are variations in the individual techniques and their application in different industries, both in Europe, Scandinavia, and the United States of America. These should not be too hurriedly disregarded. Attempts have been made to review these aspects in such a manner that a reasonable survey is provided of industrial practice. An attempt has also been made to adhere to accepted standard terminology where possible.

If I have anywhere followed the words of the pioneers of this subject more closely than is proper without using quotation marks I have done so inadvertently and ask pardon.

It should be remembered that a student cannot be expected to apply these techniques merely by studying this book. Method study, being a practical management tool, can only be learnt by practical application and exposure to problems under the guidance of experienced instructors. However, the principles underlying the procedure are comparatively simple and once they are properly understood, practice can be adapted to suit circumstances. It is essential however that the principles should first be mastered and thoroughly understood before they are adapted to suit the purpose of the individual investigation.

It is desirable that students of method study, as part of their training should become acquainted with simple statistical concepts at an early stage, as little can be achieved in activity sampling, for instance, or simple experimental methods until an understanding of these basic principles has been obtained. It has often been found appropriate to achieve this understanding, by a non-mathematical approach to the subject, such as is obtained by the use of statistical experimental kits either of the proprietary type developed by the College of Aeronautics, Cranfield, Bedfordshire, England, or those made by many instructors themselves. This kind of equipment allows experiments to be carried out on a wide range of statistical ideas and theory in a practical manner, a laboratory notebook* being kept by each student in the course of these experiments which contains not only the laboratory record sheets but also the instructions for carrying out each of the investigations.

The furniture industry has developed the method study techniques along lines that were appropriate for the tasks that it required them to perform. The product cost characteristics of the industry has contributed to this development and has also led to its greater preoccupation with method study rather than work measurement.

It is hoped that although it is written primarily for the furniture industry it may be of interest to method study trainees in other industries.

* Murdoch, J. and Barnes, J. A., *Basic Statistics Laboratory Instruction Manual*—(21 Experiments); Spiegel, M. R., *Theory and Problems of Statistics*, Schaum Publishing Co., New York.

The reader may question why there are not more case studies from the furniture industry included in the book, but to have added more individual case studies would have increased the size of the volume beyond the limits of the series.

Acknowledgements

I AM indebted to the following persons and organizations for allowing me to reproduce certain photographs, graphs, charts, diagrams, and data. To the literary executors of the late Sir Ronald A. Fisher, F.R.S., Cambridge, to Dr. Frank Yates, F.R.S., Rothamsted, and to Messrs Oliver & Boyd Ltd., Edinburgh, for permission to reprint the table of random numbers, as Fig. 25, from their book *Statistical Tables for Biological, Agricultural, and Medical Research.* To the College of Aeronautics Library, Cranfield, Bletchley, Buckinghamshire, for permission to reproduce from the College Report No. 86 by C. J. Norbury, *The Frame Interval Diagram*, Fig. 34. To Visual Planning Systems Ltd., for providing a photograph of their models and permission to reproduce this as Fig. 44. To Sir Isaac Pitman & Sons Ltd., for permission to reproduce the illustrations of Gantt charts as Figs 48 and 49. To Rozalex Ltd., and Chloride Publicity Services Ltd., for permission to reproduce the photograph of an example of a Cyclegraph, Fig. 51. To the Controller of Her Majesty's Stationery Office, for permission to reproduce the example of a Sensorimotor process chart, Fig. 58, which appears on page 17 of *Problems of Progress in Industry No. 6—Training Made Easier.* To the British Productivity Council, London, for permission to reproduce Fig. 59 from their publication *Design for Production.* To Value Engineering Ltd., London, for permission to reproduce the photograph of the impellor assembly, Fig. 60. To Associated Electrical Industries Ltd., Rugby, England, for permission to reproduce the photograph of an example of a bench layout, Fig. 63. To K. F. H. Murrell Esq. of the Unit for Research on Human Performance, in Industry, Welsh College of Advanced Technology, Cardiff, for permission to reproduce the table and diagram, Fig. 64. To the M.T.M. Association for Standards and Research, Ann Arbor, Michigan, for permission to reproduce the M.T.M. data card, Fig. 65. To the Science Museum, London, for permission to reproduce the photograph of an engineering workshop of the mid-nineteenth century (negative number 374/51) as

Fig. 67. To Richard Muther & Associates, for permission to reproduce the illustrations from "Example 2—Planning a New Office Layout" from their publication *Simplified Systematic Layout Planning* as Figs 69, 70, 71, 72, 73, and 74.

CHAPTER 1

Introduction

The Resources of Production

The successful operation of an industrial enterprise depends upon what use is made of its available resources. These resources consist of land, buildings, materials, manpower, plant, and machinery. The success achieved in utilizing the amount of each of these resources is measured in terms of the organization's productivity. This is the ratio between the available resources or input, and the production obtained from these resources or output. If the input of any one of these resources is a known quantity of units a certain percentage of production or output should be expected from this. As with the determination of machine efficiency, it is unreasonable to expect 100 per cent efficiency to be obtained from any machine, but it is reasonable to assume that the operational efficiency of the machine will come within the limits of a recognized standard. In a similar manner the expected efficiency to be obtained from a manufacturing organization should reach a reasonable standard but the productivity of many is all too frequently much lower than it should be. For example in many organizations only 50 per cent of the productive floor space, land, and buildings is used effectively. When a calculation is made to determine how much a square foot of floor space is costing the manufacturer, the situation frequently presented is not a very satisfactory one. What degree of utilization a manufacturer obtains from a unit quantity of material sometimes leaves much to be desired, particularly when the material is expensive and where materials constitute a major percentage of the product cost. The conditions associated with the utilization of manpower are also often no better, for frequently workers are only used effectively two-fifths of their time, the other fraction of their time being spent in unproductive and wasteful activities. This often is caused by no fault of their own but as a result of the bad organization of their work. Where this situation arises management is paying five days' wages for two days' productive work. In those industries where the cost of labour is a major percentage of the product cost, this is a serious situation. Similarly the utilization of plant and machinery is generally extremely low and, when this is viewed in the light of the investment in such plant and equipment, a very unfavourable situation is presented. It is conditions such as these that are reviewed, analysed, and remedied by the application of method study. For by the nature of its analytical procedure the means are provided by which the efficiency and productivity of a production unit can be examined and improved, and enables this approach now to become a systematic activity.

The area of possible method study application in an organization can be extremely wide and for convenience this is divided into five well-defined zones of activity: the analysis of components and products; the analysis of operations, whether they are performed in the factory or the office; the analysis of plant layout for the better use of factory floor area and office space; the analysis of materials handling as it occurs in the

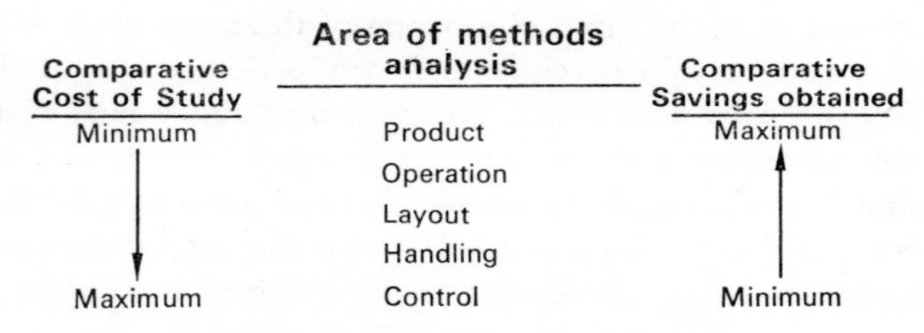

FIG. 1. Areas of methods analysis.

manufacture of a product or the production of paperwork; finally the analysis of systems and procedures for the control of production.

The benefits and savings that can be achieved from a method study in each of these areas of application will vary according to the details of the assignment and the particular aspect selected for analysis. But it has been the author's experience, having carried out numerous studies in all the five areas of application, that the greatest percentage savings are obtained from the analysis of the design of products and components, with its subsequent influence on the other areas of application. The cost of carrying out such a study is a minimum, whereas it is a maximum in the area of systems procedures and control. This is because in order to do an effective study in the area of control, some measure of review of product design, operations, layout, handling, as well as the systems and procedures of control, have to be made for the proposals to be successful. A general guide to the comparative costs of a study and the savings likely to be obtained in each of the areas of application is indicated in Fig. 1. This shows the relationship diagrammatically.

Historical Development

The history of man's endeavour to make his work more efficient, which is the development of method study, provides interesting and sometimes amusing reading. The limitations of space do not permit the discussion of this aspect at any great length, but some mention of the milestones in this development must be made to create an interest in the subject's historical associations, and to indicate that this approach to the study of working methods is not new. The few examples given will demonstrate that what is new is possibly only the formalization of the procedure and techniques by which the work problems are approached.

Those individuals in the past who are known to have applied this critical approach to their work did so in order to make the best possible use of their own available resources, and to solve some immediate problem associated with this work. They were quite frequently craftsmen who, although untrained in the methods of scientific inquiry, often achieved results which in their day were much talked about. Unlike the conventional scientific inquirer, working in the confines of his laboratory, they were at all times not only involved with the tools and processes of their craft, but at the same time had to contend with the attitudes of their workers or fellow craftsmen. These pioneers, however, had the necessary human qualities which enabled them to achieve success in the face of many difficulties. This fact can be perceived easily by anyone who is interested enough to read the lives of these remarkable people. But nothing has changed with regard to the reactions of people to such investigations, for those problems encountered by pioneers in this subject have still to be faced by practitioners today. In fact human attitudes appear to be very much as they were centuries ago. The method study practitioner is still beset with prejudice, bigotry, and actions which are not far removed from those of the Luddites. But these attitudes, whilst not being as violent in their manifestations as those of the past, are nevertheless still present in many countries of the world.

Many in the past realized the importance of studying the methods of work associated with those products that had to be produced cheaply and in large quantities. Jean R. Perronet (1708–94), a French citizen, for example, as early as 1760 made studies of the manufacture of No. 6 pins, of which in those days it took 24·3 hours to produce 12,000. Charles Babbage (1792–1871), the British economist and mathematician, also developed methods for the manufacture of pins for similar reasons. In his essay "On the economy of machinery and manufacturers" a table is given in which the time for each method and process for the manufacture of these pins is recorded.

Josiah Wedgwood (1730–95) was a person who, towards the end of his apprenticeship, developed a love for original experimenting and the study of methods, which was not altogether restricted to process study. By his approach to the manufacture of pottery he succeeded in improving the quality and output from his humble factory, and at the same time introduced much more than better methods in the shape of factory cleanliness, better utilization of materials, and all those objectives which are also the aims of method study investigations today.

By far the most interesting and spectacular method study was made by Samuel Bentham (1757–1831) and Marc Isambard Brunel (1769–1849) in 1799 on the manufacture of ships' pulley blocks. Brunel was the son of a French farmer who served in the French navy before going to America in 1793 as a political refugee. There he lived for a time and became an American citizen before coming to England in 1799. Britain was at that time embarking upon a programme of naval expansion for the protection of her colonies, thus the building of a large number of ships was necessary. However, one of the difficulties experienced in attempting to achieve this objective was the inability to produce a sufficient quantity of ships' blocks. The number of trained blockmakers available was discovered to be insufficient to produce the quantities required, as a fully rigged frigate used about 1500 of these blocks and each block was entirely made by hand at an output of ten blocks per day from one skilled worker. As the number that could be manufactured by existing blockmakers was found to fall far short of the quantities required, attempts were made to train sufficient blockmakers to produce the required quantities but this was not found to be the answer, as the period of training required to produce a skilled blockmaker was of 3 years' duration and the Admiralty was not prepared to wait for this period before the required number of ships was completed.

Bentham, as a brigadier and inspector general of dockyards, was quick to appreciate the true nature of the situation. With the creative genius of Brunel he set about solving this problem. An analysis of the present working methods was made, and the proposed solution was the development of machinery for doing these operations. These machines, which simulated the blockmakers' skill, enabled ten unskilled men to produce one hundred and ten blocks per day. The result of this study was to have wide social and industrial implications, particularly in the prison system as a result of the efforts of Sir Jeremy Bentham (1748–1833), brother of Samuel Bentham, who introduced these machines into the prisons. The production of ships' blocks by these machines was one of the first examples of line production in the manufacture of a product, as each operation in the process was performed in series, on a machine developed for this purpose, and each operated by an individual worker.

Robert Owen (1771–1858) may be considered to have been a pioneer of method study principles. In his work at the New Lanark Mills he indicated his interest in those problems which are now the recognized area of method study inquiry.

Many of the examples often have a quaint and humorous side to their story. Take, for instance, that of John Coxeter, a clothing manufacturer of Newbury in Berkshire, England, who by 1811 had built up a reputation as a master craftsman in the trade, and in the same year agreed for a 1,000 guinea wager to make a quality coat for Sir John Throckmorton, the banker, between sunrise and sunset, which would be made from wool which had that morning been growing on a sheep's back. On 25 June of that year Coxeter won his bet with nearly an hour and three quarters to spare but this was achieved only after detailed method study. That evening Sir John Throckmorton dined at the Pelican Inn at Speenhamland wearing the coat, a fine dark brown Wellington hunting kersey, double-breasted, with turned up cuffs and long tails. A local painter named Luke Clint painted a panoramic representation of the scene in oils which included the portraits of the principal characters who participated in this event.* Today the coat and the original painting may be seen in the hall of Coughton Court, a National Trust property on the fringe of the forest of Arden in Warwickshire, where the Throckmorton family are still in residence.

Some method studies in the past have been concerned with the suitability of a particular commonplace tool: Frederick Winslow Taylor (1856–1915), who, whilst a foreman of a department at the Midvale Steel Company near Philadelphia in the United States of America, was responsible for one of the most interesting studies concerned with the shovelling of iron ore for the purpose of achieving greater output. When

* The painting and the coat were subsequently shown at the Great Exhibition of 1851.

the size of the shovel blade in use at that time for this purpose is considered, approximately one and a half foot wide and the same measurement in length, it can easily be appreciated why a person of Taylor's analytical ability should have questioned its efficiency for this operation. When the shovel blade was loaded with rice coal the shovel load weighed 3½ pounds whilst when it contained iron ore the shovel load weighed 38 pounds. By method study and simple experimental method the correct size of shovel blade was determined which would enable a maximum output per day to be achieved with minimum fatigue to the operator. It was found as a result of this study that a shovel blade which enabled a load of 21½ pounds to be handled was the best for iron ore. It is notable to observe in this study that the participation of the workers concerned with this operation was obtained throughout the study and they were consulted at all stages of the investigation.

Henry L. Gantt (1861–1919), who is to be remembered for his investigations into production planning and control procedures, was a pioneer of method study principles applied to the organization of work. He expressed the conviction that "In all problems of management the human element is the most important one".

Any brief survey of those responsible for the development of method study would not be complete without mention of the considerable contributions made by Frank B. Gilbreth (1869–1924), who, assisted by his wife, Dr. Lillian Gilbreth, a university trained psychologist, was responsible for the development of many of the techniques which are now such a familiar part of the procedures of method study investigation. Their amusing family life is described in a book written by two of their children.* Gilbreth became a successful builder, but early in his career he became interested in the study of work methods. His investigations into the operations of bricklaying later developed into an interest in operator training and the development of the principles of motion economy.

Immediately after the First World War there was a general preoccupation with work measurement and incentive systems for achieving greater output. The limitations of this approach was stressed by Dr. Harold B. Maynard and his colleagues, who, as early as 1930, coined the expression "Methods Engineering" and suggested that emphasis should be placed more on the development of effective working methods than on work measurement and incentives.

* Gilbreth, F. B. jr and Gilbreth Carey, E., *Cheaper By The Dozen*, Chatto & Windus, London.

Many other contributors to method study development could be mentioned, but it has been considered sufficient to refer to them in the text of this volume when discussing those method study techniques to which they have made singular contributions.

The Method Study Procedure

Method study, as previously stated, is the systematic investigation of productive work in order to determine methods which will achieve the best use of available resources. To accomplish this aim, investigations are conducted in an organized sequence of activity. This may be briefly stated as follows.

Method Study Procedure

Diagnosis and formulation of the problem.
Collection and recording of the data.
Examination of the data.
Development of the proposed method.
Installation of the accepted method.
Maintenance of the method.

It can be seen from consideration of this procedure that it is broadly applicable not only to method study but to investigations in general. It is the adherence to this approach that enables the investigator to proceed to his particular objective, and in doing so not overlook any important aspect of the problem. The amount of effort and time devoted to each stage of this procedure will, of course, depend on the problem being investigated, and the area of the method study application. The diagnosis and formulation of the problem which is the first part of the procedure consists of selecting the work to be studied. This requires that the problem should first be identified and the objectives of the proposed investigation defined. The economic justification for the study is carefully considered and the means by which the degree of achievement of the objective may be measured. The component parts of the problem are separated and the alternative methods of approaching the problem are examined and considered in planning the investigation. When this stage is completed the recording and collection of the data can then begin. What essential information is required for the conduct of the study will be dependent on a number of factors, such as what information is to be obtained, to what degree of detail should this be collected, in what form should this be recorded, and how the information should be presented for subsequent examination. When the necessary information has been collected, and presented in the most suitable form for scrutiny, it is next examined. The analysis of the information will be made in the most appropriate manner, isolating the most useful and relevant facts so that their meaning may be clearly grasped and a clear understanding of what is occurring may be appreciated. It is at this stage that the information obtained may be marshalled in the form of charts, diagrams, or models as an aid to this critical examination, so that a clearer and more complete picture of what is involved in the problem can be obtained, and should inefficiency and waste occur this can be more clearly indicated. The development of a proposed method consists of the production of a number of answers to the method problem. Devising means to eliminate waste and inefficiency constitutes the main objective of this stage of the procedure. The ability to think creatively will be demanded of the investigator for this purpose. Any of the proposals produced may themselves be critically examined to see that they will conform to the desired results. They may also be tested or tried out in order to confirm that this is so. Simple experimental procedure will sometimes be used so that reliable inferences may be obtained from any such trial. But whether this is done will depend largely on the nature of the proposed method. In certain situations where it is not possible to actually carry out physical trials of the proposals the procedure of simulation may be resorted to. The effectiveness of any study will always be determined and for this purpose cost comparisons may be made for the evaluation of any alternative proposals. When this stage has been completed proposals and recommendations will be submitted to management in the form of a report for their consideration.

When everyone associated with the development of the proposals is fully satisfied with their effectiveness the installation of the improved method can commence. This has to be planned carefully and the use of particular techniques may be necessary to achieve this. The instruction of operators in the proposed method may also have to be considered.

The proposed method, having been successfully installed, is now periodically reviewed in order that the work methods may be checked for any amendments or subsequent improvements that may have been introduced. These if present are recorded and recognized in the standard specification, if they are considered desirable. This maintenance enables the method to be constantly reviewed and ensures that the time spent in carrying out the study will not have been wasted. Each of the elements of this procedure will now be considered individually.

Qualities Required by the Method Study Practitioner

The personal qualities required by any individual who is to successfully practice method study can for convenience be divided into three categories. Firstly he must have certain personal qualities the possession of which will depend largely on his attitude of mind. The success of any study depends largely upon the attitude with which the problem is approached and resolved, just as much as the technical ability demonstrated in its solution. Secondly the practitioner must have the will and strength of character to succeed in any investigation he has undertaken. Thirdly he must have an appreciation of the technical implications of each individual study and an understanding of the human factors associated with each.

The investigator should develop a capacity for comprehension and analysis together with a tidy mind. He should be a person of high personal standards because he will be working with personnel at all levels in an organization. He should also possess those mental qualities which the late Arthur D. Little described as the four marks of a scientific mind. The simplicity to wonder, the ability to question, the power to generalize, and the capacity to apply.

It is necessary for him to have the will and determination to succeed in his investigation and achieve the desired results, for without this quality of character the difficulties he will encounter will make it almost impossible for him to achieve the necessary results from the study. He will meet with all types of obstruction, resistance, and delaying tactics, which may aggravate and confound a person not possessing this strength of character. However, in his eagerness to obtain results the investigator must not press his case too forcibly to the point of annoyance, otherwise increased resistance on the part of personnel will be the result and this will make his objective even more difficult to obtain. It is therefore important that in his dealings with personnel the qualities of tact and diplomacy should be exercised. It is often realized that persons who may be knowledgeable in the techniques of method study will never make a success of its application as they are not able to get along with people and lack the necessary human qualities for success.

An analytical quality of mind should be developed by the investigator together with an almost tenacious quality which will be exercised in the search for data and information. This quality is often indicated in the investigator by the characteristic of not being too easily satisfied with information and the answers collected. A healthy sceptical and critical faculty should be cultivated together with a logical quality of mind. These qualities are exercised in the training of method study practitioners as well as the techniques. The same care and patience in the collection of data should be employed as would be used in a laboratory, when recording the details of an experiment. No person likely to take the "easy way" when confronted with difficulties will ever succeed in the application of method study.

The investigator should not easily agree with personnel, but any disagreement he may have with them should be supported by a convincing and logical reason for this disagreement. If the possession of the above qualities is asking too much of human nature it should be remembered that these are some of the human attributes which are demanded for success in other walks of life. It is for this reason that method study personnel are frequently recruited from those persons who are likely to proceed to higher achievement and positions in their career. For this reason management trainees are often given method study training in order that they may spend some time in this activity before proceeding to other management functions.

Technical Implications

Whilst it is not essential for the investigator to have a detailed process knowledge of the industry or area of an investigation in which he is to apply method study, an acquaintance with an industry does help considerably. In certain studies the investigator may be too easily persuaded against the suitability of one of his technical proposals if he does not possess a reasonable appreciation of a process. For this reason methods personnel are often recruited from those persons who already have adequate process knowledge. The most often repeated phrase that the investigator will encounter will be "it cannot be done". This statement is supported usually by what seems to be a perfectly valid technical argument, which, without some technical knowledge on the part of the investigator, would not be possible for him to refute. The possession of process knowledge also enables the practitioner to be an advocate for technical improvements and also, which is of considerable value, to be more readily acceptable as a person by technical personnel.

In order to achieve and maintain this necessary acceptability he must keep himself up to date with new technical information and also be able to evaluate the possible contribution it can make to his organization. If the investigator has superior technical knowledge it should never be paraded, but should be used to question the efficiency of existing techniques when these come up for review in the course of a method study. Factory personnel will be quick to perceive that an investigator has adequate technical knowledge without this being advertised.

Process knowledge will also enable the investigator to discuss technical problems with personnel in an atmosphere of mutual interest. This will invariably lead to their requesting his advice on some technical problem or improvement when mutual confidence has been attained and the appropriate climate has been created for method study application. It is always necessary for the investigator to ensure that sufficient technical knowledge is possessed by personnel who are going to be involved in the development of new methods, so that discussions productive of results may be obtained. In assignments where it is found that inadequate process knowledge is possessed by the persons involved in the study, the investigator is at a considerable disadvantage. Whilst this kind of situation is not universal it is not uncommon.

The Human Factor

Although method study is primarily concerned with technical considerations, the practitioner, by the very nature of the method study procedure, will in the course of his work be dealing with people. It is therefore necessary for him to use his imagination and become well acquainted with the human factors involved in an application as well as those of a technical nature. The best schemes can fail if the human considerations are ignored, and moderate schemes can produce quite surprising results if they are remembered. There is unfortunately a rapidly growing tendency to regard method study purely and simply as a professional technique for studying work without being sufficiently human in its application. Many of the difficulties associated with its application in industry are of a human rather than a technical nature. It is for this reason essential for the investigator to remember that for the successful study of methods the human and the technical considerations are essentially interdependent.

When conducting an investigation it is essential to consider all the relevant facts concerning the work situation. This implies paying attention not only to such matters as existing methods and the layout of the work area but also the human factors associated with them. If the study is to be successful it must recognize these things and other highly personal considerations. It should be appreciated that there is no formula for dealing with the human factor. For an activity that has reduced practically everything else to procedures and formulae this is viewed by the practitioner with some misgivings, but this fact has to be faced and only experience will enable him to contend confidently with this question.

The things which method study will change are those things which directly and immediately effect people. The results of studies, for instance, often introduce a closer control of peoples activities; any such change or control that is introduced may be felt as a constraint and pressure. Problems associated with the human factor may not be foreseen or recognized when they arise. This is particularly so with respect to the effects that a study may have on the activities of people who are not themselves the subject of the study. For this reason imagination and intelligent anticipation is essential for the assessment of how any particular change may affect them. Human reactions are the most unpredictable and all one can do is to try to anticipate the mental and emotional reactions to an investigation and the influence that the subsequent changes in method may have on personnel. It is important, therefore, to determine which departments and functions are likely to be affected by the improvements. Changes in an operator's methods affect only the operator, whilst extensive changes will quite often affect several departments. The facts concerning the effects of any new method or technical change should be understood and appreciated. Experience of local personnel and conditions can often reduce these difficulties. But everyone connected with, and likely to be affected by the study must be considered when the correct approach to the investigation is determined. Method study cannot succeed in its aim unless it is based on a free and willing co-operation between management and workers. This co-operation can only be obtained if considerable attention is paid to the human aspects of the situation being studied. This co-operation is essential at all stages of the investigation, for a study must not only have the support of the operators but also the full and declared support of management.

It should not be the intention of the practitioner to sell method study, but to sell himself as a person; for this reason time spent in establishing personal relationships, in order to obtain his acceptance as a person, is never wasted. This acceptance of the practitioner by all personnel depends for its success as much on his personal attitudes as the technical considerations previously mentioned.

When, in the course of collecting information about the present method of doing work, a choice of operators is suggested for the recording of this information, it is best to select those who are working to the specific method, as there is no object in studying methods which do not represent or are inconsistent with current standards and practice. The recording of the present method of doing the job will be of little use if the operator performs the method incorrectly.

It is best to approach those operators required for a study through the foreman or, if local policy requires it, through the shop steward. This approach to the operator should also be considered carefully. It should be one of complete frankness and at all stages of the investigation the operator should be kept fully informed of the progress of the study. He is often in a position to offer practical suggestions about his own job having possibly been associated with it for a number of years. For these reasons his full co-operation should be sought and obtained. Personnel generally like to be co-operative if they feel that the investigator is interested to hear and attaches importance to their ideas for methods improvement.

The purpose of any study must always be explained to the operator and any questions that he may ask must be answered before his work is investigated. It is necessary to include in the investigation not only the job done by the operator, and what goes on in the bench area within the individuals range of vision, but also an appreciation of what goes on in the department and the whole factory around the individual for the whole of the working day.

Care must always be exercised in the development of an operator's method to see that any existing job satisfaction is not destroyed when introducing any improvements to his existing method. People naturally like things to be efficient but they also like to be treated as people and what matters most in this particular instance is how they react when more efficient methods are introduced. Another factor that should be considered at the initial stages of a study is to determine how effective is the process of consultation. For it is important that at all times the quality of fairness and justice must not only be exercised but seen and felt to be so.

There is an understandable resistance to change that all individuals possess; it is for this reason that the investigator must be diplomatic and tactful in his approach. Resentment of criticism and resistance to change are normal factors of human behaviour. They are more likely to be overcome by recognition of their existence and by a tactful approach than by any other means. The confidence and co-operation of all levels of personnel concerned with an investigation should be obtained either prior to the study or whilst it is being conducted. Any attempt to overcome resistance to change and win co-operation must be based on an understanding of the reasons that produce this resistance. Basically it is an emotional rather than a rational or intellectual reaction. The emotions concerned, it is suggested, are fear and anxiety, and for this reason it is no use placing too much reliance on logical arguments, for the more effective the logic of an argument, in certain circumstances, the more likely is the resistor to feel frustrated and in consequence more aggressive. To dispel any anxiety, all personnel should be kept informed as the investigation proceeds and as a result of this approach co-operation is more likely to be achieved. All must have an appreciation of the aims and purpose of method study and feel that their own experience is contributing to the results that are to be achieved.

One of the barriers to the willing acceptance of improved methods is, as stated previously, that of fear, but there are a number of more common reasons for resisting change. Resistance by an operator may arise from the following causes. Fear of redundancy, fear of having to work harder, fear that older workers will not be able to master new skills, fear that a congenial work team will be broken up, fear of the dilution of craft skills, and resentment at being studied. Resistance by management may arise from the fear of loss of "empire" or from a feeling that method study is implied criticism. Fear that inefficiencies will be discovered for which they will be blamed. Feeling that their authority is being encroached upon or it may originate from their devotion to their own preferred systems or organization. Resentment of outsiders and non-specialists; apathy on the part of those due for retirement or from misconceptions of the aims and objectives of method study.

The employer who takes effective action to dispel such fears makes a major contribution to the success and effectiveness of method study application through improved relations. In the process of doing this it must be made perfectly clear by higher management that no adverse reflections will be made on anyone's work as a result of improvements which may be suggested by method study. Furthermore, management must not use the results of an investigation as personal criticism of those responsible for the old method.

People, whether they are operatives or managers, dislike being studied and being told that the methods they are using are wrong. Their reactions to this suggestion are identical. Resistance to change can and does take many forms other than open resistance. This is often evident during the recording stage of the method study procedure when information about the present method is being collected. Unless complete co-operation has been successfully obtained it is probable that attempts will be made to present to the investigator a false picture of the normal pattern of activity. There will also often be a tendency for personnel to appear much busier than they are normally and for them to do things by accepted method where they would normally employ short cuts. Sometimes they may fail to point out any unusual or typical aspects of the situation which might affect the validity of the information collected. In addition, when new methods are being developed personnel will sometimes do their utmost to make them appear less efficient than the old, and will not attempt to try and solve problems which the new methods may produce.

Resistance on the part of executives normally takes the form of a refusal to accept all or part of the recommendations or reluctance to supply the investigator with all the available data. People are often suspicious that technical progress may be in some way the main cause of redundancy, as new and more efficient methods usually mean greater production by fewer men. Where management has a policy for possible redundancy, which is acceptable to the operatives, this does help to reduce this fear. Personnel who belong to functional departments tend to regard their function as all-important, disregarding the fact that its importance rests in the contribution it makes to the achievement of the overall aims of the total organization. Often people in an emotional state need only an opportunity to let off steam and thus reduce their emotional tension. In such situations the investigator is required to be a patient and sympathetic listener. The more the investigator opposes the resistor's point of view, the more will he tend to cling to it. It is important that the investigator should never become emotionally involved in any argument, he should simply obtain all the details from the operator or person involved and review this in the peace of his own office.

One of the main criticisms by operators of a proposed method is usually concerned with their incapacity to perform the new method satisfactorily when requested to do so. In this situation, it is to be remembered that a person's ultimate capacity is just as obscurely hidden from himself as it is from an independent observer. No one who knows an old method study application well can have any doubts of the truth of this statement. The working capacity of an individual is influenced by his physical, mental, and emotional make up. Differences between individuals in these characteristics are considerable. In order to utilize the human resources of an organization to the best advantage it is important to study the relationship between a man and his job from two aspects. The first is that of fitting the man to the job; this requires studying the demands of the job on the worker and selecting for the job those workers best able to meet these demands. The second is that of fitting the job to the man; this involves an assessment of the capacities and limitations of the worker and modifying the job so that his ability to contend with it is increased. In the development of any new method the method study practitioner should always bear in mind that human beings are not machines and when they are treated as such they become unco-operative. It is seldom sufficiently realized that fewer physical limitations to the employment of personnel would exist if more attention were given to fitting the job to the man. Where a task is discovered to be performed inefficiently because of the physical limitations of the worker the usual remedy is to seek a replacement for him. It is suggested that it may well prove more economic eventually to reorganize the task so that the number of people who can perform it effectively is considerably increased. It is important that the operator should be studied with reference to the present method and also any proposals that may be introduced, as in many operations the qualities of personality, character, and temperament play an important part in influencing how the job is to be performed. Such factors as these are not generally given much attention in the selection and allocation of personnel, but they may well account for the significantly different levels of performance of workers.

The influence of fatigue and monotony occasioned by the operation of a method should also not be overlooked. Operator fatigue must always be reduced to a minimum if efficiency is to be maintained. Every effort must therefore be made in the method study application to conserve the energy of the worker, as fatigue is produced not so much from the amount of work done as from the worker's attitude to what he has to do and his work environment. The common cause of psychological fatigue is the monotony of repetitive work, boredom, inactivity, and isolation. But most people can usually find enough energy for those activities that interest them.

It is suggested that the successful application of method study will depend largely on how the human relations aspect of the assignment is conducted. However successful the method study practitioner may be in mastering and applying his techniques, if he fails to win the confidence and co-operation of the personnel associated with the investigation he will be wasting his time.

Selected References and Suggestions for Further Reading

Introduction to Work Study, International Labour Office, Geneva, 1959, chapter 2, Productivity in the Individual Enterprise.

Outline of Work Study. Part I Introduction, Part II Method Study, British Institute of Management, London.

Glossary of Work Study Terms in English, French and German, European Productivity Agency of the O.E.E.C., Paris.

Glossary of Terms in Work Study, British Standard Institution, London, B.S. 3138: 1959.

Industrial Relations Handbook, Her Majesty's Stationery Office, London, 1957.

BROWN, J. A. C., *The Social Psychology of Industry*, Penguin Books.

DALZIEL, S. and KLEIN, L., *The Human Implications of Work Study*, The Case of Pakitt Ltd., Human Sciences Unit, Warren Spring Laboratory, Stevenage, Herts., England.

MAIER, R. F., *Principles of Human Relations*, John Wiley, New York; Chapman & Hall, London, 1952.

MYERS, C. S. (Ed.), *Industrial Psychology*, Home University Library, Oxford University Press, London and New York.

RATTRAY TAYLOR, G., *Are Workers Human?*, The Falcon Press, London.

TREDGOLD, R. F., *Human Relations in Modern Industry*, Gerald Duckworth, London, 1963.

TOURAINE, A., *Acceptance and Resistance—Workers' attitudes to technical change*, Organisation for Economic Co-operation and Development, 1965.

CHAPTER 2

Diagnosis and Formulation of the Methods Problem

THE method study procedure commences with the identification of the problem that demands a solution. It provides for a clear appraisal of the problem situation and in doing this contributes considerably to the planning of the investigation. How the activities in the present method ought to be examined, how they may be isolated, and how wide an area the proposed investigation should include, are some of the questions that are answered at this stage. The extent of a proposed study, its constraints and limitations, when indicated and acknowledged by all concerned, will form the basis for the objectives whose achievement will constitute the agreed criteria of success.

Before a method is selected for study, and a proposed investigation is planned, it is essential that the investigator should consider all the various aspects of the problem so that the present conditions associated with the problem situation may be correctly diagnosed and the problem accurately identified. The factors that should be considered in order to do this can, for the convenience of the investigator, be arranged in the form of a check list. The use of this will ensure that each aspect of the proposed problem will receive the appropriate attention at this important stage of the procedure. The check list is arranged in the order in which these questions should be answered. The information obtained, as a result, will enable the investigator to advise management on the suggested conduct of the study and its possible duration. The following questionnaire or check list will give some idea of the form of these questions.

Does a methods problem exist?
What is the possible cause of the problem?
By whom was the investigation requested?
For what reason was the request made?
What is the proposed objective of the study?

By what means will it be determined that the objective of the study has been achieved?
What are the constant and variable aspects of the present method?
What are the suggested limits of the study?
What is the extent of the possible changes likely to result from a proposed study?
By what approach is the problem most likely to be solved?
What are the terms of reference suggested by management?
What are the possible savings from a proposed study?
Is it appropriate and convenient to carry out the proposed study?
Can the results from the study be used in future investigations?

Many method study investigators arrange this information in different ways, but whatever procedure is used, the result will be to determine the possibilities for improvements and to define the limits of the study. How an investigation is conducted will, of course, be influenced by the terms of reference provided by management, but the answers to the above questions will have to be obtained in order that the investigator may assist management and contribute in formulating these terms of reference correctly. By whatever means the information is collected, a preliminary investigation may be necessary if the time of the investigator is not to be wasted.

Before the commencement of an investigation the suggested area of activity for a proposed method study presents a complex picture of innumerable events, conditions, and activities together and in succession. The investigator presented with this situation has first to ascertain that a problem does in fact really exist, and then he has to review the situation in order that he may determine what follows what, or what facts are invariably connected together, then to account for these regular connections. This is done in order that the problem may be more easily identified and the correct approach and procedure selected to obtain a solution.

In many situations to determine the probable cause of a problem is not an easy task as the basic cause may have its origin in the most unexpected quarters of an organization. Further it is important to remember that to locate the cause of a problem does not mean that this will necessarily be the area for the investigation. The energies of the investigator may be directed to that facet of the problem where the effect of the ailment may require to be neutralized. The fact that a jig and fixture has been designed wrongly and produces conditions of low productivity in an operation or that a component has been designed unsatisfactorily thereby resulting in extra operations for its manufacture, does not necessarily signify that the subject for a study will be to provide proposals for the redesign of the jig and fixture or the component. The investigator's task may be, in this instance, because management cannot see their way to correct the errors by re-design, to neutralize the effect of the errors in an immediate area of the factory where difficulties are being experienced as a result of this. It may be more economical to approach the problem in this way unless management suggests that the alternative is more suitable.

For method study activity to be effective within an organization, the process of selecting subjects for possible investigation must be made as a result of a deliberate policy of management and not in a haphazard manner. If this is done correctly the energies of the method study personnel will not be dissipated on unimportant considerations. Any request for an investigation should be periodically reviewed by senior management, who will select those subjects most appropriate for study and allocate time and methods personnel for the completion of each task. Priority is usually given to those activities where the application of method study will achieve the greatest cost reduction.

The need for a method study investigation is not always indicated by the apparent conditions of the work situation. Old ways and procedures of doing work have a habit of becoming accepted and this inevitably leads to unsatisfactory features passing unrecognized. Frequently methods that were satisfactory for one set of circumstances are not necessarily appropriate for changed conditions. Because the influence of these conditions is not appreciated the unsuitability of the methods go unnoticed. Where the following conditions are recognized, however, it is almost certain that a method study is desirable: where costs are high or have increased suddenly or are higher than normal; where conditions are such as to indicate a problem such as bottlenecks, high incidence of materials handling, excessive work in progress and movement, low utilization of material, labour, machinery, floor space, or services. The need for a study to rectify such situations is obvious.

The method of approach to the present method should be one that will enable the location of the constants and variables of the subject, as this will simplify the planning of the investigation. To enable this to be done certain preliminary information about the nature of a problem and a proposed investigation has to be obtained. The constants of a present method are those aspects which cannot be altered for various reasons. For instance if the objective of an investigation is to make the best possible use of a known area of floor space this factor is a constant of the problem. If there is also associated with this same problem a condition that certain machinery will have to be included in any new rearrangement of this floor area then this also will be a constant of the problem. It is conceivable that it may not be possible to satisfy these two conditions, but the purpose of the study should be to determine in what circumstances this could be done. All the other factors of the problem are then the variable factors, which may be manipulated to obtain the desired objective of the study. The correct definition of the variable and constant aspects of a problem by methods personnel will enable management to formulate more clearly the terms of reference for a particular study. The consideration of these two aspects may be further influenced by how much management is prepared to spend on alterations and additional equipment in order to obtain the desired results.

It is essential for the investigator, early in the preliminary stages of the procedure, to clearly define the objectives of a proposed study. This is done not only to provide a goal at which to aim, but also to obviate any subsequent misunderstanding that may occur between himself and the person who has requested the study. In any methods investigation there can be many objectives, and frequently many are obtained simultaneously with those sought, but the initial choice of too many objectives produces a confusion of aims and will frequently influence the duration and complexity of a study. The purpose should therefore be to aim for an immediate objective and not one of a long-term nature.

The means by which to determine whether the results, previously agreed, have been achieved is invariably provided by a careful definition of these objectives, prior to the commencement of the study. If these objectives are reduction of costs, better use of floor area, reduction of materials handling, or a percentage increase in the production from an operation, or a reduction in the percentage of operator delays, then the results of a study, if they indicate that the desired reduction in any of these has been achieved, can easily be determined in terms of the savings in the appropriate units, whether these are pounds sterling, square feet of floor area, distance travelled in yards, or percentage increase in products produced. It is customary for the person who originally requested the study to agree to the means by which the achievements of a study may be measured, in order that there is no misunderstanding when the final proposals are produced.

A suitable solution to a methods problem is most likely to be obtained, with the minimum of effort and cost, if the direction of approach to the problem is considered carefully. There are various ways of approaching the analysis of present methods in order to achieve a solution. Consider, for example, an industrial operation which, it is suggested, should be the subject of an investigation, a review of the redesign of a product or component can frequently eliminate the necessity for the operation entirely, or reduce the activity associated with the operation considerably. Similarly, by considering a group of operations, of which the subject of the study is a member, it is possible to eliminate the operation in question by combining it with another and performing both simultaneously. By changing the sequence of operations it is often possible to eliminate certain operations altogether, as the possible reason for the additional operation in the first place was due largely because this sequence had not been considered. The elimination of operations required to manufacture a product has a marked influence on plant layout, materials handling, and the control of production. Whatever the approach of the study may be, time spent on a detailed analysis of an operation, or a series of operations, will be wasted if subsequently it is found that, by a simple and permissible amendment to factory layout or the design of a component, the operation may be eliminated altogether.

The consideration of product and component design, plant layout, materials handling, and control come within the category of what is called "primary analysis", whereas the detailed examination of an operation, at an individual worksite, comes within the category of secondary analysis. It is wise to see that primary analysis is carried out before secondary analysis is attempted.

The extent of the changes likely to result from a proposed study can invariably be anticipated as the result of experience gained in similar method studies. Knowledge of the industrial process and the exercise of some imagination will help to anticipate such changes. If the objectives of a proposed study are obtained, their influence on other aspects of the organization's productive work may be considerable. What these areas of the organization are likely to be can only be determined by experience. It is frequently necessary to be aware that the solution of one problem may create further problems in other areas of production. To anticipate changes and their influence on production is to be aware of the necessity for consultation at the appropriate stage of the method study procedure with personnel who work in those areas likely to be affected. The influence of possible changes may be of such a nature that management may not consider it desirable for a study to be made in the present circumstances, or as a result of this consideration may limit the scope of the study by the terms of reference they will provide.

The limits of any particular study are influenced by a large number of factors other than the above considerations. To obtain the facts about any method situation is impossible without search and observation. This is a mental as well as a physical activity, for in order to observe, not only must the attention be made to take a particular direction, but the investigator must be more or less conscious of what he is looking for. In other words method study observation, like ordinary perception, is selective. It is recognized that without this selective approach to the method study problem, an investigation would be prolonged unnecessarily and be more costly, as data would be collected which would make no contribution to the objectives of the study. This process of selection is influenced by considerations which will limit the area of the investigation. Such considerations as how much management is prepared to spend to obtain the proposed results of a study, will exclude from the consideration of the investigator many aspects of the problem which, if considered, would considerably influence the magnitude of the savings. However, due to the influence of policy, management may not consider it an appropriate time to include these factors in the study. This may be thought by the investigator to be a restriction of his personal opportunities for achievement, but method study application is governed by an organization's policy, and it is always recognized that greater results could have been achieved if the area of the investigation had been wider. Although this may appear to be a curtailment of the investigators activities, he need not fear this restraint, as all management functions are restrained if policy dictates that this should be so.

The terms of reference provided by senior management, which the investigator himself may have helped to define, are the guide to the proposed study. These are the instructions and means of guidance which have been developed from the suggested limits of the study. They are a means by which all personnel will be able to understand the aims and purposes of the particular investigation, and provide the authority for the investigator to carry out the study. When this is understood by all it simplifies the task of the investigator when seeking the assistance of those who are most likely to be able to help him in the conduct of the study.

The anticipated profitability of any proposed investigation may frequently be determined by a pilot study. Such a study may last only a few hours or extend to a number of days. This study will determine the magnitude of an undesirable condition or symptom which, in the light of previous experience of method studies made in similar applications, can be considerably reduced or eliminated entirely. From this an estimate of proposed savings can easily be anticipated.

With every investigation that is made the practitioner gains more experience of the conduct of studies and the development of solutions. Each investigation will inevitably lead to the consideration of other factors, as each will pose certain questions about other activities in the organization which will start a thought process that leads to the awareness of other problems. In view of this, experience gained by the conduct of studies in one area of application will almost certainly be of use in other subsequent studies. Where economic considerations do not favour a study being made, the deciding factor for a study may be obtained by considering whether the results of the study can be used in other areas of method study activity. If this is possible the cost of the study is then spread over more than one investigation.

When selecting the subject for a proposed study, timing of the commencement of the investigation is an important consideration. It may not be correct policy at a particular time to carry out a study; very good reasons may be put forward to support this, even though the conditions that are to be examined leave much to be desired, and considerable savings seem likely to be obtained. It may be that a proposed major reorganization of a department is to take place in the near future, which would make any present study inappropriate and a waste of time. As the result of this consideration the present method is suffered, however bad it may be, for the time being.

Sometimes when the changes that are likely to occur as the result of a study are appreciated, management may not want to be confronted with the necessity for making a decision concerning these changes at the present time, for it is to be remembered that these decisions may include consideration for the redeployment of personnel, a major change round of equipment and services, and possible training, to indicate only a few.

These considerations, as well as those of an economic nature, enable management to decide whether a study should be made and also influence the decision concerning its limits. It may be that other information will be required to assist in making this decision, which according to the type of investigation that is proposed may include such possible considerations as the following. The present production, whether it is normal, variable, and what proposed production is required? The number of operators who are employed on the activity in question? What is the category of the labour in question, whether skilled, semiskilled, or unskilled, their hourly rate of pay and availability? The production per operator? What equipment is used, its efficiency, cost, availability and adaptability? These are only some of the general questions posed by the investigator when he is preparing proposals for the commencement of a particular method study assignment. According to the kind of study that is proposed, different questions will, of course, be asked to determine the economic justification for an investigation. The use of questionnaires such as are contained in Chapter 5 may help in this task.

Selected References and Suggestions for Further Reading

CURRIE, R. M., *Work Study*, Pitman, 1964, chapter 5.

MUNDEL, M. E., *Motion and Time Study Principles and Practice*, Prentice-Hall, Englewood Cliffs, N. J.; Chapman & Hall, London, chapter 4.

PENNYCUICK, K., *Industrial Diagnosis*, The English Universities Press, London, 1961.

SHAW, A. G., *Purpose and Practice of Motion Study*, Harlequin Press, London, appendix A.

CHAPTER 3

Collection and Recording of the Data

Introduction

After the subject for a proposed method study has been selected, it is necessary to collect the information about the problem to be investigated. The object of this second stage of the method study procedure is to collect and record this information in the most convenient manner. All the methods of recording that are employed can be regarded as a convenient form of shorthand which, having been standardized, is easily understandable by those who may wish subsequently to follow the details the investigator has obtained. The choice of any one of the various means of collecting and recording data in method studies will depend on the nature and the objectives of the study undertaken and the degree of detail required. No investigator should attempt to obtain information in greater detail than the objectives of the study demand, as it is recognized that the greater the degree of detail the longer is the period of time required for the collection and recording of this information. Any procedure of recording that is selected must therefore be of a kind that will enable an appropriate model of the problem to be subsequently constructed, and which will be suitable for subsequent analysis, and not only be intelligible to the recorder himself but also to other persons who may wish to examine it.

The following recording techniques are available to the investigator.

(a) Process charts
  (i) Operation or outline process chart.
  (ii) Flow process chart.
  (iii) Two-handed process charts.
(b) Activity sampling
(c) Photographic methods of recording
  (i) Micromotion.
  (ii) Memomotion.

Many divergencies in methods of recording were beginning to appear in common practice as method study developed, and it was for this reason that it was considered that a valuable service would be rendered to industrial management if standards were devised for these in order primarily to maintain a common medium of expression for all practitioners in this field. The American Society of Mechanical Engineers produced a standard in 1947. This standard is now generally accepted by all those who practice method study.

However there are many variations to the standard methods of charting described which are considered appropriate in certain circumstances. Biggs and others have described possible variations, but care should be exercised in the use of non-standard conventions as the purpose of the standards would be defeated.

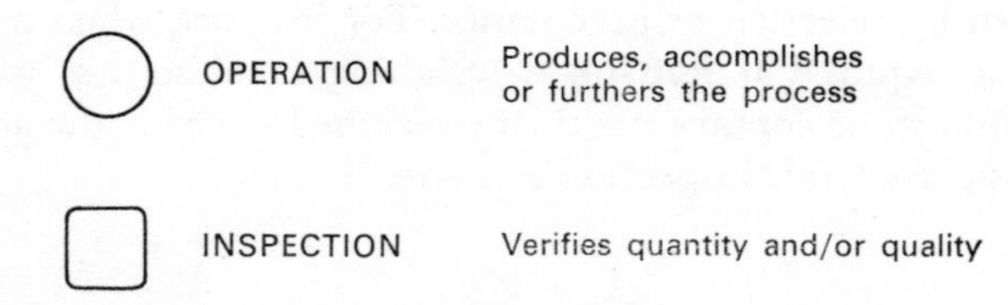

FIG. 2. The symbols of operation and inspection.

Process Charting. The Operation or Outline Process Chart

The outline process chart, as its name implies, provides a means of obtaining an overall view of the production process. It is the simplest type of process chart as it records only the salient activities in a process, namely the operations and inspections. The nature of a study may require the investigator to obtain only an outline presentation of the process under examination before possibly commencing a more detailed recording of other parts of the process, or the scope of the study may require no greater detail than that provided by this method of recording. The two symbols used to represent the standard activities of operation and inspection in the construction of this process chart are indicated in Fig. 2. The linking together of these symbols in the sequence in which the activities they represent takes place, constitutes this type of chart. This method of charting also provides a means of recording the units of time and quantity to qualify each symbol but does not indicate where the activities take place or who performs them.

An operation symbol may be made to represent different scales of an activity. For example one symbol may indicate the complete assembly of a product comprising a number of sub-assembly operations leading to a final assembly, or alternatively each of these sub-assembly and assembly operations may be indicated by an individual operation symbol. What each operation symbol will be made to represent will depend upon the details of the process recorded and the objectives of the study. The amount of activity represented by an operation symbol can thus vary from chart to chart and will depend on the amount of information the chart is intended to record. It is important that in any one chart the scale of activity depicted by each symbol should be as nearly as possible the same.

It should be remembered that those activities that resemble inspections but which are really operations should not be confused. When an inspection takes place a condition is checked against a standard and is thus followed by rejection or acceptance. For instance when a container is filled to a required weight on a weighing machine an operation is carried out but if the container is then reweighed to check the accuracy of the previous activity an inspection is made.

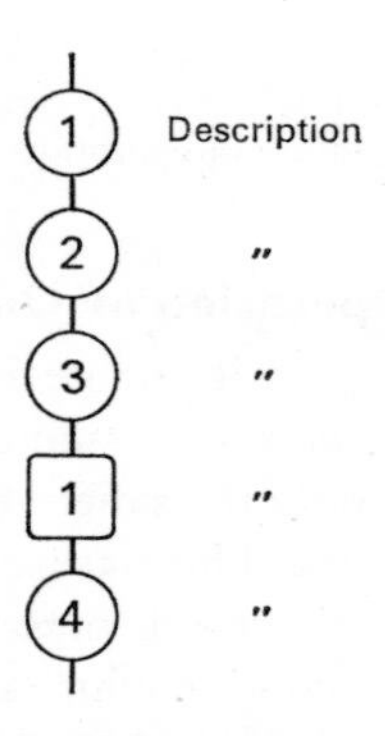

Fig. 3. A simple example of an outline process chart.

The outline process chart is constructed by joining together the symbols of operation and inspection vertically one below the other in sequence. To the right of each symbol the activity is described briefly as shown in Fig. 3. Certain standard charting conventions are used for recording complex processes and the use of these produces a recording more readily understandable not only by the investigator but also by independent persons familiar with these conventions.

Numbering of Symbols

The symbols are numbered to provide a means of quick reference and comparison so that the total number of activities of each type which represent the process can easily be determined and any individual activity identified. Each type of symbol is numbered in sequence from the beginning of the chart and its appropriate number is placed in the centre of the symbol (see Fig. 3).

Combined Symbols

Where two different activities occur at the same time and place, these are indicated by combined symbols. One symbol is made to include the other. When it is possible to determine the relative importance of the two activities the symbol of the more important activity is placed on the outside and the less important on the inside. The numbering of combined symbols is made by giving each its own serial number and these are shown inside the combined symbol separated by a hyphen. The first of the two numbers represents the outer symbol (Fig. 4).

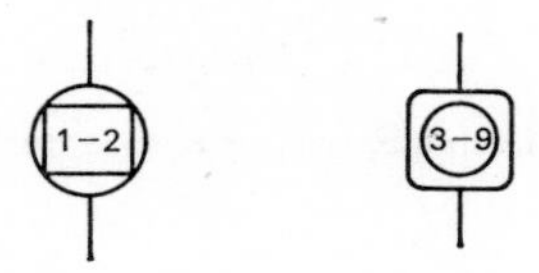

FIG. 4. Combined symbols and their numbering.

Introduction of Material

When materials, components, sub-assemblies, or accessories are brought into the process, this fact is indicated on the chart by a horizontal line and arrow which enters from the left of the vertical chart line at the appropriate point. The nature of the material or accessory is indicated by the provision of a brief description above this line (Fig. 5).

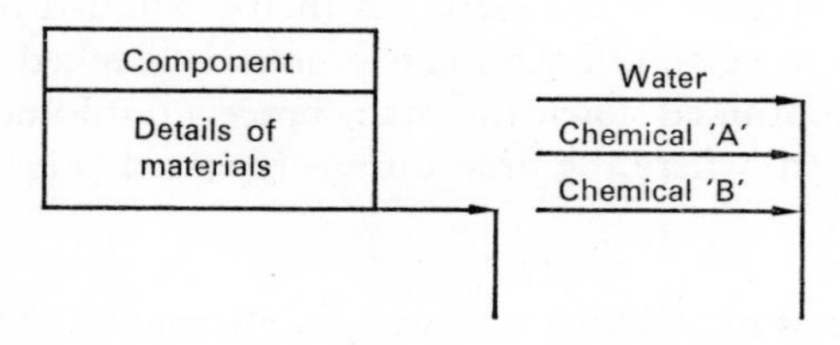

FIG. 5. Introduction of materials.

Change in Shape, Size, or Nature during Processing

Where the shape, size, or nature of a material is significantly changed as the result of an operation, and it is desired to indicate such a change so that handling or processing characteristics from one stage to another may be appreciated, this change is shown on the chart by breaking the chart line at the appropriate place and inserting a brief description of the nature of the change (Fig. 6). It should be appreciated, however, that it is not necessary to record in this manner every significant change of shape, but only those that are considered to have a direct bearing on the objectives of the study. Many changes of shape are naturally inferred from the nature of the operation that precedes it.

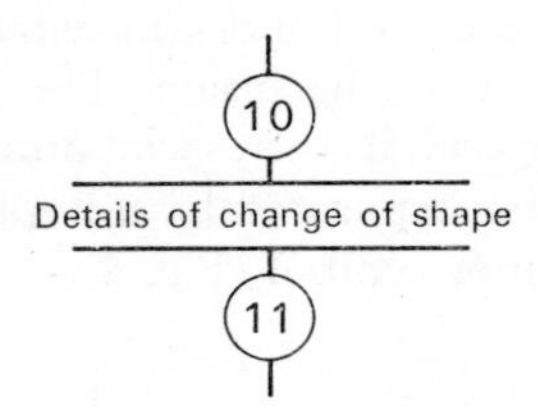

FIG. 6. Change in shape, size, or nature during processing.

Entry and Charting of Subsidiary Parts

In assembly operations the product is constructed from many components and materials, which are introduced into the sequence of processing during its manufacture. When charting activities of this kind the main process is charted on the right-hand side of the chart and the subsidiary processes are charted to its left. These are subsequently joined to each other and made to enter the main process at the appropriate points as they are required. The symbols of the main process are numbered in the conventional way until the introduction of a subsidiary process is reached. The sequence of numbering is then continued from the start of this subsidiary process until the main process is reached again, then the numbering is continued down the main process until another subsidiary process is reached, where the procedure is repeated (Fig. 7).

Alternative Routes

Often a process may divide into various alternative paths as the result of an activity which may divide material into a number of quantities,

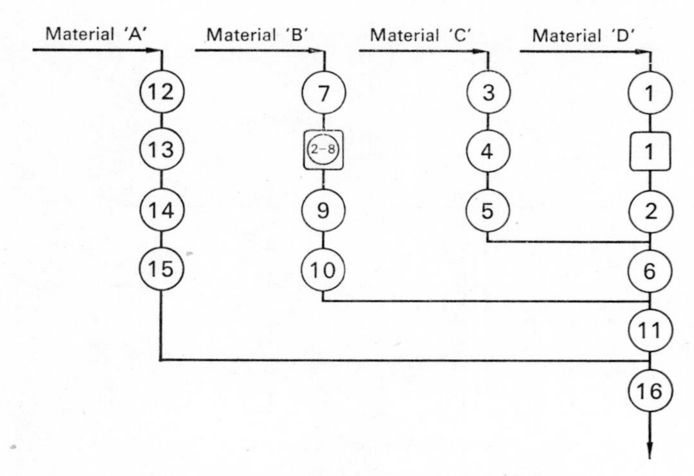

FIG. 7. Entry and charting of subsidiary processes.

each receiving subsequent processing from that point onwards. In such situations the main process line is divided into the appropriate number of branches. The right-hand branch will represent the main process line, whilst the alternative ones are indicated successively towards the left of the chart.

The proportion or percentage of the original material allocated to each branch may, if required, be indicated above the branch. The main process line is numbered in the conventional manner and the alternative paths are numbered in sequence from the right, as shown in Fig. 8.

Rejects and Material Returned for Reprocessing

As the result of an inspection rejects are often separated from correctly produced articles. Rejection, when it occurs, is indicated by a branch to the right of the main process line. The reason for rejection can be indicated by information written above and below the line, as shown in Fig. 9. Certain types of process material, which has been rejected as the result of an inspection, may be returned to an earlier location in the process sequence for further treatment; this is indicated by a branch to the right of the chart together with a suitable description, but unlike the previous example this branch is carried back to the point of re-entry of the material to the main processing (Fig. 10).

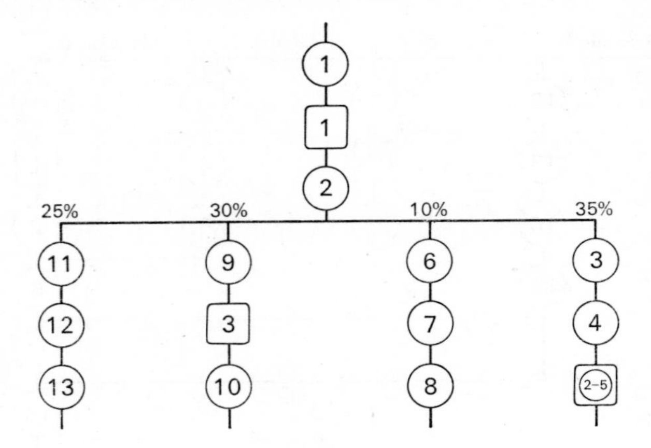

FIG. 8. Alternative routes.

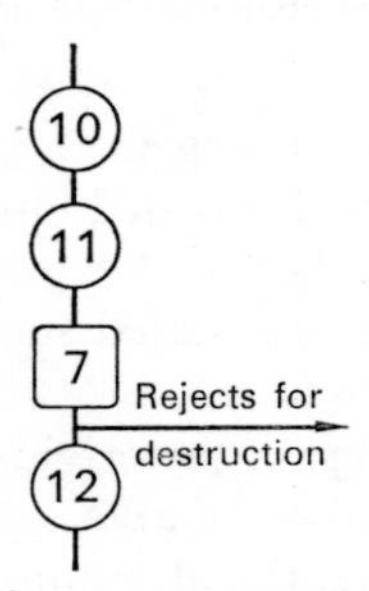

FIG. 9. Rejects for destruction.

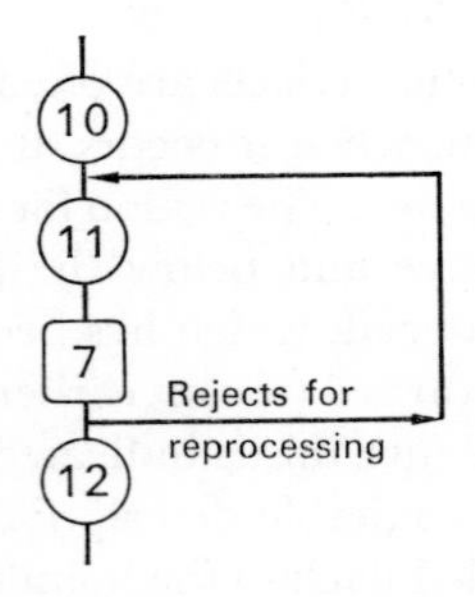

FIG. 10. Material returned for reprocessing.

Working in Parallel

Often it is necessary, in order to balance the flow of work through a process, to carry out the same operation in duplicate at more than one location or by more than one operator. This situation is indicated by dividing the chart into a number of paths, each of these representing a duplication of the operation. In the example (Fig. 11), operations six and seven are shown in parallel and represent the same operation

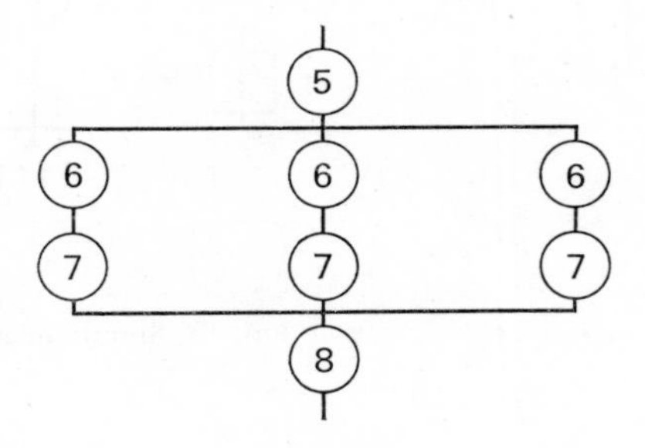

FIG. 11. Working in parallel.

being carried out independently of each other. The method of numbering, as indicated previously, is from right to left but in this case it is the same two operations. This charting convention can also be used to show that some materials may follow alternative but complementary routes during a process.

Simultaneous Operations

When simultaneous operations have to be made on the main portion of a unit and an assembled component a partial dismantling may be necessary. The dismantling operation, the simultaneous operation, and the subsequent reassembly, can be charted in the same way as that used to indicate working in parallel. In Fig. 12 a dismantling has occurred after the second operation. An operation has then been carried out on the main assembly and the dismantled portion and the two parts have then been reassembled. In Fig. 13 components are sorted into three lots, extra operations being performed on two of the lots to make them acceptable for operation eleven.

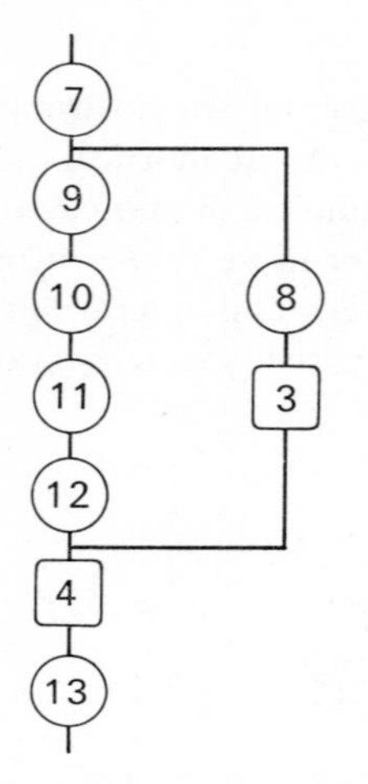

FIG. 12. Simultaneous operations.

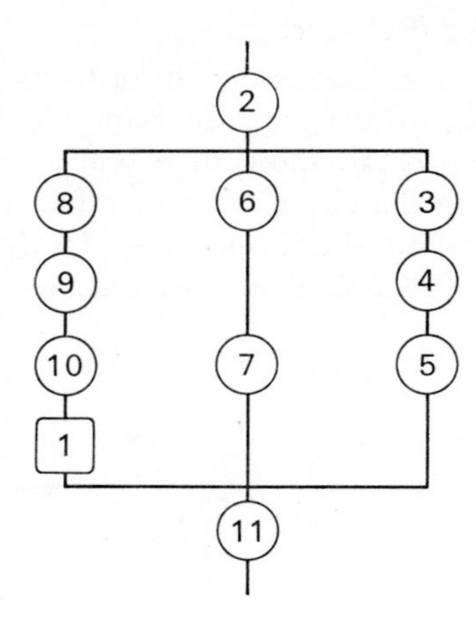

FIG. 13. Simultaneous operations.

Repeat Operations

When a certain activity has to be repeated a number of times before a process can be continued, as often occurs, for example, in batch production, it is confusing and unnecessary in such situations to show on the chart each repeated operation in full as this would increase the length of the recording. This situation is indicated by breaking the chart line at the appropriate point by two parallel lines and joining the upper line to a bracket which includes the activity to be repeated. The number of repetitions is written between these parallel lines. This convention must be applied only to a sequence which is truly repetitive. Sometimes the first and last activities of a repetitive sequence differ slightly from each other. In such a case these will be charted in the normal way and the convention will be applied only to the intervening fully repetitive sequence. Special care must be taken to ensure that the correct number of repetitions are indicated so that the appropriate continuity of numbering is preserved (Fig. 14).

When no Juncture Occurs

The operation or outline process chart is usually constructed and arranged so that the vertical and horizontal lines do not cross. If it is necessary during the process of recording to cross a vertical or horizontal line, the normal practice to indicate that no juncture is intended is to draw a small semicircle in the horizontal line at the point of intersection (Fig. 15).

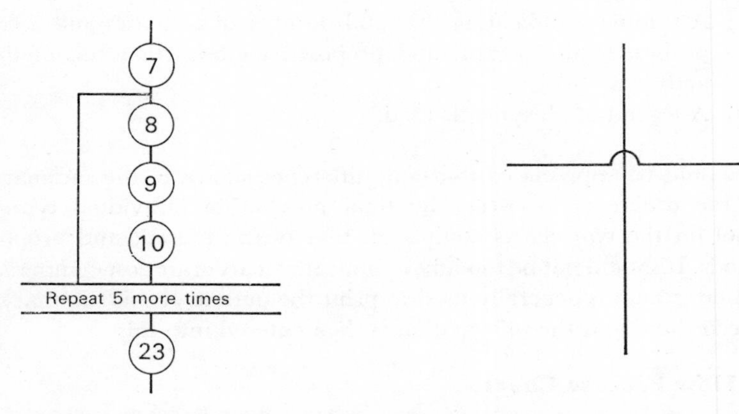

FIG. 14. Repeat operations.

FIG. 15. When no juncture occurs.

Time

It is an advantage to include on the chart the time taken for each activity. This is done by placing the time, in any convenient time unit, to the left of the chart and in line with the appropriate symbol. The total time is then indicated at the base of the recording (Fig. 16).

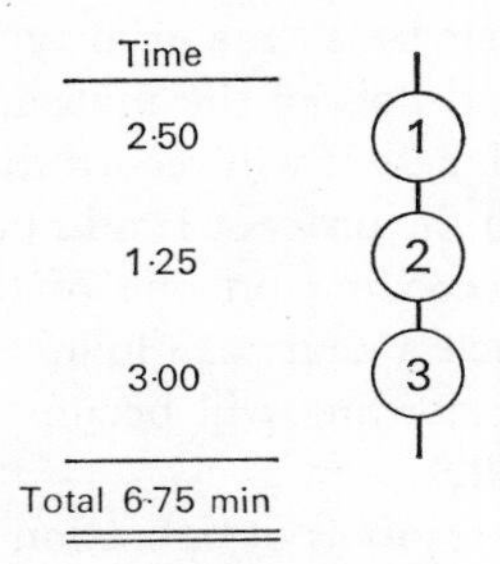

FIG. 16. Indication of time.

General Information

All process charts should be self-contained and each should possess the following information.

(i) A brief description of the process charted.
(ii) An indication of where the process chart begins and ends.
(iii) Whether the recording represents the present or the proposed method.
(iv) A summary indicating the total number of activities and a comparison of the present and proposed methods in terms of these activities.
(v) A legend of all symbols used.

It should be appreciated that any difference shown in the summary is only the difference between the total number of individual types of symbol on the two charts compared, that of the present and proposed methods. It should not be thought to indicate an accurate cost comparison. A rubber stamp is generally used to print the outline of this summary on the recording, and the information is then entered into this.

The Flow Process Chart

The outline process chart, previously described, gives only an overall view of a process, it does not give details of what occurs between the activities of operation or inspection, nor does it give information as to the movement and flow throughout the process. As this information has often to be obtained, as it is important in certain method studies, a form of chart called a flow process chart is used in such circumstances. This enables information of this type to be obtained in a convenient form for subsequent examination.

This recording can either be a "material type" chart, in which case it will record the activity and flow of the material throughout the process, or a "man" type, in which case it will record the movement and activities of the operator throughout the process. It is important that having decided for the purpose of the recording on one of these two procedures, this decision is adhered to. Such a chart can follow the activities of either but not both, otherwise the recording will become confused and subsequent analysis extremely difficult.

In addition to the two symbols of operation and inspection previously encountered in the construction of the outline process chart, three further symbols are now used, the symbols of transportation, delay, and storage. These are indicated in Fig. 17 together with a definition of each and examples of their use. In making such a chart it is not expected to draw these symbols freehand except during the actual process of recording.

Plastic templates are obtainable for achieving a satisfactory presentation of these symbols on the final chart, should this be desired.

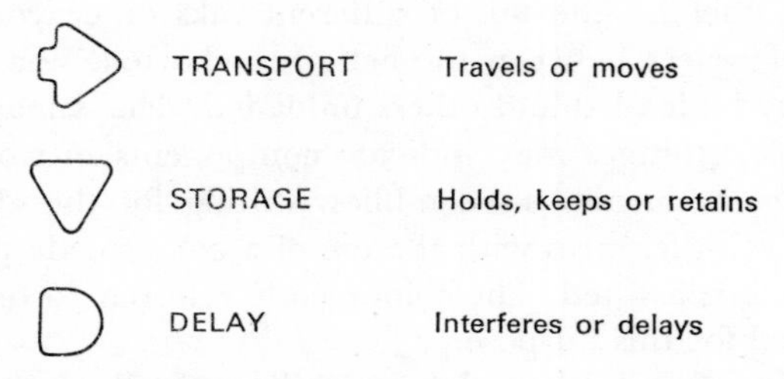

FIG. 17. Symbols in addition to those of operation and inspection used in the construction of the flow process chart.

The procedure for constructing a flow process chart is similar to that employed for the outline process chart, and the charting conventions previously described are also applicable, but with the addition of the extra three symbols. The only other addition to the conventions used for re-

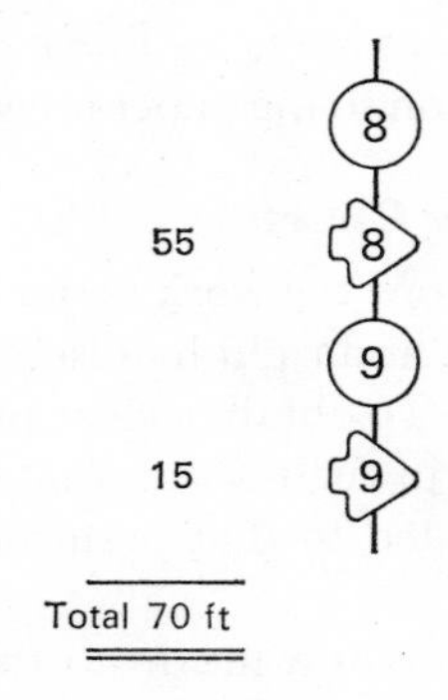

FIG. 18. Indication of distance travelled.

cording is that the transport symbol is qualified by distance moved, in suitable units of distance, to the left of the symbol. As each symbol will also be qualified with units of time, the units of distance will be placed to the left of those of time. The total distance will be shown at the base of the chart, as indicated in Fig. 18.

A process chart is but a means to an end and not an end in itself. Thus any method of charting must be flexible and its value as a visual record can always be enhanced by various devices. The full use of colouring can be obtained either by the use of different inks or crayons, to indicate particular differences between the activities charted. For example some transports may be loaded and others unloaded, delays may be avoidable or unavoidable, storages may indicate components in store, or painted articles drying, or furniture assemblies waiting for the glue to dry. By indicating these differences with the use of a colour code the elaboration of the recording is assisted. The colour code referred to on pp. 43–45 is frequently used for this purpose.

The criterion for judging the suitability of all charting devices is whether the process recorded can be easily understood. F. B. Gilbreth stated that a process chart is "A device for visualizing a process as a means of improving it", so that any aids that can further this desire are acceptable to the method study practitioner.

The flow process chart, like the outline process chart, requires a heading and a summary. The form of this summary will be the same as that for the outline process chart already described, except for the additions of the extra process symbols and the units of distance. In similar fashion to that employed elsewhere, a rubber stamp made to this design is used to affix this summary on to the paper on which this chart is recorded.

The Two-handed Process Charts

It is often necessary to record the work performed at a single work place in terms of the operators left and right hands and the occasional contribution of other body members. To obtain a clear picture of such an operation the work must be recorded in such a way that the activity performed by one part of the body is related to that performed simultaneously by the other.

A two-handed process chart is a means to this end and is a method of recording in which the activities of a worker's hands or limbs are recorded in relation to one another. There are two methods of recording commonly used to satisfy this aim. The first records the activities of the operator's two hands in terms of the A.S.M.E. symbols previously employed in the construction of the outline and the flow process charts. The second records the operator's two-handed activity in terms of what are called the "basic divisions of accomplishment".

The Two-handed Process Chart—A.S.M.E. Symbols

This type of two-handed process chart consists of two vertical columns in which are recorded the symbols indicating the activities of the left and right hands. Examples of the use of each of these symbols for the activities of the operator's hands are shown in Fig. 19. These symbols are aligned so that simultaneous movements are opposite each other. If the movements of the feet contribute to the activity two extra columns are used to record

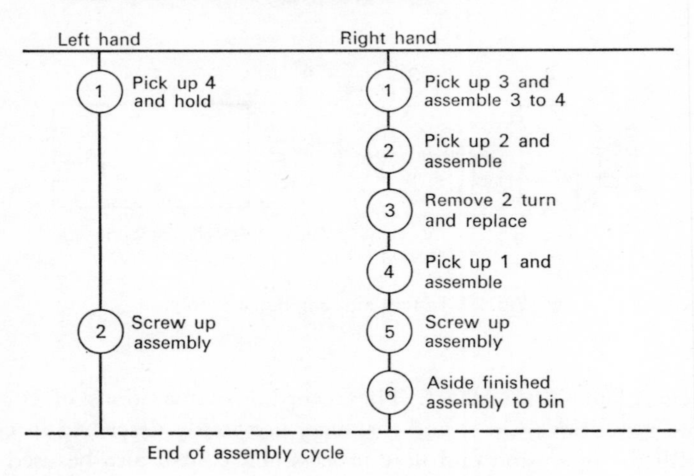

Fig. 19. Example of an outline two-handed process chart.

this. The degree of detail required will influence the scale on which this chart is constructed. As with the use of the operation or outline process chart, which gives only details of the activities of a process in terms of the operations and/or inspections, a two-handed process chart may be constructed in a similar fashion to give an overall picture of a two-handed activity in terms of the symbol of operation, should this degree of detail be considered appropriate and sufficient. The symbol of inspection is not often used in the construction of this type of chart, as it is frequently possible to record an inspection activity in terms of the operation or other symbols. The example of a two-handed process chart shown in Fig. 19

conveys an overall picture of the assembly of an air coupling (Fig. 20). This indicates that the first operations of the hands are performed simultaneously and subsequent operations are made by the right hand whilst the left hand holds the assembly.

If more information is required the other three symbols of transport, delay, and storage may be used in addition to that of operation. Fig. 21 shows the same two-handed activity in more detail using all four symbols. The numbering of the symbols is done in the conventional way, the activities of each hand being treated for this purpose separately. The symbols which are the same are numbered serially for each hand from the

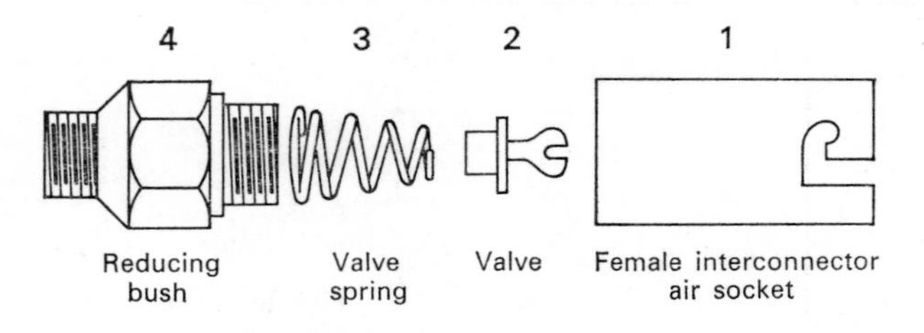

Fig. 20. Instant air coupling assembly.

commencement of the chart. The recording conventions of combined symbols, repetitions, time, and distance, previously described in connection with the operation and flow process charts, can also be used in the construction of the two-handed process chart. But it should not be forgotten that the purpose of this charting method is to provide a means of recording a two-handed activity for the purpose of subsequent examination and development of an improved method. Such development will require the application of the principles of motion economy (Chapter 9, p. 192) and the classification of movement (p. 67).

As with other forms of charting the two-handed process chart must be self-contained. For this reason a summary is prepared in a similar manner to that for other process charts.

This type of two-handed process chart is a valuable technique of recording but its use has certain limitations, one of these being the difficulty of recording the precise details of the individual activities of the hands by symbols which are comparatively broad for this purpose.

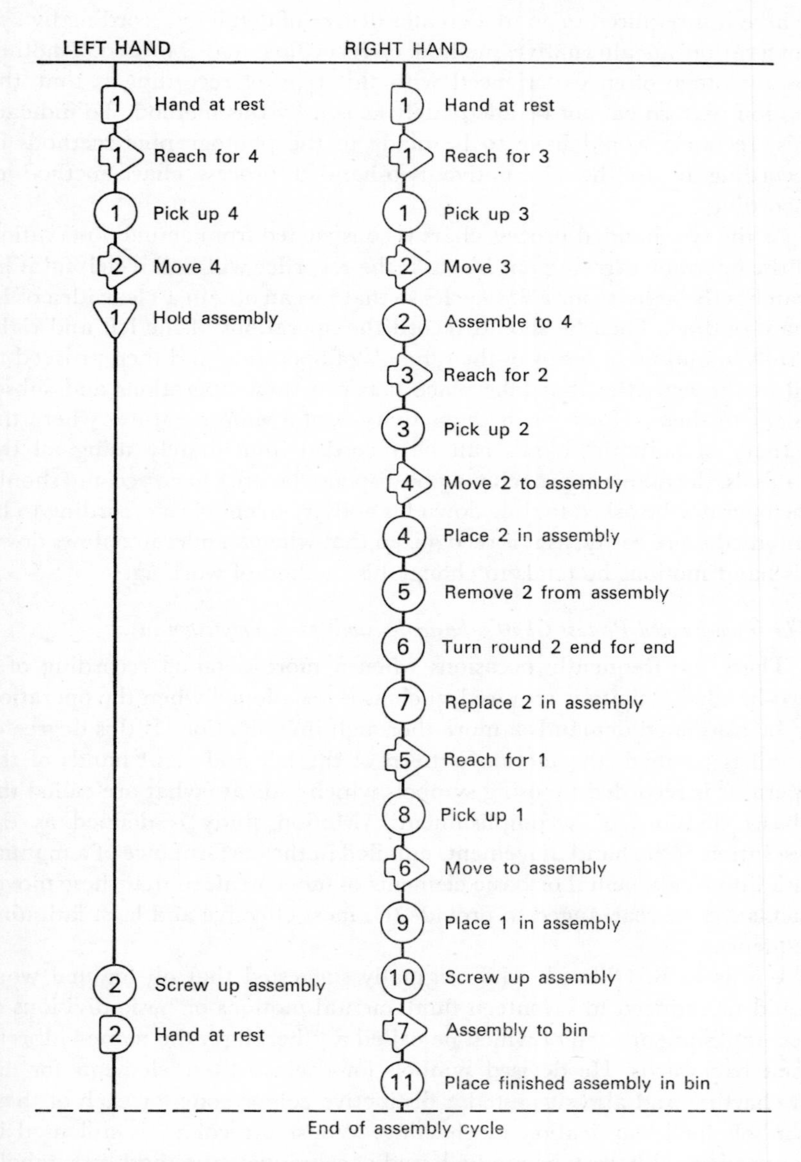

FIG. 21. More detailed example of the two-handed process chart for the air-coupling assembly.

Where it is required to go to a greater degree of detail in recording by eye observation an alternative method of recording may be used. Another disadvantage often experienced with this type of recording is that the motion pattern cannot be adequately shown by this method. To indicate this, recourse would have to be made to the photographic methods of recording or to the alternative two-handed process chart method of recording.

As the two-handed process chart is constructed from actual observation of the operator carrying out his task, the recorder will find it helpful if he watches the activity for a few cycles so that he can obtain a clear idea of its main outline. Then he should record the operations of the left and right hands in outline in terms of the symbols of operation and then proceed to fill in the activities that take place between these operations and subsequent to them. However, if the activity is of a simple nature, where the activity of both the hands can be recorded immediately using all the symbols, the above approach may be dispensed with. On no account should the operator be asked to slow down his activity to enable a recording to be obtained more easily, as it is recognized that when an operator slows down his hand motions he tends to change his method of working.

The Two-handed Process Chart—basic divisions of accomplishment

There are frequently occasions when a more detailed recording of a two-handed activity is required, such as is occasioned when the operation to be examined demands a more thorough investigation. If this degree of detail is justified, the motion pattern of the left and right hands of the operator is recorded by using symbols which indicate what are called the "basic divisions of accomplishment". Motion study is defined as the resolution of the hand movements entailed in the performance of a manual task into fundamental or basic elements of movement, so that these movements can be rearranged to provide the most effective and least fatiguing sequence.

It was F. B. Gilbreth who originally suggested that all manual work could be reduced to seventeen fundamental motions or basic divisions of accomplishment each of which he called a "therblig", the name Gilbreth spelt backwards. He devised symbols for each of these elements for use in charting and also suggested a distinctive colour code for each of these symbols for identification in charting. Whilst the colour is still used in connection with certain method study techniques, the therblig symbols, which have been superseded by the modern abbreviations suggested by the Standard of the American Society of Mechanical Engineers, now have only historical interest. This revision of the original Gilbreth symbols was undertaken to permit an easier understanding of their purpose, as it was thought that their use often suggested elaboration and complication where it did not exist.

The classification of these basic divisions of accomplishment, the name by which these elements are now known, is given below by the letter symbol suggested by the American Society of Mechanical Engineers. A definition of each of these basic elements is also given.

With a knowledge of these basic elements of movement it is possible to prepare a two-handed process chart by direct observation of the operator's activities. However, skill and experience are required in order to do this. This method of recording should not be confused with a similar but more detailed chart known as the simo chart, which will be described subsequently in connection with a technique known as "micromotion study", this chart is obtained as the result of film analysis. It is in connection with this photographic method of recording that the colour code equivalents to these elements are used. They are also shown here for convenience.

It is important to remember that these basic elements are used to describe the motions of the hands. They are not applicable when mechanical means are used for performing some of these elements. It is difficult to define in words the exact nature of each of these basic elements of motion and for this reason a film of these elements is normally used to train method analysts in their identification and understanding.

The Basic Divisions of Accomplishment

Reach (R) — When the purpose is to move the hand. It begins when the hand is moved without a load and ends when the hand touches an object. (Olive green.)

Move (M) — When the purpose is to carry an object to a destination. The hand begins to move with an object and ends when the object reaches its destination. (Mineral green.)

Change Direction (CD) — When a change in the path or plane, along which a reach or a move is taking place, occurs through defects in the operation method. (Green.)

Grasp (G) — When the purpose is to gain control of an object or objects with the fingers. It begins when the hand touches the object and ends when control is obtained. (Crimson lake.)

Hold (H) — When the control of an object is obtained. It begins when the movement of an object, controlled by the hand, ceases and ends when movement commences again. (Gold.)

Release load (RL) — When the control of an object is relinquished. The motion used to shake a sticky object from the fingers is not described by this basic element. Release load begins when the hand and part begins to separate and ends when the hand has lost contact with the part. (Pale vermilion.)

Preposition (PP) — The preparation of the object being moved for the best subsequent basic element, which is usually that of position. It is not performed as an independent motion. Preposition of tools and objects at a work site is not preposition in this sense but is a function of planning. (Light blue.)

Disengage (D) — To break contact between one object and another. As the objects are separated the resistance suddenly ends. If two objects are loosely connected and where clearance occurs between them the motion is that of a move and not a disengage. It begins when the parts begin to separate and ends when complete separation is obtained. (Light violet.)

Position (P) — To line up an object with another. This motion begins when the part begins to line up and ends when the process of lining up is completed (Prussian blue.)

Search (S) — To seek or locate an object. If the operation work area layout is correctly arranged this motion would not occur. It begins when the hand starts to find an object and ends when it is located. (Black.)

Select (SE) — To choose between several objects. This motion begins when the hand touches several objects and ends when the hand has located an individual object. (Light grey.)

Plan (PL) — The hesitation that occurs when an operator decides on a next course of action. This element begins when the hand is idle, or makes random movements while the operator decides on appropriate action, and ends when the action has been determined. (Vandyke brown.)

Examine (E) — To determine the quality of an object. This element begins when a hand begins to feel or view an object and ends when it ceases to do this. (Burnt Sienna.)

Avoidable Delay (AD) — Some movement or idleness which is not part of the regular motion sequence. It begins when a deviation from a

	standard method commences and ends when a return to the standard method is made. (Lemon cadmium.)
Unavoidable Delay (UD)	The stopping of an activity produced as a result of the poor arrangement of the motion pattern or by bad methods. It begins when idleness commences and ends when work begins again. (Yellow ochre.)
Rest to Overcome Fatigue (F)	A delay necessary for the operator to recover from exertion. It begins when rest commences and ends when the hand begins work again. (Deep chrome.)
Balancing Delay (BD)	This begins when one hand waits for the other and occurs in instances where the work cannot be arranged so that the cycle times of each hand are the same. It ends when the hands are working together again. (Orange.)
Do (DO)	This begins when an operation is commenced and ends when it is completed in full or in part. (Magenta.)

An example of a two-handed process chart constructed with these symbols is shown below for the purpose of indicating the form that this takes. It is constructed for the simple operation of putting the top of a fountain pen on its base.

LEFT HAND			RIGHT HAND
Reach for fountain pen top	R	R	Reach for fountain pen base
Grasp pen top	G	G	Grasp pen base
Move to put together	M	M	Move to put together
Align top to base	PP	PP	Align base to top
Position top to base	P	P	Position base to top
Hold top	H	DO	Push home base to top
Hold top	H	DO	Engage screw thread and tighten
Hand to desk	R	M	Move pen to desk
Hand at rest on desk	UD	RL	Place pen on desk

It is appreciated that in this particular example the activity could equally be recorded with the A.S.M.E. charting symbol, but where finer detail is required than is obtained by the use of these symbols, this method of charting, using the symbols of the basic divisions of accomplishment, is advisable.

Method Study Investigation Forms

In order to assist in the recording of the more straightforward types of activity, standard method study investigation forms have been designed to simplify this process. It is not possible to design such forms to cover all the eventualities of charting. It is for this reason that complex processes are not generally recorded on them. However, some of the usual conventions can be applied to these forms, and common sense will indicate where modification of the standard chart can be made during the process of recording. For instance where it is required to indicate combined symbols the appropriate symbols can be joined by a horizontal line.

Standard forms have been designed for the following methods of charting, the operation or outline process chart (Fig. 22), the flow process chart, and the two-handed process chart (Fig. 23). Each of these are of foolscap size and consist of a top sheet, which includes a summary, and continuation sheets.

Activity Sampling

Introduction

Activity sampling is a procedure of recording used for obtaining an estimate of the proportions of time spent in occurrences which make up sections of a total activity. The required information is obtained by making a large number of instantaneous observations over a representative period of time. It is based on the fact that the percentage number of observations recorded for a particular activity is a measure of the percentage of time during which that activity occurs.

The technique was originated by L. H. C. Tippett at the British cotton industry research association in 1927, for the purpose of discovering the cause and duration of loom stoppages with a view to estimating how much of the productive capacity was lost through various causes. Previously he had used methods which were found to be tedious and unnecessarily protracted. The possibility of using such a technique for general use was further developed by R. L. Morrow in a paper presented to the American Society of Mechanical Engineers in 1940 and later published in 1946. It

Process Chart

Ref. No. ____________
Page ______ Of ______

Summary

	Present		Proposal		Difference	
	No.	Time	No.	Time	No.	Time
○ Operations						
□ Inspections						
⇨ Transportation						
D Delays						
▽ Storages						
Distance travelled		Feet		Feet		Feet

Job ____________

Man or Material ____________
Chart begins ____________
Chart ends ____________
Charted by ____________ Date ______

Details of {Present / Proposed} Method	Quantity	Operation, Inspection, Transportation, Delay, Storage	Distance in feet	Time	Analysis — Why?: What?	Where?	When?	Who?	How?
		○ □ ⇨ D ▽							
		○ □ ⇨ D ▽							
		○ □ ⇨ D ▽							

FIG. 22. Process chart form.

TWO-HANDED PROCESS CHART

PRESENT
PROPOSED METHOD

REF. NO. ______
PAGE ______ OF ______

SUMMARY

	PRESENT		PROPOSED		DIFFERENCE	
	LH	RH	LH	RH	LH	RH
○						
⇨						
▽						
D						
TOTAL						

JOB ______

CHART BEGINS ______

CHART ENDS ______

CHARTED BY ______ DATE ______

OPERATOR ______

LAYOUT	PARTS SKETCH

LEFT HAND	MOVEMENT CLASS	DELAY	HOLD	TRANSPORT*	OPERATION	OPERATION	TRANSPORT*	HOLD	DELAY	MOVEMENT CLASS	RIGHT HAND
		D	▽	⇦	○	○	⇨	▽	D		
		D	▽	⇦	○	○	⇨	▽	D		
		D	▽	⇦	○	○	⇨	▽	D		
		D	▽	⇦	○	○	⇨	▽	D		
		D	▽	⇦	○	○	⇨	▽	D		
		D	▽	⇦	○	○	⇨	▽	D		
		D	▽	⇦	○	○	⇨	▽	D		
		D	▽	⇦	○	○	⇨	▽	D		
		D	▽	⇦	○	○	⇨	▽	D		
		D	▽	⇦	○	○	⇨	▽	D		
		D	▽	⇦	○	○	⇨	▽	D		

Fig. 23. Two-handed process chart form.

has subsequently had wide application in method study investigations and has been used in numerous industries and locations other than the furniture industry, such as department stores, iron foundries, in the building and construction industries for study of site gangs, machine utilization in the tobacco industry, clerical operations in offices, and the division of labour between staff in hospitals.

The procedure has in the past been given various names by those who have contributed to its development and application. Studies using this technique have been named variously "snap reading", "ratio delay", "work sampling", "activity ratio", "machine utilization", and "random observation studies". Whilst each of these names describes a particular aspect of its application they are not of a sufficiently general nature to provide an all embracing title. The term "activity sampling" will be used to describe the procedure. This was suggested by the British Standards Institute as being a more appropriate one.

Procedure

The theoretical basis of activity sampling is similar to that used in statistical quality control for determining the proportion of defective articles in a batch. As its name implies it is essentially a sampling technique.

If management wish to know the division of the total time spent by an operator during a working day in effective and non-effective activities, it is possible for this information to be obtained by continuous observation over the stated period. However, this might be tiresome and tedious and might produce unrepresentative data due to the continuous presence of the investigator. Where details are to be obtained of the percentage activities of a number of operators working simultaneously, the use of activity sampling is essential as it would be difficult to obtain this information by any other means, unless the photographic methods of recording were used. This technique therefore enables the sampling of moments of activity at intervals over a given period of time to obtain an estimate of the required information.

If it is decided that activity sampling is an appropriate means of obtaining the required information for a particular method study the following procedure will have to be adhered to.

Activity sampling procedure:

(i) Determine purpose of the study.

(ii) Consult with personnel.
(iii) Determine degree of accuracy required.
(iv) Plan the study:
 (a) Total number of observations required.
 (b) Interval between observations.
 (c) Position of the observer.
 (d) Duration of the study.
 (e) Design study form.
(v) Make observations and record the results.
(vi) Compute the results.
(vii) Presentation of the results in suitable form.

The investigator should determine carefully in conjunction with management the purpose of the particular activity sampling study. This purpose is invariably to determine the percentage occurrence of certain activities, but what these activities should be demands careful thought. As a means of clarifying this point it is appropriate to construct a "tree" of activities and delays which have to be considered to achieve the aims of the study. As a result of doing this the investigator will be able to set out the heading under which the observations will be recorded. In certain circumstances the study may consist of finding out the proportion of time during which a group of men and equipment is working or not working. In this case a "tree" would be constructed as shown in Fig. 24. Often, however, it is necessary to obtain details of the division of the work carried out into its various activities and the nature of the non-working periods. In such

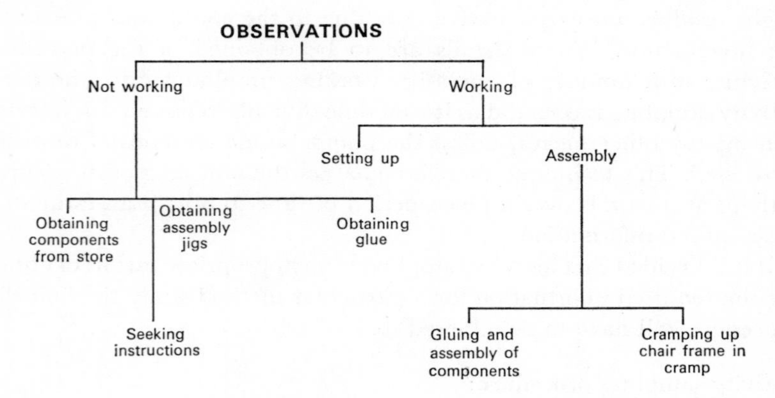

Fig. 24. Activity sampling observations—tree of activities.

situations the tree would be extended to include these other activities as indicated in the figure. A diagram of this kind thus becomes the basis for the planning of the study. Particular subjects for observation will be grouped together under one of the headings indicated as it should be realized that it is not possible to consider and observe too many subjects simultaneously for the study would become humanly impossible to make. It is usually only reasonable to make an instantaneous observation of a few activities and subjects at any one time, as to how many will depend on the skill and experience of the observer. But there has always to be a compromise in such circumstances, between what information is required by the study and the ability of the observer at the instant of making the observation to decide in what categories each of the activities fall. It is normally found impossible in practice to distinguish between certain kinds of delay, thus it may be found convenient for them in certain circumstances to be grouped together. If a large number of activities have to be considered it is usually necessary in such instances to carry out two studies. Before the actual details of this aspect of the proposed study are finalized, it is always found helpful to make a preliminary study to identify the subjects to be recorded and to estimate their percentage occurrence.

The investigator should consult with all personnel who are likely to be associated with the study before it is commenced. This is done in order to acquaint them with the aims of this type of study, what will be involved, and to seek their co-operation.

Having decided on the subjects and activities that are to be observed, the next decision that has to be made is to decide on the limits of accuracy appropriate to the objectives of the investigation. The degree of accuracy usually found acceptable for such studies is ± 5 per cent of the percentage activity. There are occasions where coarser limits are sometimes acceptable to management, particularly where only an indication of percentage activities is required. But usually because the use of activity sampling brings to light some very unfavourable aspects of a work situation, the accuracy of the results is the first thing that is questioned. It is for this reason that an accuracy not larger than ± 5 per cent is selected. It is important to remember that the degree of accuracy required will influence the duration of the study and the total number of observations that will eventually have to be made.

Having decided on the activities that are to be studied and the degree of accuracy that will be acceptable, the actual planning of the proposed study now has to begin. This is commenced by the determination of the total number of observations required to achieve the objects of the study, and the accuracy required. An accurate indication of the occurrence of the activities, to the limits required, will not be obtained if a sufficient number of observations is not taken.

To obtain the number of observations required for any study the following formula is used:

$$N = \frac{4P(100-P)}{L^2},$$

where N is the number of observations required for the given accuracy, P is the percentage occurrence of the activity being analysed, L is the limit of error considered acceptable.

At the commencement of the study P should either be estimated in order to apply it to this formula, or a pilot study should be taken of possibly 150 observations in order that a value for P can be determined for substitution in this formula. For instance, if as a result of a pilot study it was determined that the percentage occurrence of a particular activity was 10 per cent, and that an accuracy of $\pm$ 5 per cent was acceptable, the total number of observations necessary to achieve this accuracy would be determined as follows:

$$N = \frac{4P(100-P)}{L^2} = \frac{4 \times 10(100-10)}{5^2} = \frac{40 \times 90}{25} = 144 \text{ observations.}$$

The observer can be certain, in making this number of observations, that 95 per cent of the time or 954 cases out of 1000 that the true value of P will be somewhere between $P - L$ and $P + L$. For example if $L = \pm$ 2 per cent and the percentage occurrence being analysed is 28 per cent then the real value of P will be 28 per cent $\pm$ 2 per cent. In the majority of cases 95 per cent or $\pm$ 5 per cent certainty or confidence limit is adequate for most activity sampling studies.

In order to determine the limit of error or L for the percentage occurrence of an activity that has been observed, so that a check may be made to see that a sufficient number of observations has been obtained for this activity, the following formula is used:

$$L = \pm 2\sqrt{\left[\frac{P(100-P)}{N}\right]}.$$

If, for example, after taking 150 observations in a particular study the investigator wishes to find the degree of accuracy or limit of error for an activity, which is 10 per cent of the observation time or total number of observations, he will use the above formula substituting these figures in the formula.

$$L = \pm 2\sqrt{\left[\frac{P(100 - P)}{N}\right]} = \pm 2 \times \sqrt{\left[\frac{10(100 - 10)}{150}\right]}$$

$$= \pm 2 \times \sqrt{\left(\frac{900}{150}\right)} \qquad = \pm 2 \times \sqrt{6}$$

$$= \pm 2 \times 2{\cdot}45 \qquad = \pm 4{\cdot}90 \text{ per cent}$$

$$\therefore L = \pm 4{\cdot}90 \text{ per cent and } P = 10 \text{ per cent} \pm 4{\cdot}90 \text{ per cent.}$$

The next consideration in planning the proposed study is the interval to be allowed between observations. This interval may be either of fixed duration, such as, for example, one observation every minute, or of random duration, in which case the interval between the observations will be of variable duration. This variability or randomness is obtained by the use of what are called "random numbers".

If the observations are made at random intervals the elapsed time between the observations will depend on the design of the study to be undertaken and the total number of observations that have to be obtained within a given period of time. Frequently this period of time is the duration of the activity or the given representative period, or this length of time is all that management can allow for the study.

Randomness of the observations is obtained by the interpretation of random numbers (Fig. 25). These can be found in any textbook of statistical tables. These numbers are used in this particular instance to indicate the time at which each observation should be made. To do this the random numbers are interpretated in various ways according to the requirements and conditions of the study. When the manner in which these numbers are to be interpreted has been decided, the selection and planning of a schedule of observation can then be made. For example in the following line of random numbers taken from the table, 10 47 42 75 22, the first digit can be made to indicate the hour and the second digit the minutes past the hour. Since most plants work between the hours of 8 and 12, and after a meal break from 1 to 5, any numbers falling outside these times can

TABLE XXXIII. RANDOM NUMBERS (I)

03 47 43 73 86	36 96 47 36 61	46 98 63 71 62	33 26 16 80 45	60 11 14 10 95
97 74 24 67 62	42 81 14 57 20	42 53 32 37 32	27 07 36 07 51	24 51 79 89 73
16 76 62 27 66	56 50 26 71 07	32 90 79 78 53	13 55 38 58 59	88 97 54 14 10
12 56 85 99 26	96 96 68 27 31	05 03 72 93 15	57 12 10 14 21	88 26 49 81 76
55 59 56 35 64	38 54 82 46 22	31 62 43 09 90	06 18 44 32 53	23 83 01 30 30
16 22 77 94 39	49 54 43 54 82	17 37 93 23 78	87 35 20 96 43	84 26 34 91 64
84 42 17 53 31	57 24 55 06 88	77 04 74 47 67	21 76 33 50 25	83 92 12 06 76
63 01 63 78 59	16 95 55 67 19	98 10 50 71 75	12 86 73 58 07	44 39 52 38 79
33 21 12 34 29	78 64 56 07 82	52 42 07 44 38	15 51 00 13 42	99 66 02 79 54
57 60 86 32 44	09 47 27 96 54	49 17 46 09 62	90 52 84 77 27	08 02 73 43 28
18 18 07 92 46	44 17 16 58 09	79 83 86 19 62	06 76 50 03 10	55 23 64 05 05
26 62 38 97 75	84 16 07 44 99	83 11 46 32 24	20 14 85 88 45	10 93 72 88 71
23 42 40 64 74	82 97 77 77 81	07 45 32 14 08	32 98 94 07 72	93 85 79 10 75
52 36 28 19 95	50 92 26 11 97	00 56 76 31 38	80 22 02 53 53	86 60 42 04 53
37 85 94 35 12	83 39 50 08 30	42 34 07 96 88	54 42 06 87 98	35 85 29 48 39
70 29 17 12 13	40 33 20 38 26	13 89 51 03 74	17 76 37 13 04	07 74 21 19 30
56 62 18 37 35	96 83 50 87 75	97 12 25 93 47	70 33 24 03 54	97 77 46 44 80
99 49 57 22 77	88 42 95 45 72	16 64 36 16 00	04 43 18 66 79	94 77 24 21 90
16 08 15 04 72	33 27 14 34 09	45 59 34 68 49	12 72 07 34 45	99 27 72 95 14
31 16 93 32 43	50 27 89 87 19	20 15 37 00 49	52 85 66 60 44	38 68 88 11 80
68 34 30 13 70	55 74 30 77 40	44 22 78 84 26	04 33 46 09 52	68 07 97 06 57
74 57 25 65 76	59 29 97 68 60	71 91 38 67 54	13 58 18 24 76	15 54 55 95 52
27 42 37 86 53	48 55 90 65 72	96 57 69 36 10	96 46 92 42 45	97 60 49 04 91
00 39 68 29 61	66 37 32 20 30	77 84 57 03 29	10 45 65 04 26	11 04 96 67 24
29 94 98 94 24	68 49 69 10 82	53 75 91 93 30	34 25 20 57 27	40 48 73 51 92
16 90 82 66 59	83 62 64 11 12	67 19 00 71 74	60 47 21 29 68	02 02 37 03 31
11 27 94 75 06	06 09 19 74 66	02 94 37 34 02	76 70 90 30 86	38 45 94 30 38
35 24 10 16 20	33 32 51 26 38	79 78 45 04 91	16 92 53 56 16	02 75 50 95 98
38 23 16 86 38	42 38 97 01 50	87 75 66 81 41	40 01 74 91 62	48 51 84 08 32
31 96 25 91 47	96 44 33 49 13	34 86 82 53 91	00 52 43 48 85	27 55 26 89 62
56 67 40 67 14	64 05 71 95 86	11 05 65 09 68	76 83 20 37 90	57 16 00 11 66
14 90 84 45 11	75 73 88 05 90	52 27 41 14 86	22 98 12 22 08	07 52 74 95 80
68 05 51 18 00	33 96 02 75 19	07 60 62 93 55	59 33 82 43 90	49 37 38 44 59
20 46 78 73 90	97 51 40 14 02	04 02 33 31 08	39 54 16 49 36	47 95 93 13 30
64 19 58 97 79	15 06 15 93 20	01 90 10 75 06	40 78 78 89 62	02 67 74 17 33
05 26 93 70 60	22 35 85 15 13	92 03 51 59 77	59 56 78 06 83	52 91 05 70 74
07 97 10 88 23	09 98 42 99 64	61 71 62 99 15	06 51 29 16 93	58 05 77 09 51
68 71 86 85 85	54 87 66 47 54	73 32 08 11 12	44 95 92 63 16	29 56 24 29 48
26 99 61 65 53	58 37 78 80 70	42 10 50 67 42	32 17 55 85 74	94 44 67 16 94
14 65 52 68 75	87 59 36 22 41	26 78 63 06 55	13 08 27 01 50	15 29 39 39 43
17 53 77 58 71	71 41 61 50 72	12 41 94 96 26	44 95 27 36 99	02 96 74 30 83
90 26 59 21 19	23 52 23 33 12	96 93 02 18 39	07 02 18 36 07	25 99 32 70 23
41 23 52 55 99	31 04 49 69 96	10 47 48 45 88	13 41 43 89 20	97 17 14 49 17
60 20 50 81 69	31 99 73 68 68	35 81 33 03 76	24 30 12 48 60	18 99 10 72 34
91 25 38 05 90	94 58 28 41 36	45 37 59 03 09	90 35 57 29 12	82 62 54 65 60
34 50 57 74 37	98 80 33 00 91	09 77 93 19 82	74 94 80 04 04	45 07 31 66 49
85 22 04 39 43	73 81 53 94 79	33 62 46 86 28	08 31 54 46 31	53 94 13 38 47
09 79 13 77 48	73 82 97 22 21	05 03 27 24 83	72 89 44 05 60	35 80 39 94 88
88 75 80 18 14	22 95 75 42 49	39 32 82 22 49	02 48 07 70 37	16 04 61 67 87
90 96 23 70 00	39 00 03 06 90	55 85 78 38 36	94 37 30 69 32	90 89 00 76 33

FIG. 25. Table of random numbers. (Abridged from Table XXIII of Fisher and Yates, *Statistical Tables for Biological, Agricultural, and Medical Research*, published by Oliver & Boyd Ltd., Edinburgh, and by permission of the authors and publishers.)

be discarded. If, for example, 200 observations have to be made in one day, 200 numbers are obtained from a table of random numbers and each is placed on a form in the sequence in which they are selected; they are then in the order in which they will be used, and this constitutes the schedule of the required observations.

However, the above numbers may be interpreted as minute intervals between observations if desired. For instance if the factory commences work at 7.30, then the first observations would be made on this basis at 7.40, i.e. 7.30 plus the random number 10, and the next at 8.27, the next at 9.9, and so on. Observations are not made during the periods of scheduled rest, such as lunch, tea breaks, which occur during the time limits of the study.

If the activity presented for sampling is not periodic or cyclic in any way, effective randomization can usually be achieved by taking observations at constant time intervals, where conditions and circumstances similar to those obtained in the photographic technique of memomotion are present. But an interval between observations of approximately one minute or less is the usual period required for studies conducted in this way. Whatever the interval that may be chosen, and this applies to both fixed and random intervals, it must be of sufficient duration to allow the observer to be able to comply with the physical demands of the particular study.

Studies may be made with the observer recording his observations throughout the duration of the investigation from one location, or alternatively a study may be conducted from a number of predetermined observation points, which the observer will visit in a planned sequence, preferably at random. This procedure is frequently adopted in situations where a large number of machines or men cannot be observed simultaneously from one position. If this method is proposed for a particular study, it is important to see that the interval chosen between observations is such that it will allow the observer to record the information that he has observed from one position, and get to his next location in time to make his next observation. This is an important consideration in studies conducted on building sites or in factories where congestion and obstruction may occur. For this reason a safety margin of time should be allowed for in planning the time interval between observations in such studies. Consideration of this factor will also influence the minimum interval duration that may be selected in connection with a particular type of study.

The next consideration is the duration of the study. One of the advantages of an activity sampling study is that it can be spread over a longer period of time than other forms of recording. This enables a more representative sample of an activity to be obtained. Normally, however, studies can be taken over a period of hours or days and the period extended for a long enough duration to ensure that all the variables of an activity are sampled. A representative period, for instance, in a retail shop would require that the observations be made over at least a week, since the pattern of trade varies from Monday to Saturday. The duration of a study will primarily be indicated and influenced by the number of observations that have to be obtained to secure a certain degree of accuracy. If the required number of observations is large and it is only possible to obtain a certain quantity of these per day, then to comply with the basic requirements of the study, the approximate duration of the sampling is obviously indicated. A study is made to obtain certain information; if this can be secured in a short span of time there is nothing gained by prolonging the study further. Thus the duration of an activity sampling study is the minimum

ACTIVITIES	OPERATOR					TOTAL
	1	2	3	4	5	
CONTACT FOREMAN.				✓		
OBTAIN MATERIALS.		✓				
INSPECTION.			✓			
STACK PARTS.						
FILL IN JOB CARD	✓					
SET UP					✓	
DELAY						
ABSENT						
WORK M/C						

Fig. 26. Example of activity sampling observation sheet for the study of a number of operators.

time that it takes to obtain the desired information to the accuracy required. When experience has been gained the duration for a proposed study will suggest itself.

The design of the observation sheet to be used in a particular study demands close attention if difficulties are not to be subsequently experienced during the actual study. There is no standard form as each observation sheet has to be designed for the individual requirements of a study. But whilst each observation sheet is different, they all have certain features in common with each other. Each will show the particular equipment or operator that is to be observed and the appropriate activity or delay that occurs at the instant of making the observation. Each will also normally provide enough space for a tally mark or tick to be entered against the operator, machine activity, or type of delay observed. A form for one such arrangement is indicated in Fig. 26, where the observer uses a single sheet for several operators or machines. The purpose of the particular study, for which the form was designed, was to determine the relative proportion of time during which a group of fifteen machines were (a) working or actually processing timber, (b) running but not processing timber, (c) being set up or prepared for the next job, or (d) idle.

Alternatively an observation sheet can be designed as in Fig. 27 or as in Fig. 28. In both of these examples there is a column for each of the

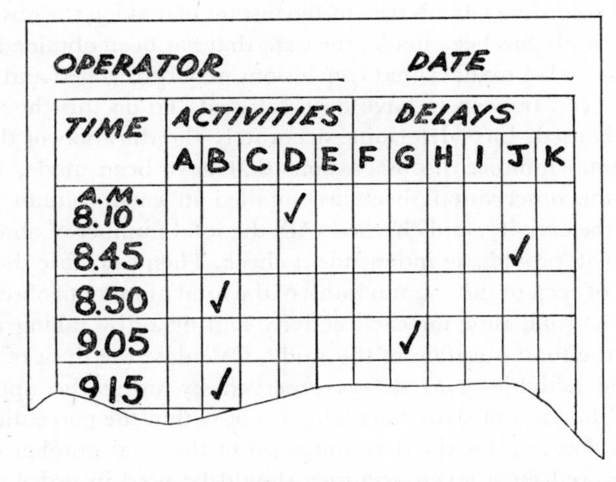

FIG. 27. Example of activity sampling observation sheet for the study of one operator.

subjects to be observed, and according to the activity seen at the instant of looking up from the form, at the area of activity, a tick or letter denoting the subject is placed in the appropriate column below the activity or delay observed.

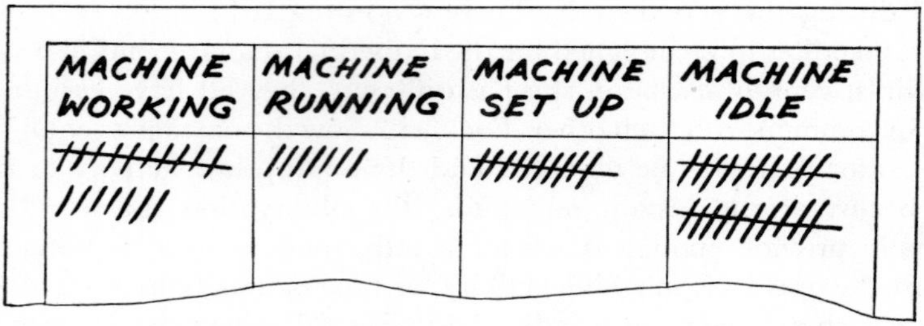

MACHINE WORKING	MACHINE RUNNING	MACHINE SET UP	MACHINE IDLE
////////// ///////	///////	//////////	////////// //////////

FIG. 28. Example of activity sampling observation sheet for the study of a number of machines.

It is essential, in the process of making the observations, to see that these observations are free from any form of bias, assumptions, or anticipations, which are likely to have been produced as a result of any preconceived knowledge of the activity. Although the conduct of a study does not demand any great degree of skill, scrupulous honesty, however, is required in recording what is seen at the instant of making the observation.

After the study has been made, the data that has been obtained must be presented in such a manner that conclusions may be reached and the aims of the study can be seen to have been satisfied. To do this the following procedure is used. First determine accurately the duration of the study. Then the total number of observations that have been made. If all the marks on the observation sheet are totalled in each column for each element of the activity, and checked with the total number of observations made, this will provide an independent check. Then calculate the relative percentage of each of the column totals of the total number of observations. Calculate the total time for each activity and delay by taking that percentage of the total duration of the study. Calculate the limit of error for each of the activities and delays observed by using the appropriate formula. If the limit of error calculated is not within the percentage limits desired, the formula for the determination of the total number of observations required for a given accuracy should be used in order to obtain an idea of the additional number of observations that would have to be taken to obtain the degree of confidence desired. The results of the study are then arranged in the form of a summary, indicating the percentage of each activity, the time spent on each activity, and the actual and possible range between which each of the activities will possibly lie. The simplicity of the calculations can best be appreciated by a simple example. Figure 29 shows an observation sheet used in the study of the activities of a "Wadkin"

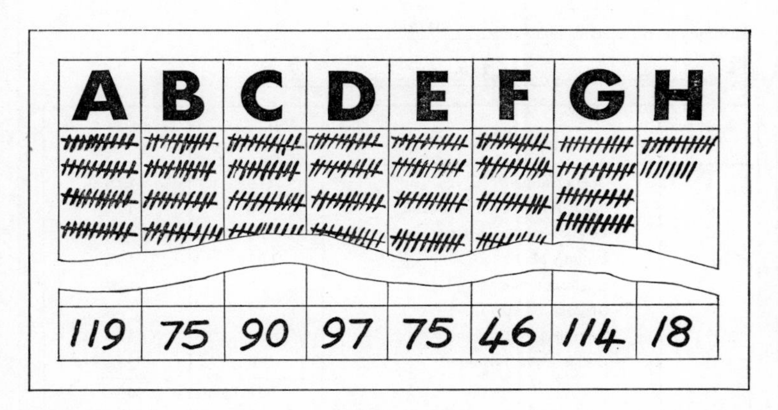

Fig. 29. Activity sampling observation sheet for the study of a crosscut saw.

hydraulic cross-cut saw. The summary of this study is shown in Fig. 30 and the calculations to determine the objectives of the study are as follows:

(a) *The percentage frequency of each of the activities*

This is obtained by counting up the number of observations for each activity and expressing each total as a percentage of the total number of observations. This is shown on the activity sampling summary (Fig. 30).

(b) *The percentage time consumed by activity A and for the activities A and H*

Activity A.

Estimated percentage of total time is 19 per cent.

Total observation time is 120 min.

19 per cent of 120 min is $\frac{19}{100} \times 120 = 23$.

The observed time for activity A is 23 min.

Activity Sampling Summary

Study No 17 Date 20.9.64

Subject WADKIN HYDRAULIC CROSS CUT SAW Location ROUGH MILL.

Observers ONE Workers ONE

Required No of Observations 634

Representative Period 2 HOURS

Activity Ref.	Activity	No of Observations	Estimated % of Total Time
A	Collect timber	119	19%
B	Place timber on roller table	75	12%
C	Position timber against stop	90	14%
D	Cutting plank	97	15%
E	Stack cut pieces	75	12%
F	Dispose of scrap	46	7%
G	Counting cut pieces	114	18%
H	Contact supervision	18	3%
		634 Total	100

The object of the study is to determine the following:-

(a) The percentage frequency of each of the activities.

(b) The percentage time consumed by activity A and for the activities A and H.

(c) The limit of error for activity A.

(d) The percentage limits between which the true value of activity A may be expected to lie.

The observations sheet used for this study is shown in Fig 29.

FIG. 30. Activity sampling summary.

Activities A and H.

Estimated percentage of total time consumed by activities A and H is $19 + 3 = 22$ per cent.

Total observation time is 120 min.

22 per cent of 120 min is $\frac{22}{100} \times 120 = 26 \cdot 4$.

The observed time for activity A and H is 26·4 min.

(c) *The limit of error for activity A*

$$L = \pm 2\sqrt{\left[\frac{P(100 - P)}{N}\right]} = \pm 2 \times \sqrt{\left[\frac{19(100 - 19)}{634}\right]}$$

$$= \pm 2 \times \sqrt{\left(\frac{19 \times 81}{634}\right)}$$

$$L = \pm 2 \times \sqrt{\left(\frac{1539}{634}\right)} = \pm 2 \times \sqrt{2 \cdot 43} = \pm 2 \times 1 \cdot 56$$

$$L = \pm 3 \cdot 12 \text{ per cent.}$$

The limit of error for activity A is $\pm 3 \cdot 12$ per cent.

(d) *The percentage limits between which the true value of activity A may be expected to lie*

The observed time for activity A is 23 min $\pm 3 \cdot 12$ per cent.
The actual time for activity A lies between 23 + 3·12 per cent or 23 — 3·12 per cent or 23·7176 min and 22·282 min respectively.

If necessary this calculation may be made for each of the activities if their accuracy is considered critical.

Photographic Methods of Recording

Introduction

The method study photographic procedures of recording consist of the following techniques:

(a) Micromotion.
(b) Memomotion.

The use of either of these can be regarded as an essential and convenient procedure, which in certain circumstances will almost certainly be demanded. Although their use involves the making of films and photographs, it should be remembered that it is not necessary to make a technically perfect film in every respect. As long as the film will show in a reasonably satisfactory manner the activity to be studied, this is all that is desired. However if a photographically acceptable film is obtained in the process of recording information it will greatly assist the subsequent presentation of these activities to factory personnel and management, should this be desired.

Many method study investigators find it convenient to use still photographs to record details of conditions and situations in a work environment to support and illustrate written information. This form of evidence, in situations that are continually changing, enables the investigator to support his argument, which would otherwise be difficult to do. Polaroid cameras, which enable the production of these photographs and their immediate development, have been found particularly successful for this purpose.

Micromotion

This technique was originated by F. B. Gilbreth for the recording and subsequent analysis of the movements of an operator's two hands. It provides a means of obtaining a complete record of the activity and the method used, and simplifies the subsequent task of methods improvement in this area of investigation. As it is not always possible to record the two-handed activity of an operator by the conventional two-handed process chart, by reason of the speed at which the operator is carrying out his task, this technique provides the only means by which recordings of such situations can be made.

It is only on work of a highly repetitive nature and with a substantial life, that micromotion is economically justified, but there can be other advantages to be obtained from its use. It permits greater detail to be obtained and records the activity with greater accuracy than the other methods of recording can provide. It is often in certain circumstances considered to be more convenient where speed and accuracy of recording are demanded, as it provides a positive record without errors. The use of the procedure of analysis associated with this method of recording aids in the development of method study personnel, by enabling them to obtain a clear understanding of the basic divisions of accomplishment, so that they are subsequently more able to make accurate motion studies by personal observation. The fact that a method is recorded on a film also facilitates the instruction of new operators—as they can see the old and new procedures and make comparisons they will thus be encouraged to appreciate the opportunities afforded by looking for similar possibilities in other work. A film may also form the basis for the production of a sensorimotor process chart used in connection with analytical training procedures (Chapter 7).

There are certain features in the use of micromotion which are considered by many to be a possible disadvantage. For instance the delay

Fig. 31. Microchronometer.

between obtaining the data and the processing of the film, so that it is available for analysis, is often considered to be one, but this need not be so as the processed film can be obtained usually on the fourth day after filming from the processing laboratories who specialize in this type of service. Another consideration is the expense of the equipment and apparatus. This can be considerable, but where it is economically justified this need not be a problem particularly as many trade and industrial advisory organizations have this equipment and are prepared to lend this with specialist staff for making a film recording for the individual firm. With the wider use of 8 mm film this has itself reduced the total cost when compared with the expense of 16 mm film and equipment. The analysis of the film, whilst it consumes time and as such is an expensive procedure, when compared with the time taken in the use of the conventional charting methods on comparable activities there appears very little difference in terms of time. However, these considerations need not worry the practitioner unduly as the use of this technique is obligatory if a recording of certain activities is to be made at all.

Procedure

Micromotion study involves three separate phases of activity.

(a) Filming.
(b) Film analysis.
(c) Graphic presentation of the method for study criticism and improvement.

Each of these phases of the activity is equally important but demands the possession of different skills from method study personnel.

The following equipment is required for carrying out a micromotion study. A 16 mm camera together with a suitable tripod which should be one that will hold the camera firmly in position in the average conditions of an industrial work area. An exposure meter is also required, to see that the lighting conditions of the work place do not affect the quality of the film to be taken. Lights are usually optional by reason of the high-quality film that can now be purchased. Other equipment required is a timing device and an electric drive. The timing device usually employed is called a microchronometer (Fig. 31). Its face is divided into a hundred divisions and it possesses two hands. The large hand makes 20 r.p.m. and the small hand 2 r.p.m. Since in some cases variations in the speed of filming, other than the normal, i.e. 16 f.p.s., is often necessary, the use of the microchronometer is desirable to identify the speed of the filming from the developed film. It was originally developed in the days of the hand-cranked camera, where the speed of filming was subject to variations. It is also desirable always to include the timing device in the field of view of the camera, so that proof of the continuous nature of the film can be made, and to be able to identify at any future occasion the speed of the filming and the length of any section of the film damaged and removed.

The electric drive is an important addition to the equipment required for filming, as the camera, whilst making the film, is normally driven by a spring mechanism which allows filming for only a period of very short duration. Where it is necessary to film continuously for much longer periods, to obviate the necessity of constantly pausing to rewind the camera, which would be an inconvenience, the electric drive is used. This can be battery driven or derive its source of power direct from the mains supply. This permits the taking of longer series of pictures without the pauses necessary to rewind and also enables a choice of filming speeds to be obtained where it is thought necessary to increase or decrease the speed of filming above or below the normal 16 f.p.s.

The procedure of filming demands the observance of six basic rules. Firstly, the co-operation of the shop steward, the operator, and supervisor should be obtained. Notification of the intention to film should be made well in advance. Secondly, the camera should be placed as close to the activity to be filmed as possible and it should be arranged so that the camera view includes all the work area and the operation. The film should then be made with as little inconvenience as possible. Thirdly, the appropriate speed of filming for the particular operation should be selected and the electric drive set to this. The normal speed of filming is often not appropriate in certain circumstances. An increased number of frames per second above the normal is often required where the hand movements are very fast and the distance travelled by the hands is short. Fourthly, the best exposure possible should be obtained. The length of the exposure will be influenced by the speed of filming, in frames per second, and the exposure interval by the sensitivity of the film, which is always indicated on the film carton, and the quality of the light available.

If a microchronometer is to be used, make sure that its position is such that it will be included in the film and that its location does not interfere in any way with the operation to be recorded. If, due to circumstances and the individual nature of the work area, this cannot be done, then a wink counter may be used. This is attached to the camera and operates when the camera is filming. When the film is subsequently developed the number of each frame is clearly shown at the bottom of the picture. This numbering device was originally designed to read to 1/2000th of a minute, as it was this element of time that was regarded by F. B. Gilbreth as the normal for the quickest element of movement and was termed a "wink" by him.

Sixth, a record of all the details of the making of the film should be made so that subsequent filming may be improved. For this purpose a film record sheet is completed (see Fig. 38).

Film analysis commences when the processed film is returned from the laboratory where it has been developed. It is desirable to form this film into a continuous loop for analysis so that it may be projected over and over again. By doing this a much clearer idea is obtained of how the operation is performed. This loop should show at least two cycles of the operation, one of which should have been filmed at about 64 f.p.s. and the other at the normal speed of 16 f.p.s. The first cycle when projected at normal speed will thus give a slow motion effect and make details of the operation easier to follow. Having projected the film loop a number of times in a film analyser so that the main details of the operation have now become familiar to the analyst, the film is then stopped near the commencement of the operation cycle and the film moved frame by frame to the exact starting point. The film projector or analyser is specially designed for the analysis of such film. It enables film to be projected at infinitely variable speeds above or below the normal and also allows the film to be projected forwards or backwards either continuously or by hand, frame by frame. The analyser incorporates a frame counter which is simply a numbering device which indicates the number of frames of the film being analysed that have passed between two points on the film. This is an aid in determining the time for a basic element, for as the speed at which the film has been taken is known in terms of frames per second, the time that has elapsed during the period of a number of frames can thus be easily obtained. This frame counter is adjusted to zero on the film analysis projector at the commencement of the study of the film or if a timing device or microchronometer has been placed in the field of the camera during filming, a note is made of its reading.

It is now necessary not only to analyse the film in a particular way but also to record the details obtained from this in a manner suitable for subsequent examination. A film analysis record sheet (Fig. 32) is used for

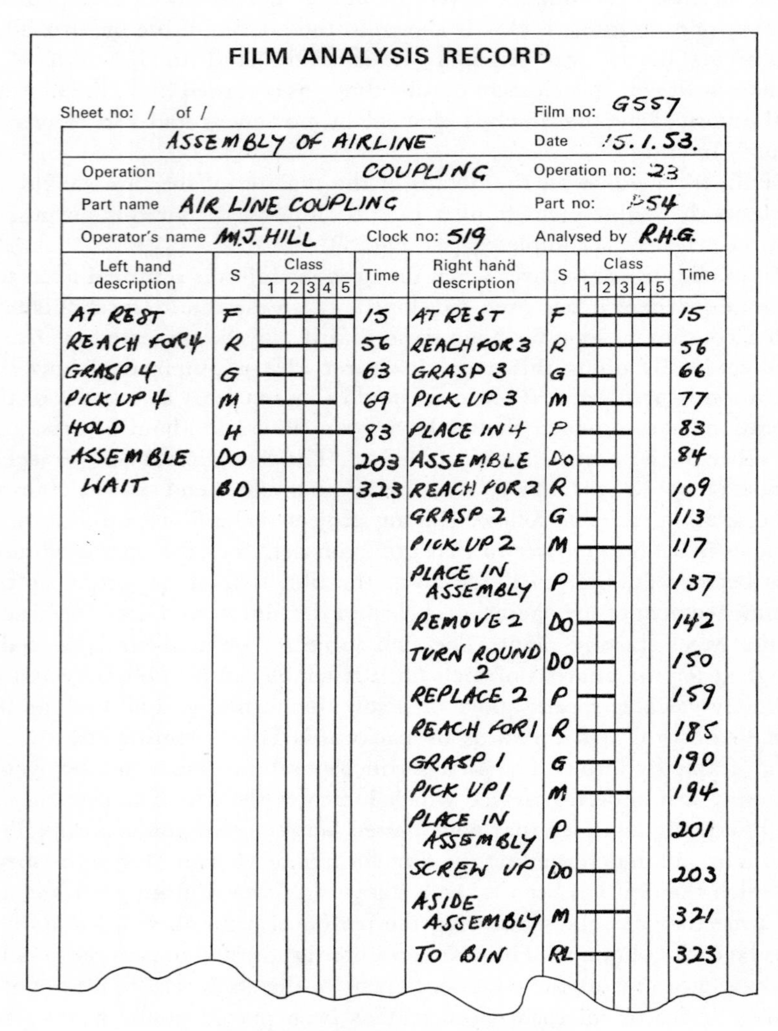

FILM ANALYSIS RECORD

Sheet no: / of / — Film no: G557

ASSEMBLY OF AIRLINE — Date 15.1.53.

Operation COUPLING — Operation no: 23

Part name AIR LINE COUPLING — Part no: P54

Operator's name M.J. HILL — Clock no: 519 — Analysed by R.H.G.

Left hand description	S	Class 1 2 3 4 5	Time	Right hand description	S	Class 1 2 3 4 5	Time
AT REST	F		15	AT REST	F		15
REACH FOR 4	R		56	REACH FOR 3	R		56
GRASP 4	G		63	GRASP 3	G		66
PICK UP 4	M		69	PICK UP 3	M		77
HOLD	H		83	PLACE IN 4	P		83
ASSEMBLE	DO		203	ASSEMBLE	DO		84
WAIT	BD		323	REACH FOR 2	R		109
				GRASP 2	G		113
				PICK UP 2	M		117
				PLACE IN ASSEMBLY	P		137
				REMOVE 2	DO		142
				TURN ROUND 2	DO		150
				REPLACE 2	P		159
				REACH FOR 1	R		185
				GRASP 1	G		190
				PICK UP 1	M		194
				PLACE IN ASSEMBLY	P		201
				SCREW UP	DO		203
				ASIDE ASSEMBLY	M		321
				TO BIN	RL		323

FIG. 32. A film analysis record sheet.

the purpose of recording the results obtained from the study of the activity performed by the operator's two hands. Its use provides a means of studying each hand separately and independently and this greatly simplifies the procedure of film analysis.

The details entered on this record sheet, in the columns for the description of the left- and right-hand activities, will be as brief in their wording as possible. In the column headed with an S is placed the symbol for the basic division of accomplishment or basic motion element observed. In the column headed "Class" is recorded the class of movement observed in carrying out this basic motion.

Gilbreth classified these movements into five categories. When a movement of the hand is observed using any of these, the movement is classified by a number. It is the object of methods improvement in manual operations to reduce the movements being reviewed to the lowest number classification possible, if this aspect is to be considered. But this aspect is a concern of film analysis.

The Classification of Movement

1. Fingers only (I).
2. Fingers and wrist (II).
3. Fingers wrist and lower arm (III).
4. Fingers wrist lower and upper arm (IV).
5. Fingers wrist lower and upper arm and shoulder (V).

The numbers placed in the column under the heading "Time" on the film analysis record sheet indicate the number of frames that have elapsed during a basic motion element.

From the details entered on this record sheet a special type of two-handed process chart known as a "simultaneous motion time chart", or simo chart, is subsequently constructed. It is this that is afterwards examined in order to obtain improvements to the operation.

To commence the analysis of the film and the filling in of the film analysis sheet either the right- or left-hand is selected first for study. The motion element or basic division of accomplishment being used by the hand selected at the commencement of the operation is noted. Then the film is moved through the projector frame by frame observing at the same time the class of movement employed, and noting when the end of the motion element is reached. When this is completed the frame counter reading is noted, as this will indicate the number of frames of film that have been used for this motion element. This figure is recorded in the column marked "Time" on the film analysis record sheet. Now in line with the frame counter reading the symbol of the motion element seen to have been employed is recorded. The other motion elements employed by the particular hand in carrying out the operation are similarly charted and this procedure is continued until all the movements of the hand have been analysed and recorded. Then the same procedure is repeated for the other hand and the details recorded on the other half of the record sheet. Having recorded the activities of both the left and right hands in this manner on the film analysis record sheet, a simo chart can now be constructed from this data. A record of this kind is shown in Fig. 33. This is constructed nearly always from the data shown on the film analysis sheet but some film analysts leave out the intermediate stage of the film analysis sheet.

To construct a simo chart, a standard form is obtained, and the left-hand description and the symbol of the basic element for the activity is entered on it from the film analysis sheet. The number of frames that have elapsed during the production of the element is converted into a suitable linear measurement, by selecting a unit of length to represent one frame. Thus 15 frames will be represented by fifteen times this unit measured from the top of the column marked "Time". This duration is marked on the chart and a line drawn across from this column to where the class of movement made during this element has been entered. The area of the simo chart bounded on the one side by the number of elapsed frames represented in measurement units, and on the other by the horizontal line drawn to the class of movement, represents a significant feature of the chart. This area is coloured with a crayon of the appropriate value represented by the colour code for each of the basic divisions of accomplishment. This colour code which was indicated in introducing the basic divisions of accomplishment is particularly effective for the immediate recognition of certain ineffective elements on these charts.

The completion of a simo chart provides a very detailed analysis of how a particular operation is performed. It is this that will form the basis for the analysis and development of an improved method. It should again be pointed out that it is only on certain activities, where this method of recording is necessary and where it can be economically justified, that this procedure should be used. The analysis of film for micromotion study can be very time consuming; an idea of how long this activity can take is indicated by the fact that a skilled film analyst can do a maximum of 400 ft of film per day.

SIMO CHART

Sheet no: / of / Film no: G557.

Operation: ASSEMBLY OF AIR LINE COUPLING. Date 15. 1. 53

Operation no: 23

Part name: AIR LINE COUPLING Part no: P54

Operator's name: M. J. HILL. Clock no: 519 Analysed by R.H.G

Left hand description	S	Class 5 4 3 2 1	Time	Class 1 2 3 4 5	S	Right hand description
AT REST	F		10		F	AT REST
REACH FOR BUSH.	R		20 30 40 50		R	REACH FOR VALVE SPRING.
GRASP BUSH	G		60		G	GRASP SPRING
PICK UP BUSH	M					
HOLD BUSH	H		70		M	PICK UP SPRING
			80		P	PLACE IN BUSH
ASSEMBLE	DO				DO	ASSEMBLE

FIG. 33. Example of a simo chart.

Memomotion

Memomotion is the name given by its inventor, Dr. Marvin E. Mundel, to a special type of cine photography used in method study in which the film is taken at low speeds, such as 1 f.p.s. Such an arrangement permits an hour's work to be recorded on about 100 ft of film. Work which has been done over a long period can thus be reviewed by film in a short space of time. A hundred feet of film can be projected within four minutes at the normal projection speed of 16 f.p.s. Memomotion has all the advantages of micromotion study and embraces its three phases of filming, film analysis, and graphic presentation. The particular method of analysis and the subsequent presentation of the data for criticism will depend on the nature of the problem for which this technique has been used.

The technique originated in 1946 when Dr. Mundel was commissioned to investigate the conditions of cooking meals in a large hotel, to provide information for an article for *Life* magazine. Due to the nature of the problem he had decided to use photographic methods of recording. If the subject had been recorded by the conventional micromotion cine photography it would have required 120,000 ft of film and an exorbitant time for analysis. The subject was eventually photographed at 1 f.p.s., thus reducing the length of film required to 7,500 ft.

The first user of a similar type of technique was F. B. Gilbreth in 1916 when he was making studies of group activities. The apparatus used by him for this purpose was a hand crank camera. Time-lapse photography using a motor driven camera has, however, long been used for the study of plant and flower growth. The Gilbreths, it should be remembered, had made films that were taken at one picture or frame every 10 minutes.

Memomotion studies can be made in a manner similar to activity sampling studies, where eye observation is superseded by the camera which samples the situation or activity at a constant or random time interval. As many industrial operations are not machine-paced or cyclic, sampling by photography at a constant time interval is appropriate provided certain conditions are met. Activity sampling by the use of a camera has certain advantages where a large number of conditions and objectives have to be observed simultaneously.

Memomotion studies are frequently used to study the flow of men and materials, or the use of material handling equipment in a given area, or the activities of an operator at work, the equipment he uses, and the flow of material to and from his work site. The information contained on film of such studies may be analysed in a number of ways, and the data presented in a manner depending on what is desired from the study.

It is a valuable tool of method study, which can be used where other procedures of recording would either be impractical or uneconomical. It has been found valuable in the study of methods concerned with such subjects as air-port organization, self-service and department stores, banks, traffic flow on highways, building and construction sites, and the armed services.

The use of this technique enables an investigator to select the objective of the study subsequent to the recording, as it is not always possible to define the actual nature of the problem, in certain circumstances, until after sufficient data has been obtained. Another advantage of this procedure is that it reduces the film cost to a fraction of that of normal filming and the time required for film analysis. It permits the recording of activities that have a cycle time greater than 4 minutes. This could not be done with micromotion study, as the maximum length of a 16 mm film that can be loaded into the camera is 100 ft, as this contains approximately 4,000 frames, filming at 16 f.p.s. would take about 4 min to use. At 2 f.p.s. 100 ft would take 34 min to film and at 1 f.p.s. 100 ft would take 68 min to use. Therefore by varying the speed of filming in frames per unit of time, activities of different durations may be recorded

The application of this type of photographic technique has certain apparent disadvantages and limitations, which may be overcome by the use of ingenious devices. It is not always possible, for example, to include within the film picture the whole area to be studied, but this is overcome by the use of a wide-angle lens, and other means such as elevating the camera above the work area or travelling from one previously selected location to another at predetermined intervals, as is done in activity sampling. However, when large areas are filmed at half-second intervals between frames, the film interval may still be too large to obtain details of the operator's hand movements; thus if the study requires this detail, the operators should be the subject of an individual study or in groups. If the interval between frames is too long it may be subsequently difficult to tell the type of motion performed by an operator; this would be a disadvantage where memomotion is being used for long-cycle micromotion studies, such as where the operator's cycle of activity is greater than 4 min. The use of memomotion has been developed sufficiently for its use to be now recognized as extending over a wide area of industrial application.

However, the successful application of memomotion study requires that the following sequence of activity be adhered to.

(a) Preparation.
(b) Filming and data collection.
(c) Film analysis.

Preparation consists in deciding on the form the application will take and the frame interval that should be used, arranging the location of the camera, discussing the proposed filming and study with shop personnel and supervision, seeing that adequate notice is given before filming is commenced and what additional information will have to be obtained to supplement that obtained by the film.

The application of memomotion in method study investigations is broadly divided into the following types of study.

(a) Single-operator repetition work.
(b) Area studies of groups of men and/or machines.
(c) Team studies.
(d) Utilization studies.

Studies in each of these areas of application demand that individual consideration be given to the problems associated with each.

In studies concerned with single-operator repetitive work the technique is used as an alternative to micromotion where the duration of the operator's cycle of activity is greater than 4 min. The selection of the correct frame interval therefore is a critical factor in this type of study. Studies of this kind tend to indicate more clearly the features of bad movements, for when the film is projected, they have a tendency to appear rapid and jerky. There appears to be a more favourable attitude towards studies of this kind by management and operatives, when compared to the other methods of recording. It provides the investigator with a more convenient means of convincing management of the need for improvements than is usually achieved by other means.

In area, team, and utilization studies, which are concerned with the investigation of machines and personnel, use is frequently made of frame intervals of longer duration than those used in single operator work. Difficulty is often experienced in such studies with how to determine whether a machine is working or not or whether an avoidable or unavoidable delay exists. Various methods are often used to overcome these difficulties, such as painting revolving parts with stripes so that when a machine is working the stripes will not be seen. Also where a machine is indicated to be working by the position of certain controls or leavers, these are frequently painted white so that their position will be more easily determined on the film during the analysis. The identification of personnel as they move about the work area may also be difficult in certain circumstances. Where the provision of dust jackets suitably marked to identify each operator is not possible, the use of coloured film, which is not much more expensive than black and white, will enable the identification of operators to be more easily obtained.

The selection of the appropriate frame interval will depend on the type of activity it is proposed to study and the degree of detail required. A guide to the selection of the frame interval for individual studies is provided by the frame interval diagram (Fig. 34). This is based on research carried out by J. C. Norbury in 1954. This indicates the interval to be used according to the cycle or area of the proposed study. To use the diagrams, select the row opposite the work cycle or area size to be studied, and move to the colour representing the type of information required; this will indicate the frame interval that it is advisable to use for that particular type of study. This diagram should only be used as a guide, as each study requires individual consideration. Such problems as seeing that the film expires at a certain time and that the film is loaded in the camera during breaks in production are some of these considerations. It is to be remembered that 100 ft of film or 4,000 frames will take a considerable time to analyse, at least 4 hr on the most simple activities. For this reason it is recommended that the amount of film used for any particular study should be restricted to 100 ft if circumstances permit this.

In area studies the amount of film used can often be reduced by filming for a short period at 1 sec intervals and the remainder at longer intervals. This will give details of the individual operators and in the second part details of the utilization of men and machines.

Having decided on the frame interval, the process of filming is a simple procedure. The modern film is of such quality that it enables films to be taken in poor light and the accuracy of the exposure need not be critical. On film made in poor light and under-exposed, which is frequently the case in memomotion filming, the analysis can be aided by projecting the film over a short distance on to a small screen or shadow box. A shadow box is the name given to a device which consists of a wooden box, the top of which is open and which is positioned on its side in front of the projector. The film is then projected into this box, the image being seen on its

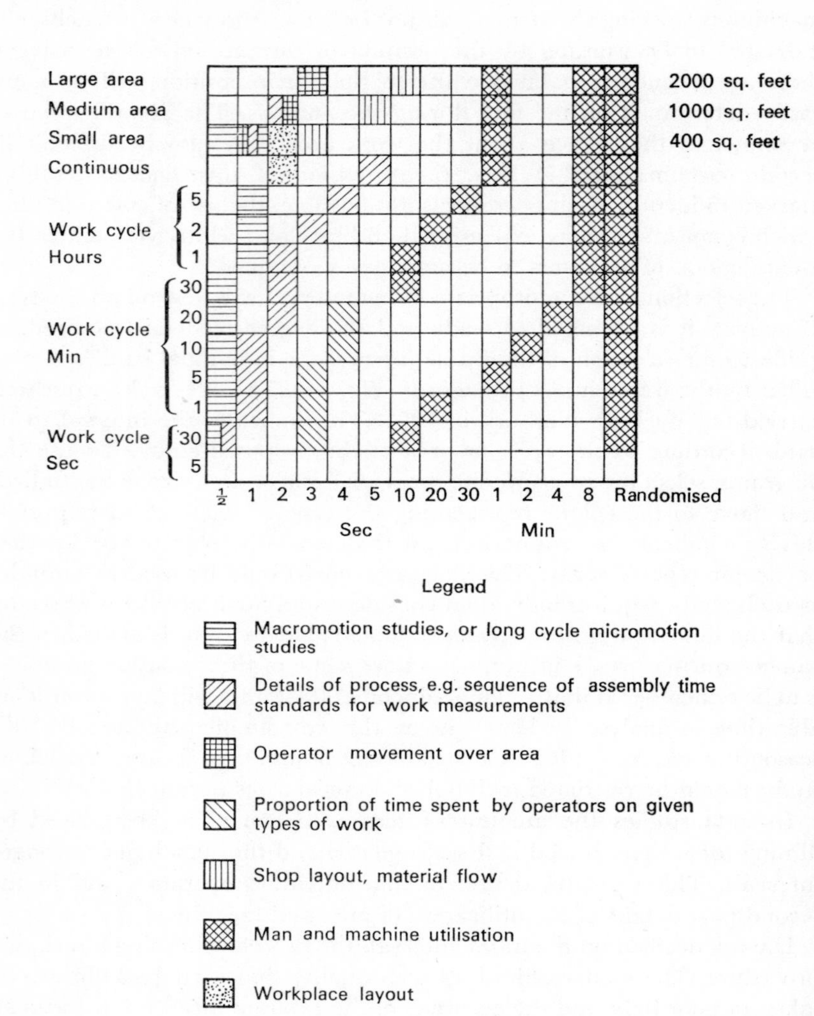

Diagram showing frame intervals for individual studies

FIG. 34. Memomotion analysis—frame interval diagram.

inside base. This device enables the viewing of a film without interference from light.

The film projector and analyser used for memomotion studies should preferably be one where frame by frame analysis can be made, and the film projected at the normal speed of 16 mm in both directions. It is an advantage if the projection speed can be controlled so that the film can be projected slowly or at higher speeds.

The analysis of memomotion films differs according to the type of study that has been recorded. On long-cycle micromotion studies where an individual operator carries out an operation whose work cycles are greater than 4 min the procedure of analysis will conform to that used for normal micromotion studies. This will consist of the conventional frame-by-frame analysis and the information obtained subsequently recorded on a simo chart.

In area studies, however, outline process charts are frequently prepared for each operator and each considered separately, and the film will be studied in addition and in conjunction with a floor plan for factors that are liable to affect production or the activity.

In team studies, which are particular types of area studies, each frame of the film records the simultaneous actions of each subject of the team. A film of this type is analysed in order to produce a multiple activity chart. A point in the cycle of activities is selected at which to start the analysis, and then the film is analysed frame by frame, the number of frames that elapse between the commencement and end of each element of the activity being recorded.

Utilization studies are those concerned with the use of men and machines whilst carrying out various activities. This type of study is analysed in conjunction with the memomotion analysis sheet prepared for such studies and shown in Fig. 35. From this a summary sheet is prepared showing the percentage utilization of the subjects selected for review. The form of this summary is indicated in Fig. 36. Where a number of operators are being analysed in the study a separate analysis and summary sheet is usually prepared for each operator.

To obtain the appropriate time interval between each frame whilst filming, a piece of equipment called a "time lapse controller" or "synchrolapse" is used, this is attached by an actuator to the cine camera and operates this at the time interval selected on the dial. An example of a simple arrangement is shown in Fig. 37. Random intervals for filming each frame can be obtained by actuating the camera at the random

Filming duration 54 minutes

Quantity of film used 100ft.

Frame interval One frame per minute

MEMOMOTION ANALYSIS SHEET

Study subject Preparation of Meal

Film number 808-1 Sheet number 1

Description	Counter	Time	Symbol	AB	TUS	ASK	AST	APS	TST	AUS	TAAF	DAC	TPS	TSK	TB
AT BENCH	00000	3	AB	3											
TO UTENSIL STORE	00003	4	TUS		4										
AT UTENSIL STORE	00007	3	AUS							3					
AT FRIGIDAIRE	00010	3	TAAF								3				
CONVERSATION	00013	3	DAC									3			
AT UTENSIL STORE	00016	6	AUS												
TO BENCH	00022	3	TB												3
TO PRODUCE STORE	00025	4	TPS										4		
AT PRODUCE STORE	00029	14	APS					14							
AT BENCH	00043	6	AB	6											
TO PRODUCE STORE	00049	4	TPS										4		
AT PRODUCE STORE	00053	5	APS					5							
TO BENCH	00058	3	TB												3
TO PRODUCE STORE	00061	4	TPS										4		

FIG. 35. Section of memomotion analysis sheet.

MEMOMOTION ANALYSIS-SUMMARY

Preparation of Meal in Domestic Kitchen

Description of activity	Symbol	Frames	Importance	Percentage of Time used
At bench	AB	1750	1	54·0
At sink	ASK	693	2	21·5
At stove	AST	349	3	10·8
At produce store	APS	100	4	3·1
To bench	TB	67	5	2·1
To sink	TSK	63	6	1·9
To produce store	TPS	54	7	1·7
Delay & conversation	DAC	52	8	1·6
To & at frigidaire	TAAF	35	9	1·1
At utensil store	AUS	28	10	·9
To utensil store	TUS	25	11	·8
To stove	TST	17	12	·5
		3233		100·0

FIG. 36. Memomotion analysis—summary of study.

Fig. 37. Time lapse control unit.

MOTION-PICTURE DATA SHEET

Place				Film No.
Operation				Op. No.
Part Name				Part No.
Machine Name		Machine Number		Dept.
Operator Name & No.				Date
Experience On Job		Material		
Begin	Finish	Elapsed	Units Finished	Rating
Camera Make	Camera Serial No.	Camera Speed in Frames/sec.	Lens	
Distance of Camera from Subject	Focus Setting	Exposure Meter Reading	Diaphragm Opening	
Kind of Film	Sensitivity Rating	No. of Spots	Wattage	A B C D

⊕ Spot Light

➡ Camera

Ⅰ Window

Tools, Jigs, Gauges:—

Made By

Fig. 38. Motion-picture data sheet.

intervals of time selected, as for activity sampling, or if small random intervals are required a special random time lapse controller may be obtained for this purpose.

With the availability of relatively low-cost cine photographic equipment and the greater interest in photography, the two photographic techniques of recording described are now well within the comprehension of most method study practitioners.

So that a complete record of filming can be obtained a motion-picture data sheet (Fig. 38) is completed for each study. This ensures that a mistake will not be repeated and that all aspects of the filming will have been considered.

Selected References and Suggestions for Further Reading

Process Charts

Operation and Flow Process Chart Standard, 1947, The American Society of Mechanical Engineers, New York.

BIGGS, G. R., Improved numbering of process charts, *Work Study and Management,* vol. 8, No. 10, October 1964, pp. 470–1.

CURRIE, R. M., *Work Study,* Pitman, chapter 5.

Activity Sampling

BARNES, R. M., *Work Sampling,* John Wiley, New York; Chapman & Hall, London, 1957.

BARNES, R. M., *Work Sampling,* W. C. Brown Company, Dubuque, Iowa, 1956.

KNIGHT, A. V., *An Investigation into Operating Methods in the Hardware Department of a Store,* Retail Distributors Association, London, 1955.

MORROW, R. L., *Time Study and Motion Economy,* with procedures for method improvement, The Ronald Press Company, New York, 1957, chapter 16, The Ratio Delay Study.

Micromotion

ALGAR, S. M., 8 mm Cine Photography for Work Study, *Work Study and Management,* vol. 8, No. 10, October 1964, pp. 464–6.

BARNES, R. M., *Motion and Time Study,* Micromotion study, John Wiley, New York; Chapman & Hall, London, chapters 10, 11, 12.

PIERCE, H., *How to use Photography in Work Study,* Kodak Limited, Industrial Engineering Department, England.

Memomotion

MUNDEL, M. E., *Motion and Time Study,* Prentice-Hall, chapter 14, Memomotion Study.

NORBURY, C. J., *The Application of Memomotion to Industrial Operation,* College Report No. 86, The College of Aeronautics, Cranfield, Bedfordshire, England.

CHAPTER 4

Construction of a Model of the Problem

WHEN the required information about the present method has been collected, it will consist of recordings of the various aspects of the problem. It may be considered necessary to integrate these facts to determine the interrelations between the various factors in order to make suitable predictions which will allow a solution of the methods problem. The means by which this is accomplished is by the construction of a "model" of the problem situation.

The more complicated a methods problem is and the more elements that it contains the more the methods analyst becomes dependent on the use of a model of the problem situation. Models are merely copies in symbolic form of the relationships that exist between the components of a system, and it is important to remember that the argument put forward by the model has little to do with the symbols that are selected. Models may be constructed from words, symbols, diagrams, numbers, letters, or any material that will serve to represent the conditions of the problem and the relationships involved. It is to indicate the relationships that exist in the problem that is important. All the means available to construct a model are useless unless this relationship is indicated correctly. It is also important to remember that the way in which a problem is presented may influence the speed and manner in which the problem is solved. The intelligent solution of any methods problem also depends on the way the information about the problem is presented and seen. Fixation is overcome and insight attained by a sudden shift in the way the problem objects involved in it are viewed. It is for this reason that the construction of a model of a problem by whatever means that are available is so important. Stafford Beer has suggested that "a model is no more than a description into which the real situation can be mapped".*

* Cybernetics and operations research, *Operations Research Quarterly*, vol. 10, No. 1, March 1959, p. 15.

Models may be representational, analogous, or symbolic.* The representational or iconic model is a pictorial or visual image of the subject for investigation such as is obtained by a photograph, a picture, a globe, a model aircraft, or toy automobile, to name only a few examples. This type of model is the simplest form to conceive and is most easily understood. But as its purpose is primarily descriptive it seldom suggests relationships. The analogue model is one that uses a set of analogous properties to represent another set of properties. This type of model is successful in representing the dynamic situations in processes or systems and is well suited for the determination of the effects of changes in an actual system. Examples of this type of model are graphs, charts, and diagrams, the use of water flow to represent "flow" of electricity in wires.

A symbolic model employs symbols to represent the properties of a situation or system. The most common example of this type of model is an algebraic formula or equation. It is the most difficult to conceive and is generally the most abstract.

The use of one particular kind of model to represent a problem situation may often be more appropriate than another. To appreciate the reasons for this enables the correct selection to be made when the occasion demands. An appreciation of the three basic types of model will enable the methods analyst to think of other possible forms of presentation and not to be too ready to accept the conventional forms in situations where they may not be applicable. Occasions frequently arise where the presentation of a problem situation in a particular manner is more appropriate than by the use of another method. This should not suggest that the investigator should always strive for some original form of presentation and disregard the standard methods that have been found suitable by experience for such situations. But whatever means are suggested, the success or failure of the proposal may depend on the ease with which the features of the problem can be communicated to those whose participation is solicited. Whether the model presents the conditions of the problem in the simplest form possible as an aid to the systematic approach to its solution, or whether the suitability of a model is suggested by the fact that it forms the basis for the statement of similar types of problem, it should be appreciated that there is a large number of factors to be considered in the selection of any one method of presentation.

There are in method study many conventional models for presenting

* Churchman, C. W., Ackoff, R. L. and Arnoff, E. L., *Introduction to Operations Research*, John Wiley, New York and London, chapter 7.

problem situations in all the areas of methods application. Many of these will be mentioned in those chapters dealing with these specific areas of application.

The following terms indicate different conventional models which are the normal means of presenting methods problems.

(a) Flow diagrams.
(b) String diagrams.
(c) Travel charts.
(d) Three-dimensional models and templates.
(e) Multiple activity charts.
  (i) Man–machine charts.
  (ii) Gantt charts.
  (iii) Network charts.
(f) Kinetograms.
  (i) Cyclegraphs.
  (ii) Chronocyclegraphs.
(g) Relationship diagrams.
(h) Numerical data charts.

Flow Diagrams

The flow process chart indicates the sequence and nature of movement but does not indicate the paths of movement associated with it. For the solution of problems concerned with movement the characteristics of such paths may include many undesirable features such as back tracking unnecessarily long movements and congestion. To indicate these a flow diagram is constructed. This is a diagram made to the appropriate scale which shows the location of the specific activities carried out and the routes followed by workers' materials or equipment in the performance of the tasks.

To construct a flow diagram of this kind a plan of the work area is first obtained; this should be to a suitable scale. The area shown may be either a complete workshop or an operator's work area. The suitability of the scale is determined by the ability to transfer the information onto the plan. The usual scale is a quarter inch to the foot. Having obtained this plan of the work area, which will indicate walls, machines, benches, and roof supports, the information from the flow process chart in terms of numerals and symbols is transferred to this plan by placing the symbol of operation, inspection, delay, and storage in the exact place on the plan where the activity occurs and the transport symbol between the locations where the movement takes place.

As the flow process chart is either a material or man-type recording the subject of the diagram will trace either the movement of material or men throughout the process. When the flow diagram is constructed it will be stated whether it is a material or man-type presentation.

The routes followed by transportations are indicated by joining the

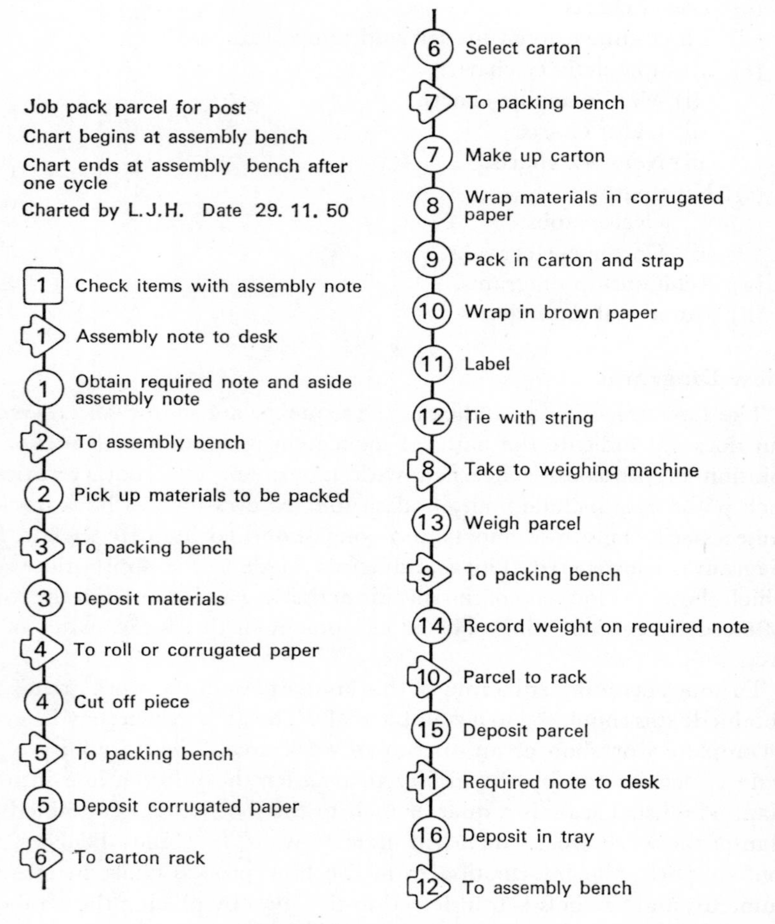

FIG. 39. Flow process chart.

symbols in sequence by a line which represents as near as possible the path of movement taken by the man or material. The direction of movement is shown by the numbered transport symbols and the direction in which they are pointing. The flow process chart (Fig. 39) is used to construct the flow diagram shown in Fig. 40.

The above indicates how to construct a two-dimensional flow diagram. However, distance moved in a vertical plane may be a significant aspect of some process activity and as important as that in the horizontal plane. To indicate these a three-dimensional flow diagram may be constructed by making either an isometric or oblique projection of the process area to scale, and transferring the flow process chart onto it, or by placing the plan of each of the floor areas of, for example, a three-storey building one above the other, on the surface of a large piece of paper. The movement between each floor plan will then be a movement in a vertical direction between these floor plans.

When the movement is complex the use of colour to indicate lines and symbols makes the problem of the identification of movements much easier.

Another type of flow diagram may be constructed to indicate the movement of paperwork or control forms. This, whilst basically the same as the two-dimensional flow process chart, will use instead of a plan of the work area, a large sheet of paper which is divided into a number of vertical columns. Each of these columns will depict a department or station involved in the delivery or departure of paper communications. The number of these columns will depend on the number of departments or stations it is desired to include in the flow diagram. The details from a flow process chart are transferred to this, and the result is a flow diagram, material type, showing the flow and communication pattern of a paperwork control procedure, and the individual operations performed on each of the forms. A simple example of such a diagram is shown in Fig. 41.

Where it is necessary to show the movement of information not only between the various departments or stations but also between the various pieces of paper or forms in a control procedure, the relevant forms involved in the system are pasted onto a large piece of cartridge paper, and the entries on these forms are indicated. The movement of the information from one piece of paper to another and from one department to the other is indicated by lines and symbols as in the conventional flow diagram. The result is a more detailed kind of material-type flow diagram which can be very useful when investigating the movement of information concerned with a paperwork control procedure or system.

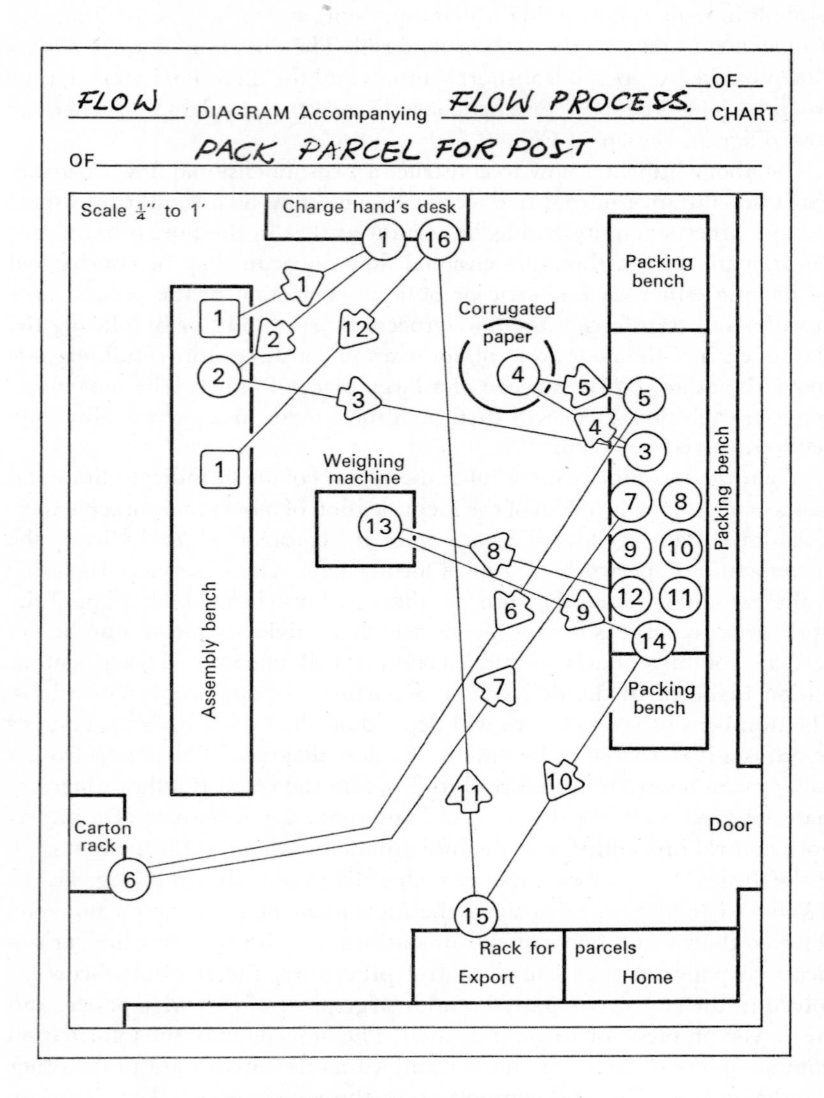

Fig. 40. Two-dimensional flow diagram.

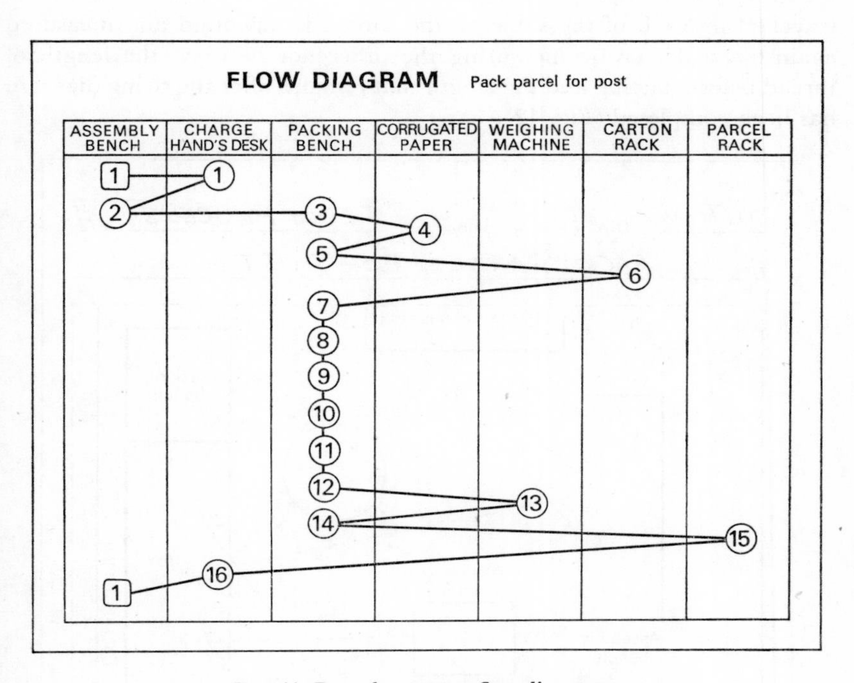

Fig. 41. Procedure type—flow diagram.

String Diagrams

The flow diagram is often found unsuitable for the purpose of indicating movement over periods of long duration or where the complexity of the flow process charting is such that it would not be possible to transfer this on to even a large-scale plan of the work area. It is in such circumstances that a string diagram is found to be more suitable. To construct a diagram of this kind a scale drawing of the area of the process to be studied is obtained, this is then fixed to a sheet of fibre board, pins are driven into the plan and thus into the board at the points where movement begins and ends. A thread is then wound round these pins in the sequence in which each of the points was visited whilst the movements were being recorded. This thread is made to represent the actual path of movement followed by the subject charted.

A composite string diagram can be made by using different coloured threads and map pins. To calculate from the diagram the actual distance travelled by each of the subjects, the thread is unwound and measured against a scale, or by measuring the difference between the length of thread before starting and the length that remains after the string diagram has been completed (Fig. 42).

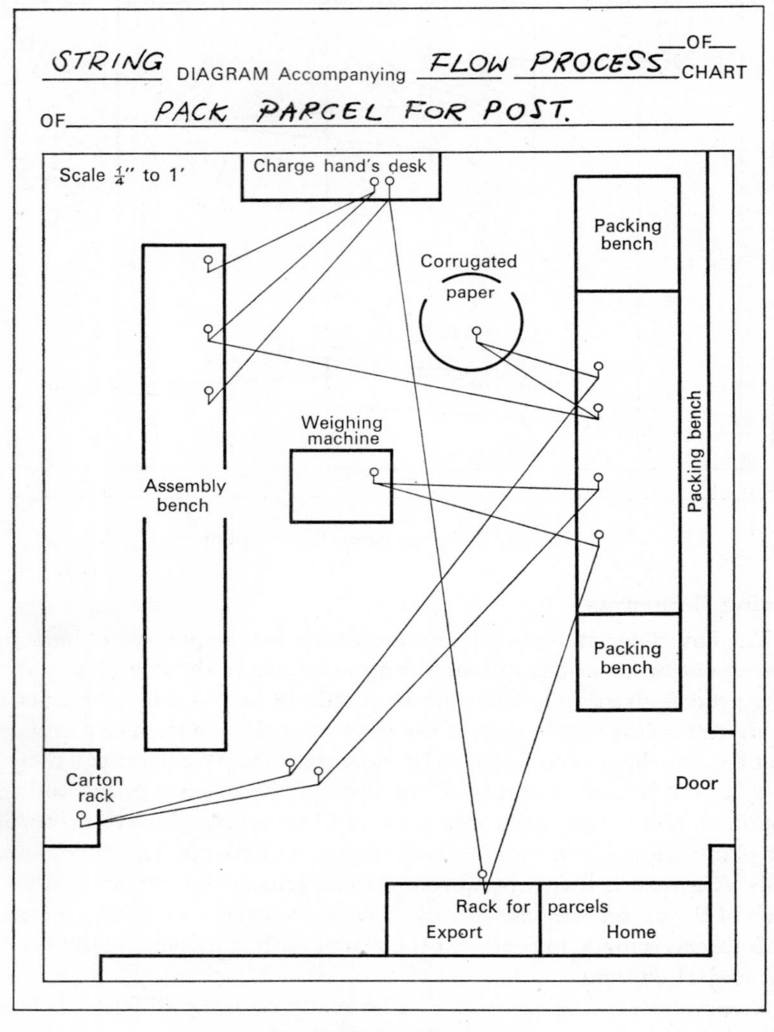

Fig. 42. String diagram.

The principal use of the string diagram is to investigate the movement of groups of workers or an operator whilst attending several machines. The movement of components or assemblies during assembly operations or the study of the movement occasioned by different suggested layouts.

Travel Charts

Where the use of the flow diagram and the string diagram would not be appropriate, due possibly to the complexity of the movement or where these two diagrams would be difficult to follow, an alternative device can be used called the travel chart. This enables the study of complex movement patterns to be made. The basis on which it is constructed is the destination fare chart used by transport companies.

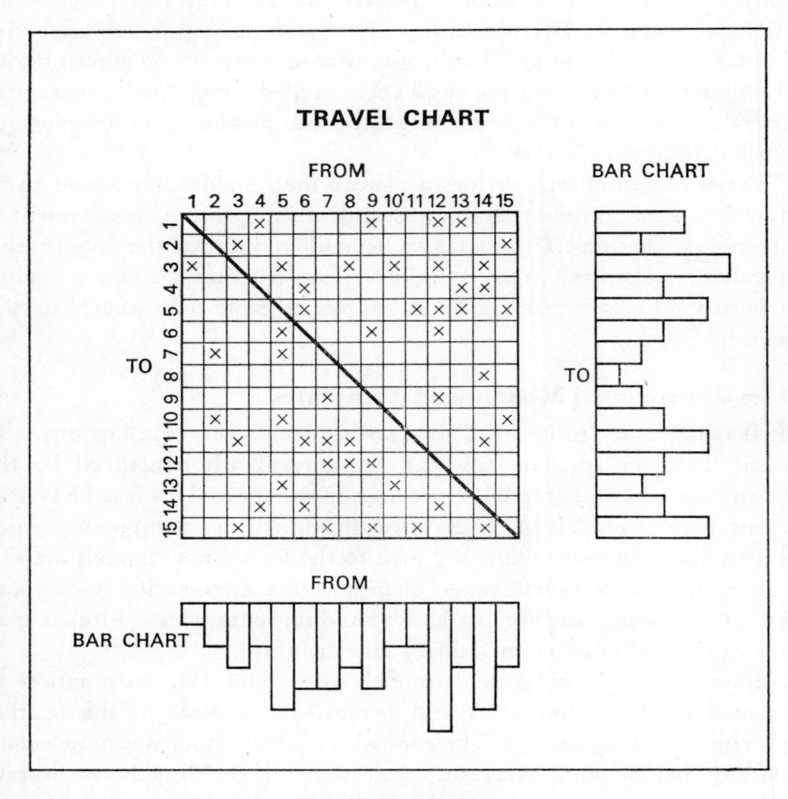

Fig. 43. Travel chart.

The chart is constructed by first producing a grid of squares to the required number and to the most suitable size. Each of the squares may be as large as two inches or as small as half an inch. The stations or points from which movement occurs are listed at the top of the grid on the horizontal axis. These are referred to as contributor stations. The points to which the movement occurs are listed on the vertical axis, in the same sequence as they are listed at the top. This vertical list of stations is referred to as receiver stations. The information obtained from flow process charts is then transferred to this chart in the following manner. A cross or tick or a coloured map pin is placed in the appropriate square each time a movement occurs from a contributor station to a receiver station. When the chart is completed the percentage volume of movement from a contributor station and a receiver station and vice versa is immediately apparent. By substituting the crosses, ticks, or coloured pins for distance, weights of unit loads, numbers of journeys, or other quantitative figures, the chart can convey a very detailed picture of the characteristics of the movement between departments, machines, or benches, or other locations in a factory.

The use of this chart provides a picture that enables movement to be reduced to a minimum or eliminated altogether by the rearrangement of machines or locations. The chart can be made to indicate the quantitative figures set against each area or station by constructing bar charts against the horizontal and vertical axes. A simple example of a travel chart is shown in Fig. 43.

Three-dimensional Models and Templates

If it is necessary to indicate the existing conditions of a layout, or to present these for revision, this can be conveniently visualized by the construction of a scale model of the area in question. This is achieved by the purchase of models of the relevant machines and equipment, which are made to a standard scale of $\frac{3}{8}$ inch to the foot. These models may be obtained for the complete range of proprietary engineering and woodworking machines, and for materials handling equipment. Models may also be obtained of office machinery and furniture.

The practice of using these models stimulates the imagination of personnel at the planning stage and increases the accuracy of the location of machines and equipment. Their use also enables important dimensions, including height and overhead clearance, to be directly measured. Explanation is frequently reduced to a minimum, as the proposed layout

FIG. 44. Layout planning models.

can be quickly understood by shop-floor workers, supervision, and management. The accurate and attractive presentation that is achieved encourages an interest in the appearance of the shop. It is often said that a shop that has an attractive appearance engenders a greater spirit of efficiency. In using these models colour can be used to enhance the realism of the model and produce greater interest. Colour coding is a valuable means of indicating phase development or the source of individual items of equipment.

On the first use of these models the initial costs are recovered and permanent planning equipment is afterwards available should amendments to the layout be desirable at a future date.

The path of movement associated with a proposed layout can be easily perceived and such is the atmosphere of actuality produced by the use of these models that greater interest in the problem and a sense of participation is often obtained as a result. This is indicated by the suggestions which are often offered by personnel for the solution of the various problems associated with the layout. A situation presented in this form enables those who are to be consulted on aspects from lighting, heating, electrical and dust extraction, installation, ventilation, maintenance and safety, to quickly visualize the implications of these considerations. Figure 44 provides an indication of the quality and features of some of these models.

Templates are used as an alternative to three-dimensional models where the expense incurred in the purchase of these models is not justified, and where the amount of drawing and tracing must be kept to a minimum. A separate template of the base silhouette of each machine is made to the appropriate scale. These can be made from the scale plan of a machine obtained from the operational manual provided with the machine or from trade literature. The silhouettes can be cut from a variety of materials such as laminated wood, carding, plastic, or metal. However, the general practice is to cut them from coloured card. These templates are not only made to indicate the base silhouette of the machine but also its operational area, which includes the space occupied by pallets or stillages, the operator, and the floor area required for maintenance and cleaning. This operational area can be painted another colour to provide a distinctive contrast. Some suppliers of proprietary equipment provide these templates printed on transparent plastic material for ease in the construction of layouts. If these are used, a photographic record can be made more easily of a present or proposed layout, thus reducing the work in the drawing

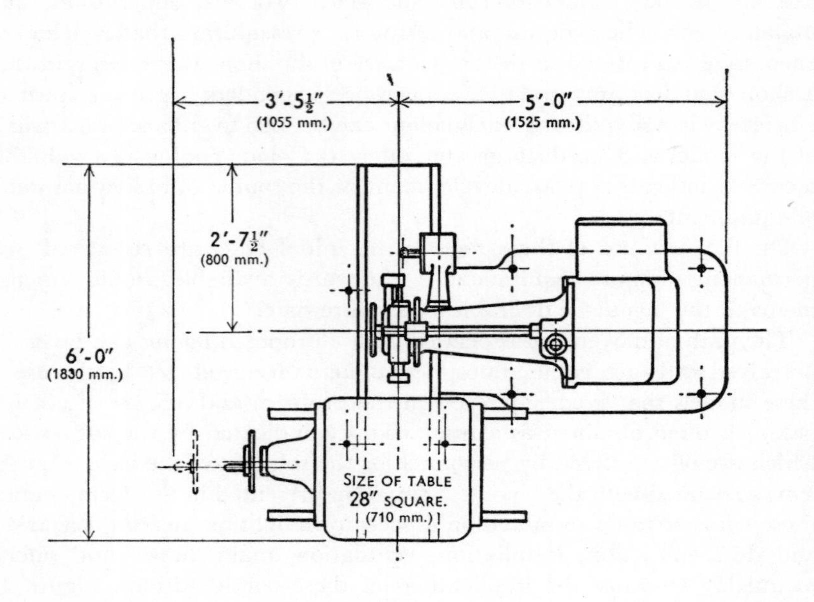

FIG. 45. Layout template.

office. Figure 45 shows a plan of a machine obtained from trade literature and a template silhouette constructed from it.

Multiple Activity Charts

Introduction

It is sometimes necessary to construct a diagram or chart of the activities of more than one subject or activity, in order to appreciate the relationship of one to the others. By the examination of the simultaneous activities of each of the subjects ineffective time in the work may be eliminated. Charts of this kind fall into the following categories.

(a) Man–machine charts.
(b) Gantt charts.
(c) Network charts.

Man–machine chart

This chart is concerned with the presentation of the simultaneous activity of a number of machines and men, or one man and his machine, or the work of a team or group of workers. It is constructed by plotting the process and activities of each of the subjects side by side against a common time scale (Fig. 46). The activity of each of the subjects is represented by a bar or strip, which is divided to indicate the various divisions of the activity it is desired to show. These different activities, which may only be working or delay in some particular instances, may be further subdivided to indicate whether the delays are avoidable or unavoidable and whether transport or movement occurs. These strips or bars are coloured, hatched, or shaded, to illustrate the different activities that take place, a particular colour or shading serving to indicate a particular activity common to all the subjects of the multiple activity. For instance, throughout the chart the colour red may indicate delay and blue be made to denote productive work. These subdivisions are constructed to scale, their length being in accordance with the duration of the activity they represent.

In constructing the chart it is advisable to use squared paper as this simplifies the procedure. Before commencing the construction the scope of the chart and the subjects to be charted should first be carefully defined. Each subject is then assigned a separate strip on the chart. The activities and subjects that it is desired to compare in this manner will have already been the subject of a flow process chart recording, constructed to the

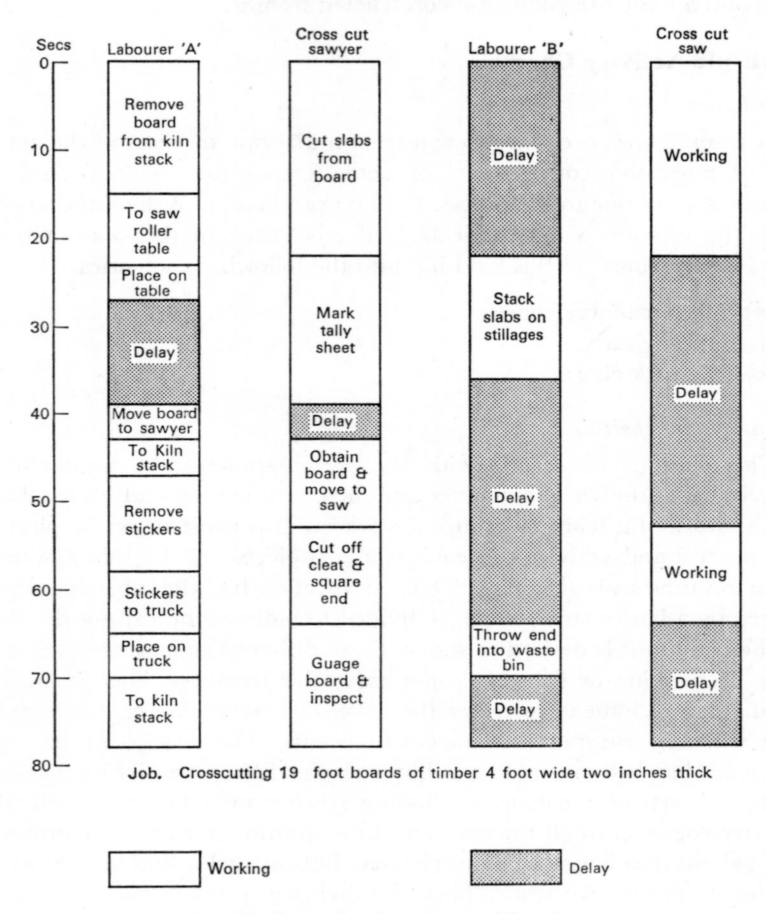

FIG. 46. Example of a man–machine chart.

detail required. As the basis of the multiple activity chart is the time scale, each of the symbols of the flow process chart will be qualified by an accurately determined time value, and a datum mark made on the activity of each subject of the proposed chart so that the simultaneous points in the cycle of activities of each subject can be lined up. The time values should be as accurate as the objectives of the chart permit.

The multiple activity chart when constructed should be self-contained, and where possible the following information should accompany the chart: a flow process chart recording of each of the subjects from which the man–machine chart was constructed; a flow diagram indicating the movement of the subjects of the chart in relation to the work area. Both these will be useful when the activity is examined in order to obtain improvements. These details should be accompanied by an adequate description of the operation method, whether the chart presents the present or proposed method, where the chart begins and ends, and details of the time scale used. If any abbreviations, legends, or colours, have been used, an indication must be given as to what they refer. A summary of the features of the present method in terms of percentage utilization should be given and subsequently when a proposed method has been recommended the differ-

ACTIVITY	PRESENT				PROPOSED				DIFFERENCE			
	Subject A		Subject B		Subject A		Subject B		Subject A		Subject B	
	Time	%	Time	%	Time	%	Time	%	Time	%	Time	%
Working												
Delay												

FIG. 47. Simple summary for the man–machine chart. (May be enlarged according to the number of activities and subjects studied.)

ence in the percentage utilization of both methods. An example of a simple summary of this type is shown in Fig. 47. A flow diagram, flow process chart, accompanying the completed man–machine chart, all contribute to a detailed picture of an activity to be investigated.

Gantt charts

This form of multiple activity chart was developed by Henry L. Gantt (1861–1919) who was one of the pioneers in the development of management science. It was first used for the planning of the utilization of machines according to the time required to do the work, then it was developed for making plans and getting them executed. It is a valuable tool of method study as it provides an infinite variety of ways of presenting facts concerning methods of work and production. It has been found of considerable value for the analysis of team and memomotion utilization studies. Similar problems in the analysis of work on construction sites, for example, and the presentation of the information obtained from memomotion film analysis of such sites, have been greatly assisted by its use. It has also been found valuable in planning preventative maintenance in factories and the recording of stores issues and receipts. It in no way supersedes the man–machine chart but it has been found to be most useful where a multiple activity of long duration is to be studied. It is a type of monitoring chart and in this respect is used for the analysis of actual against planned. In instances where the activity takes place over an extended period such as twelve months, or where there are a large number of subjects in the multiple activity, the Gantt chart is invariably used.

The Gantt chart is constructed in various ways according to the particular purpose for which it is to be used. When it is used to indicate the activities of men and machines it shows the relation between what has been accomplished with what could have been accomplished. When it is used as a project planning chart it is used as a means of planning the work to avoid idleness and the delays of men and equipment. On this type of chart is indicated the work that has been accomplished, the order of its importance, and the sequence of the work that was planned. When it is used as a load chart its purpose is to acquaint personnel with the load ahead of plant equipment or men, so that effective deployment of these resources may be made, and information may be given for quoting for future work as a means of indicating what kind of work must be declined, where congestion is likely to occur, what additional equipment, plant, and manpower will be required, what extension of the production line will be required to complete the work, and if there is insufficient work what action should be taken. All these questions are answered by consulting the Gantt chart when it is used as a load chart. When the chart is used as a progress chart its purpose is to get work done by showing a comparison of what has been accomplished with reference to a plan and the reasons for the failure to adhere to this plan.

The use of the various types of Gantt chart presupposes that a plan has been agreed upon and that this has been recorded on to one of the types of chart in such a manner that the plan thus detailed will be understood by all personnel. Thus by a comparison of what has been done with what was planned, the reasons why the plan has fallen short of the actual can be ascertained. These reasons can be recorded on the chart and thus throughout the whole period of the plan and its execution the information can be concentrated on a single sheet in a compact way. The continuity thus obtained emphasizes any break in the records and any lack of information as to what has taken place.

Data is recorded on the Gantt charts from left to right across the sheet against a time base, as is the case in the simple form of multiple activity chart; thus the passing of time can be visualized.

The most satisfactory size for this type of chart is 10 in. by 16 in. But in many instances they may be as large as half imperial size paper. Where the conventional chart layout is frequently used standard preprinted

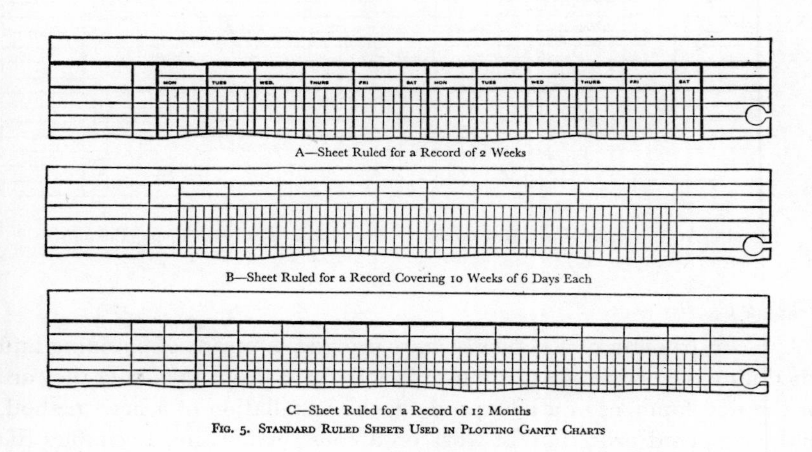

Fig. 48. Standard Gantt chart sheets. (From Clark, *The Gantt Chart*, Pitman.)

sheets are used (Fig. 48). These are easily obtainable from drawing office stationers. But in most method study situations because of the infinite variety of their uses and layout these are frequently prepared in a drawing office for the purpose of the individual study. In the use of these charts various conventions are employed for describing the different situations that arise. No purpose would be served by explaining each and every one as their selection and use depends on the purpose to which the chart is applied. Those who are interested in pursuing this subject further are recommended to consult the references at the end of the chapter. Figure 49 shows an example of a Gantt chart of the type described.

DEPT. E	NO.	OCT. 19 MON.	20 TUES.	21 WED.	22 THURS.	23 FRI.	24 SAT.	26 MON.	27 TUES.	28 WED.	29 THURS.	30 FRI.	31 SAT.
A.D. Jones, Foreman													
F. Curtis	61												
J. Christian	109												
G. Fuller	235												
V. Oldham	96												
J. Fish	79												
O. Evans	59												
W. Storer	205												
W. Page	93												
L. Clark	38												
I. Kimball	62												
F. Harris	97												
P. Foreman	1												
C. Dorset	221												
S. Sergeant	258												
M. Hall	52												
A. Martin	176												
F. Lucas	100												
J. Benjamin	209												
O. Coker	81	HIRED 10/21						LEFT SHOP					
J. Dawson	150	HIRED 10/21											
J. Stevens	115	HIRED 10/22											
K. Cary	71												
S. Rose	272							HIRED 10/27					
J. Norris	281							HIRED 10/27					

FIG. 49. An example of a Gantt chart. (From Clark, *The Gantt Chart*, Pitman.)

Network Charts

The construction of a network chart provides a means of planning and scheduling the operations of a multiple activity or project whether they are for the development of a new product, the installation of a new method, or the proposed procedure of work on a construction site. It enables the monitoring of the progress of the multiple activities and an indication of those areas where improvements are required to enable the proposed completion dates to be achieved. Like other method study techniques that are available to the practitioner, it should not be used in circumstances where a simpler method is available, due to the amount of work that is sometimes involved. In major installations and projects its use is imperative as the conventional method of using the Gantt chart has certain disadvantages.

All that is required for the construction of a network chart is some logical thinking, elementary calculations, and the ability to produce reasonable estimates of activity duration. The network chart may be determined directly from flow process chart recordings of the activities where certain conditions are appropriate.

A network chart permits the logical planning of the elements of the work to be performed and the correct sequencing of each of the individual activities. It provides a means of indicating those critical operations whose non-completion in a required time will rob the schedule of its effectiveness. Its construction enables bottlenecks to be anticipated and the relationship between different activities to be indicated, thus enabling correct decisions to be made. If all the activities that must be accomplished are known and the duration of each can be estimated, then these activities can be shown in the form of a network chart. From this the duration of the total project and the activities controlling its completion within a prescribed time can be determined and the effect of delays on any of its elements evaluated. It can also be used to determine realistic completion dates, thus making adjustments possible to achieve these.

The method to be adopted for the construction of a network chart consists of the following procedure. The method to be critically examined is first divided into individual operations by constructing operation or outline process charts for all the work or activities that must be accomplished to complete the plan. These will list the activities in the order in which they will be performed and indicate at the same time, for each operation, what activity must immediately precede it and what work can follow it or be made concurrently. When this list is completed they are set out in the form of a network chart in which each individual job and event is arranged according to its logical sequence and systematically numbered for easy identification and reference. This chart then becomes a graphical representation of the plan or method by which the work will be accomplished. Figure 50 indicates the form of such a network and though it is a simple example it serves to illustrate the basic procedure. It can be seen that the duration of an activity is represented by an arrow the tail of which marks the beginning and its head the finish. An operation symbol is drawn where two or more arrows join and this symbolizes an operation or an event or simply a point in time marking the beginning or end of one or more activities. Thus this event is the point where the successful completion of all preceding activities permits the commencement of succeeding work. The length of the arrows and their angular position have no significance. The work flow is indicated by the direction of the head of the arrow.

The next step is to estimate the time required to accomplish each of the operations in order to determine the possible duration of the project and to construct a time schedule for its accomplishment. As each arrow represents a duration of an activity each must be qualified with a time value with one exception. This exception occurs when an arrow is used simply to show that one particular operation or event, must have been reached or completed before the other. This type of arrow is called a "dummy" and is indicated by the broken tail of an arrow as is shown in the illustration where arrow 11–12 indicates that event 11 must be reached before event 12.

Each operation symbol signifying an event is identified by a number placed in its centre. These numbers cannot be allocated until the operations have been assembled into a network chart recording. When this has

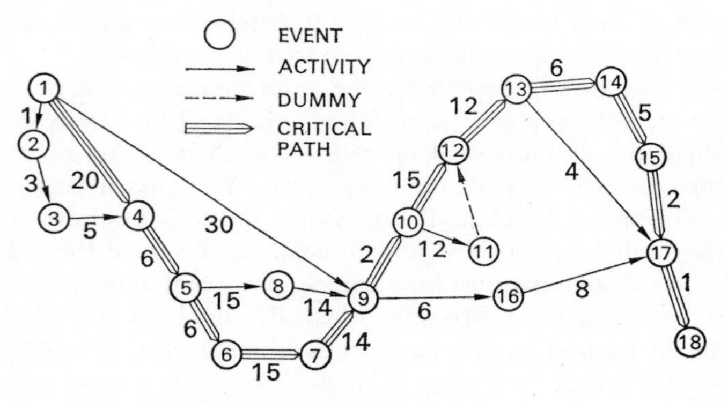

FIG. 50. Simple example of a network chart.

been constructed the following questions must be answered for each of the operations in order to obtain this number sequence.

What operations precede the operation?
What jobs run concurrently with the operation?
What jobs follow the operation?
What controls the start of the operation?
What controls the finish of the operation?

When the answers to these questions have been obtained, the events are numbered successively from the beginning to the end of the network. An initial event is one that has subsequent activities emerging from it, but none entering it. When the initial event is determined this is numbered one. To number the subsequent activities all arrows emerging from numbered events should be disregarded. This will indicate at least one new "initial" event. These should be numbered two, three, etc., the order in which this is done not being important. Deleting emergent arrows should be continued in this way until the final event is reached. This final event is the one which has no arrows emerging from it. When this numbering is completed all the operations or events from the beginning to the end of the network will have been defined.

The examination of the network that has been constructed divides these operations or events into two main categories, namely critical and noncritical operations. Critical operations are those that directly influence the overall duration of the project and if, as they frequently do, they form a chain through the network, this is known as a critical path. Noncritical operations are those that are not on this path and which have no influence on the duration of the project. Because time is required for the completion of each activity, the path through the network which gives the longest aggregate time can then be determined. Thus the only way in which the time required to complete the project can be reduced is by decreasing the time for the accomplishment of one or more of the activities on the critical path. Expediting activities not on this critical path would have no effect on the duration of the project. The addition of the times for each activity along this critical path will give a total time for the duration of the project. The critical path in Fig. 50 is indicated by doubled tailed arrows but a coloured crayon is often an appropriate means of indicating this on a network, and in various publications on this subject, other conventions are often seen to be used for this purpose.

In a network there is frequently seen to be more time available than is needed for the accomplishment of the noncritical activities, and often a specific period of time during which noncritical operations may be completed. Some of these noncritical activities can often be commenced comparatively late at the beginning of the multiple activity and still not adversely affect the duration of the project.

The difference between the earliest time and the latest time for completing a noncritical activity is called "float". It is sometimes advisable to absorb this "float" in order to avoid having an activity completed too far in advance, or possibly, as in the case of the construction industry, having equipment standing idle for several days. But it should be remembered that if the "float" is completely absorbed there will be no time for the other noncritical activities to be completed, and in consequence these activities will then become critical.

It is important to note that the duration of a project can be changed by altering the method for its accomplishment, as is seen to be the practice for all multiple activities. This can be done, for example, by assigning more men and equipment to activities where they could be used to advantage or by working overtime. The availibity of equipment can also influence the complete plan of the project.

One of the advantages that is obtained from the use of network charts and their subsequent examination is that various methods can be tested to arrive at the one best method with regard to available resources, cost, and time factors. It enables the method analyst to see simultaneously all the interrelationships between the activities, and in the course of this a plan of improvements which might otherwise be overlooked is frequently suggested.

In the development of many projects it is not possible to estimate the activity times with any degree of accuracy. In such cases it is usual to use the weighted mean of three values, the most optimistic, the most pessimistic, and the most likely to obtain a reasonable assessment of duration. Otherwise the procedure is essentially the same.

There are various ways in which the activities along the critical path may be shortened; these involve the consideration of alternative methods and their time and cost relationships, and relating activity completion times to both direct and indirect cost, in order to determine the required time reduction to achieve this at least cost. Any methods used for the more speedy accomplishment of the activities not on the critical path would not reduce the project duration, except as a means of making available men and equipment necessary to shorten completion times for the critical activities.

As the result of the examination of the network, a time schedule is constructed with a detailed plan of the methods to be adopted together with the prescribed starting and completion dates, manpower and equipment, to be assigned to the work, and the material deliveries. As the actual progress of the work never corresponds to the planned progress, it may be necessary to adjust the schedule periodically. The same procedure is adopted to do this as was previously used to prepare the schedule.

It should be remembered that the ultimate success of the application of a network chart is achieved by detailed method study and not by the complexities of the network procedures themselves.

It has obviously not been possible to deal with this procedure in any great detail within the space allowed in this volume. But appropriate publications are available which deal adequately with this method of presentation. Selected references are given at the end of this chapter for those who wish to proceed further in their understanding of this technique.

Kinetograms—Cyclegraphs and Chronocyclegraphs

It is frequently desired to visualize the pattern of the path of movement of an operator's left and right hands in relation to the work place layout or the operation that has to be performed. To obtain this kinetograms are constructed for the particular work being investigated. These can be likened to the string diagram but whilst the string diagram is concerned with movement in two dimensions the kinetogram provides a picture of movement in the three-dimensional plane.

In the investigation of certain operator tasks the use of these is of considerable benefit. In analytical training, for example, when information is being collected about the task, their use enables the determination of much information which would otherwise be unseen concerning the motion pattern and the degree of control required in the production of the elements of the work. Where it is necessary to determine the comparative skill of operators this may be done by the use of these as the skilled operator will invariably tend to have a clear motion pattern with its appearance of continuity, whereas the motion pattern of the less skilled operator will indicate pauses and hesitations which it would not be possible to see by eye observation. Also in the design of equipment and the arrangement of controls the use of kinetograms are of inestimable value.

The use of kinetograms as a method of analysis was being developed by F. B. Gilbreth at the time of his death in 1924. He elaborated on a method originated by M. Marey in France in the nineteenth century. Subsequent development and the application of Gilbreth's contributions in this field have been made by Anne G. Shaw.

A motion picture of a two-handed activity shows only parts of the movement in an operation cycle at any one time, and when a recording of a continuous movement pattern is desired it is found unsuitable. To obtain this information two still photographs are taken and superimposed photographically on each other. The first exposure is of point sources of light, such as may be obtained from ordinary flash-lamp bulbs connected to a source of electrical supply by flex, and which are attached to the operator's hands during the performance of the operation cycle. A print of such an exposure shows continuous lines of light which follow the motion pattern used in the task. To relate these light patterns to the actual operation a still photograph of the operator and the work site is superimposed on the first exposure. The resulting print of these two exposures is called a cyclegraph (Fig. 51). However, the cyclegraph only gives a single path of movement for each hand and conveys no idea of speed and direction of the movement. In order to obtain these characteristics a modification of the cyclegraph apparatus was developed. By means of a simple piece of electrical apparatus the lights attached to the operators hands were arranged to flash on and off at various predetermined rates per second. An arrangement which will effect this is called a kinetographic flash unit; this is shown in Fig. 52.

To provide for the varying speeds of an operator's hand movements during such a study it is necessary to adjust the speed of the light flashes so that 10, 20, and 30 cycles or flashes per second are available. This piece of proprietary equipment, illustrated, allows for a sufficient range of flashes per second to be obtained. A print obtained from such an exposure, where the lights are made to operate in this manner, will show breaks in the light tracings and, from these, direction, speed, acceleration, and retardation in the operation cycle is easily obtained. Direction of movement is indicated by the fact that owing to the quick flashing on and the slow flashing off each light break is tapered, as shown in Fig. 53, and the

FIG. 53. Features of chronocyclegraph light flash.

direction of the motion is towards the narrower end. The length of the breaks will vary with the speed of movement, being long when the hand motion is fast, and short when the motion is slow. An accelaration of the hand movement is indicated by the progressive increase in the length of the successive breaks whilst a retardation is shown by the reverse. A photograph that provides these features is called a chronocyclegraph (Fig. 54). With both types of kinetograms, the use of coloured film, and different coloured light bulbs attached to both of the operator's hands, it is possible to differentiate between the hand movements in complex motion patterns.

Much additional experimentation is being carried out with this technique with regard to its use for the comparison of motion patterns, where a complete understanding of this is required to determine a preferable

Fig. 51. Example of a cyclegraph.

Fig. 52. Kinetographic flash unit.

Fig. 54. Examples of chronocyclegraphs.

way of performing an operation, or operating a piece of equipment, to improve aspects of equipment design by trial and error at the work place, and the identification of bad features of working.

The use of these procedures for constructing a model of a motion pattern is further enhanced by the combination of polaroid photography and the chronocyclegraphic flash unit. The advantage of having a photograph developed within a minute of having taken it, with the added opportunity of being able to modify and improve the layout of the work area immediately, encourages a wider interest in the use of this technique. Chronocyclegraph and cyclegraph photographs can be mounted in a stereoscopic viewer. This enables the photograph to be viewed in true three-dimensional proportions.

Relationship Diagrams

Situations are constantly arising in method study where the use of other kinds of relationship diagram is surprisingly appropriate. The use of the pictorial representation of a problem situation has developed from this need. Many individuals find that their use enables them to think with far greater ease, when they can visualize an argument or situation pictorially with pencil, paper, and a diagram. This often makes clear to them a situation which they might otherwise have had difficulty in comprehending if the information had been presented in another form. The diagrammatic methods of presenting relationships in industrial problems forms an intensely interesting field of method study activity.

The family-tree relationship diagram is a simple but familiar example of one type that falls within this category. It can be appreciated that the use of this is the quickest way of determining a relationship between two people. Another example well known in the manuals of logic is the "tree of Porphyry" which provides a means of classifying and indicating relationships in a similar manner. Another example is described by Cushen which was used for the selection of a material for the manufacture of a particular product. This form of presentation enabled a choice of materials to be made from a number of alternatives with respect to the performance requirements demanded from the product, and the influence that the material would have on the other components to which it was to be assembled. Symbols were used in this particular case to represent the various qualities of the materials, and a list was prepared indicating undesirable combinations of materials. This was supplemented by another list indicating desired performance characteristics. The relationship diagram, constructed as a result from this information, enabled seventy-three of the ninety possible materials to be discarded from further consideration within one hour, leaving seventeen materials for additional study. Fifteen of the remainder were then considered unsuitable on the basis of cost, leaving two which were then subjected to more detailed analysis.

Another area where the use of this kind of diagram has been found successful is with the methods analysis of components and products, and the following example may be taken as typical of the kind of problem that it has been found appropriate to present in this manner. In a furniture factory that manufactured a large range of fireside chairs it was desirable to determine the possibilities for standardizing on the inside corner brackets or braces used to stiffen the seat framing. It was found that there were seventy-six different individual bracket components. A list was prepared of these which recorded all their individual features and qualities. As a result of the manner in which this information was presented, each was compared, and it was found that it was possible to reduce the number of this particular component from seventy-six to three brackets. It is frequently difficult to understand in cases of this kind why possibilities of this kind are not seen before. Needless to say the method of presenting the information and indicating the relationships contributed considerably to the solution of such a problem.

Some quite complex situations are often presented in this manner in a simple and understandable form. The example of a certain manufacturer of hydraulic pumps, who wished to simplify the design of his products in order to assist production, is an instance of this. From information provided by the sales department a relationship diagram was prepared which represented the complete range of small pumps that were likely to be required in reasonable quantities. From this it was possible to determine that pumps of 50,000 different specifications could be obtained from 750 standard parts.

It is appreciated that the majority of the examples quoted of the application of these diagrams appear to be applied to the analysis of components and products. But these diagrams have been successfully used in other areas of method study application, particularly in plant layout; the relationship charts of Muther described in Chapter 10 are examples of this. The "yes–no" flow diagrams which are used in the method study analysis of control procedures, and which are discussed in Chapter 12 represent yet another kind of relationship diagram, although dissimilar from those previously mentioned. This type of diagram provides a means of indicating the complicated relationships that exist in a control procedure, without fear of introducing possible ambiguities so often present in descriptions of such situations when presented in another form.

Numerical Data Charts

The investigator will frequently require to know the trends, differences, and relationships that exist between numerical data associated with a particular methods situation. For this reason he is invariably familiar with the construction of graphs, methods of charting data, and the construction of formula from them. In certain areas of method study application they are just as valuable for presenting and understanding a methods situation as the other charts and diagrams previously mentioned. It is also important to realize that in the analysis and solution of methods problems, charts of this kind are often less time-consuming to use, less susceptible to error, and more readily understood than equivalent methods. In certain circumstances the various kinds of graph can be used to solve aspects of methods investigations quickly and easily without recourse to difficult mathematics. They are also used to indicate significant trends or results in the method situation and are a means of presenting to management complex results in an easily understandable form.

In certain circumstances it is sometimes an advantage to obtain the assistance of a person who is familiar with the mathematical aspects of graphical presentation. But this is not always necessary as the methods frequently employed by method investigators enable the construction of these graphs in a relatively simple way. Various publications are obtainable which describe in detail these simple methods. These enable quite complex graphs to be constructed without great difficulty.

The graphic methods fall into three categories. Firstly, there are those for the illustration of numerical data such as pictorial charts, pie charts, bar or columnar charts, and others of a similar kind. Secondly, there are those which are used for the analysis of data which comprise the majority of the various types of graph. Thirdly, there are those that are used for computation and calculation. These include alignment charts or nomograms and multivariable graphs and calculating charts.

The methods analyst should also be able to obtain and design a simple formula or an algebraic expression from a graph when this is desired. By substituting known values for the variable elements in the formula, he may see how these values will affect the system or method he is investigating.

The extent to which method study activity in industry has made use of these graphic methods of charting is indicated by Müller. Frequent use is made of these methods in all the areas of method study, but particularly in operation analysis, the analysis of products and components, material utilization studies, materials handling, activity sampling, and control studies.

Selected References and Suggestions for Further Reading

Flow and String Diagrams

CURRIE, R. M., *Work Study*, Pitman, London, chapter 5.

MORROW, R. L., *Time Study and Motion Economy with Procedures for Method Improvement*, Ronald Press, New York, chapter 3.

Travel Chart

CURRIE, R. M., *Work Study*, Pitman, London, p. 213.

MUTHER, R., *Systematic Layout Planning*, Industrial Education Institute, Boston 16, Massachusetts, U.S.A., and Industrial Education International Ltd., Fleet St. London, chapter 4, p. 14.

Three-dimensional Models and Templates

Visual Planning Systems Ltd., Alperton, Wembley, Middlesex, England.

MUTHER, R., *Systematic Layout Planning*, chapter 12.

Man–Machine Charts

MUNDEL, M. E., *Motion and Time Study Principles and Practice*, Prentice-Hall, N.J. and London, chapters 10 and 11.

Gantt Chart

CLARK, W., *The Gantt Chart*, Pitman, London; Ronald Press, New York.

Gantt Chart, Standard Planning Sheets, W. Johnson & Sons Ltd., London, W.1.

Network Charts

BATTERSBY, A., *Network Analysis for Planning and Scheduling*, Macmillan, London, 1964.

LOCKYER, K. G., *An Introduction to Critical Path Analysis*, Pitman, London, 1964.

LOWE, C. W., *Critical Path Analysis by Bar Chart*, Business Publications Ltd., London.

LOCKYER, K. G., *Critical Path Analysis Problems and Solutions*, Pitman, London.

Kinetograms—Cyclegraphs and Chronocyclegraphs

MUNDEL, M. E., *Motion and Time Study Principles and Practice*, chapter 15.

NORBURY, R., *The Cranfield Report—A Comparative Study of Hand Movements in Typing*, I.B.M. United Kingdom Ltd., London.

PRESTON, T. A., New Techniques for Chronocyclegraphs, *Work Study and Management*, vol. 9, No. 7, July 1965, pp. 301–5.

SHAW, A. G., *Purpose and Practice of Motion Study*, The Harlequin Press, Manchester and London, England, chapter 4.

Relationship Diagrams

BAILEY, C. A. R., *Sets and Logic Series: 1 and 2 Contemporary School Mathematics*, Edward Arnold, London.

CUSHEN, W. E., Symbolic logic in operations research, pp. 187–202 of *Operations Research for Management*, vol. I, edited by J. F. McCloskey and F. N. Trefethen, The Johns Hopkins Press, Baltimore.

GARDNER, M., *Logic Machines and Diagrams*, McGraw-Hill, London and New York.

LOVIS, F. B., *Computers*—Contemporary School Mathematics Second Series, Edward Arnold, London, chapter 3, Flow Diagrams.

MUTHER, R. and WHEELER, J. D., *Simplified Systematic Layout Planning*, Management and Industrial Research Publications, Kansas City 8, Missouri, p. 2, Charting the relationships.

SPLAINE, M., A "Yes–No" technique for work study practitioners, *Work Study and Management*, vol. 7, No. 12, December 1963, pp. 551–4.

"*Design for Production*". A report of a visit to the U.S.A. in 1952 of a British specialist team on design for production, p. 27. Graph for the simplification of the design of a range of hydraulic pumps, British Productivity Council, London.

SCHEERER, M., Problem solving, *Scientific American*, vol. 208, No. 4, April 1963.

LUCHINS, A. S., Mechanization in Problem Solving: The Effect of Einstelling, *Psychological Monographs*, vol. 54, No. 6, whole No. 248, pp. 1–95, 1942.

SCHEERER, M., GOLDSTEIN, K. and BORING, E. C., A demonstration of insight. The horse and rider puzzle, *The American Journal of Psychology*, vol. 54, No. 3, pp. 437–8, July 1941.

Numerical Data Charts

ARKIN, H. and COLTON, R. R., *Statistical Methods*, College Outline Series, Barnes & Noble, New York; Constable, London. chapter 18, Graphic Presentation.

CARROL, P., *How to Chart Data*, McGraw-Hill, London and New York.

HOELSCHER, R. P., ARNOLD, J. N., and PIERCE, S. H., *Graphic Aids in Engineering Computation*, McGraw-Hill, London and New York.

MÜLLER, W., *Arbeitsstudien und Vorkalkula'ion in Holzbetrieben*, Carl Hanser – Verlag, Munchen.

NIEBEL, B. W., *Motion and Time Study*, Richard D. Irwin, Homewood, Illinois, chapter 18, Formula Construction, pp. 306–33.

SHERLOCK, A. J., *Probability and Statistics*, Second Series, Edward Arnold, London, chapters 1 and 2, Contemporary School Mathematics.

CHAPTER 5

Examination of the Data

Introduction

After the required information about the present method has been collected and presented in the most suitable form for an overall appreciation of the problem situation to be obtained, the next stage of the method study procedure is to subject this information to a critical examination. This is done in order to determine the means by which the work problem may be solved and improvements to the present method effected. This stage, however, is never commenced before the investigator is sure that all the relevant facts concerning the present method have been obtained.

The procedure of examination may be conducted in any of three ways. Either by the use of what are called questionnaires or check lists, or by the method study procedure of critical analysis, or by the application of the heuristic procedure of analysis. The use of any of these available procedures of examination will depend upon the circumstances associated with the investigation, how it is presented for analysis, and in what area of method study application the problem occurs. But it should be appreciated that each method of examination is but a means to an end, that of considering all aspects of the information in such a way that no facet of the problem is overlooked.

The process of conducting this analysis, irrespective of the method selected for use, demands a degree of intense concentration and application. This type of mental activity can be time-consuming and one that is beset with many difficulties. Only those who can apply themselves with diligence will be successful at this stage of the method study procedure.

Proficiency in this analysis is dependent on other factors besides the intensity of the application. The results that are likely to be obtained from any analysis will depend on the manner in which the information is approached and the ability of the investigator to obtain the answers to many of the questions. This approach should consist of an attitude of mind that examines the facts as they exist and not as they should or are said to exist, an attitude that reviews the information without preconceived ideas, as these can often influence the interpretation of these facts. An approach that challenges with a healthy scepticism all the aspects of the problem in a detailed and logical manner, accepting no answer until it is proved correct. An attitude that gives continued and detailed scrutiny of the facts and avoids hasty judgements.

Invariably during the examination hunches will come to mind, but the details of these should be recorded on paper as they occur, and left until the stage is reached when their validity can be investigated.

No proposals for improving the method being examined should be made until every unsatisfactory aspect of the present method has been fully examined.

Throughout the process of the analysis, by whatever means it may be made, the object of the investigation should never be forgotten. The use of each of these procedures of examination will now be discussed individually.

Questionnaires and Check Lists

It is often necessary during the stage of critical examination to obtain the active participation of those persons who are closely concerned with the situation under review. This is frequently obtained as the result of informal discussion groups assembled for this purpose. So that these discussions may be guided along lines that will produce the desired results, questionnaires or check lists are used. These are selected to cover the area or subject of the method study application that is the topic of discussion.

These questionnaires cover a wide field of inquiry. They are obtainable for process analysis, as well as for investigations in all five areas of method study application, and for the individual review of methods of recording. The questionnaires shown in this chapter are only a selection of those that are available to the investigator. Mention is made of others, either in the suggested references at the end of this chapter, or the appropriate sections of this volume concerned with the individual areas of method study activity.

They should not be used in circumstances where the conventional form of critical examination could be used, as it is possible that important aspects of a problem not covered by a question may be overlooked.

The following set of general questionnaires which have been used by method study investigators for many years was developed by R. L.

Morrow.* Their use will help to stimulate ideas for improvement in the areas for which they have been devised. It is to be appreciated that they form a basis for a questioning sequence, and thus may be added to according to circumstances and the type of work being investigated.

Operation Questionnaire

1. What is the purpose of the operation?
2. Is the operation necessary? Why?
3. Would some other operation better serve the purpose?
4. Have changed conditions modified its importance?
5. Can it be eliminated by use of different materials?
6. Can it be eliminated by improved tools?
7. Can it be eliminated by improved methods?
8. Can the design be changed to eliminate the operation?
9. Can it be partially eliminated?
10. Can it be divided into two or more short operations, or to eliminate hold-up operations in a progressive line?
11. Can it be combined with some other operation?
12. Can the sequence of the operation be changed?

Inspection Requirement Questionnaire

1. What finish is obtained on the work?
2. Is this grade of finish necessary? Why?
3. Can a cheaper finish be used and be suitable?
4. Can a better finish be obtained at same cost?
5. Is inspection visual or by gauges?
6. What are the tolerances?
7. Are these tolerances closer than necessary?
8. Should this work be gauged?
9. How frequently should the work be gauged?
10. How many pieces should be gauged at a time?
11. Are gauges of correct type for this work?
12. Are gauges in good condition?

Material Specification Questionnaire

1. Kind and type of material?
2. Grade and quality?

* Robert Lee Morrow, *Motion Economy and Work Measurement*, 2nd edn., Copyright 1957, Ronald Press, New York.

3. Is the material best for the part?
4. Would cheaper material be as good?
5. Should better material be used?
6. Weight of part?
7. Stock defects, such as form, shape, finish?
8. Dimensions of material?
9. Size of material best for least waste?
10. Can scrap or waste be reduced in other ways?
11. Will any such changes affect the economy of previous or subsequent operations?

Materials and Work in Process Handling Questionnaire

1. What is the nature of materials or parts handled?
2. What are the quantities handled?
3. Is the handling in units or containers?
4. Is the flow continuous or intermittent?
5. Does the material travel set the pace of operations?
6. What operations are performed while materials are moving?
7. What distance do the items travel while under operation?
8. What kinds of handling apparatus are used—cranes, hoists, trucks, conveyors, etc.?
9. Can operations be combined to reduce materials handling?
10. Can the operator deliver the part to the next operation when he disposes of it?

Machine and Auxiliary Equipment Questionnaire

1. Can this work be done more economically by hand or on a machine?
2. If work is done on a machine, what kind is used?
3. Is this the best kind of machine for the purpose?
4. Is machine hand-operated or automatic?
5. Is machine of correct size for the work?
6. Can the present machine be improved for this operation?
7. Is machine in first-class condition?
8. Is machine modern or out of date?
9. If the latter, would it be an advantage, economically, to have a modern machine?
10. Is machine in its proper location with respect to preceding and succeeding operations?
11. Can operator handle one or more machines?

12. Is method of drive satisfactory?
13. What is the drive speed? Is this correct?
14. How often should machine be lubricated?
15. What lubrication is used? Is it the best for the purpose?
16. Is machine properly safeguarded?
17. Are gravity feed containers used to deliver work to the point of operation?
18. Is drop delivery used for the finished article?

Tools, Jigs, and Fixtures Questionnaire

1. What tools are used?
2. Are these tools correct for the purpose?
3. Has the operator a sufficient number of tools?
4. What cutting speed is used? Feed?
5. What cutting speed should be used? Feed?
6. How frequently are tools ground, using proper feeds and speeds?
7. Are tools properly ground and set? By whom?
8. Can a power screwdriver, wrench, or similar tool be used?
9. Is a jig or fixture used? If not, how could one be used?
10. Can jig or fixture be improved? How?
11. Is method of locking jig or fixture as quick and convenient as possible?
12. Do all screws and wing nuts turn easily?
13. Is jig or fixture in first-class condition?
14. Are stops used for locating jig or fixture?
15. Should they be used?
16. How many pieces does jig or fixture hold?
17. Can this number be advantageously increased?
18. Is a cutting lubricant or coolant used? Kind?
19. Should a lubricant or coolant be used? Kind?
20. What volume of lubricant or coolant is used?
21. What volume of lubricant or coolant should be used?
22. How are chips, scrap, waste, and dust removed?
23. Would a larger volume of lubricant or coolant remove chips automatically? And how would it affect economy?
24. Is air blast used to remove chips?
25. Could air blast be used?

Preparation and Set-up Questionnaire

1. How does operator obtain his work, tools, or supplies?

2. Are there any delays at storeroom or toolroom?
3. In what quantities does he get his work?
4. Are these the proper quantities?
5. Could work be delivered to workplace?
6. If work is delivered is it in most convenient form for operator to use?
7. How is finished work removed?
8. Is this the most economical method?
9. Does delivery method affect subsequent operation?
10. Does operator make his own set-up, or are special set-up men provided?

Workplace Layout Questionnaire

1. Is the workplace laid out to conform to the principles of motion economy?
2. Are tools pre-positioned?
3. Are materials properly located?
4. Is height of bench or machine proper for operator?
5. Should work or operator be raised?
6. Can a chair or stool be used by operator?
7. If used, is chair or stool of proper height with reference to the work?
8. Are lighting conditions good?
9. Are temperature, humidity, and ventilation best for employee and work?
10. Can comfort and convenience of employee be increased? How?

Process Questionnaires

It may frequently be necessary for details of the manufacturing process to be obtained. To simplify the collection of these data recourse is often made to process check lists or questionnaires which enable the person who is obtaining these details to do so without fear of missing an important feature, and making it unnecessary for him to be knowledgeable in the technical aspects of the process. These questionnaires are usually provided by those methods personnel who are familiar with the process and its up-to-date aspects. These questionnaires list all the variables of a process which are likely to affect its efficiency. When these are made for a particular industry and process they are of universal application anywhere in that industry, where that process is in operation. They are also often useful for training methods analysts and apprentices in particular processes, as they exercise them in fact-finding and analysis.

A simple example is given of one that is used for checking an aspect of a furniture manufacturing process.

Wood Sanding Process Questionnaire

1. What type of timber is to be sanded?
2. Is the component in the appropriate condition for sanding?
3. Has it been thoroughly conditioned and seasoned?
4. Is the moisture content too high?
5. Has the component been machined correctly?
6. What are the machining qualities of the timber?
7. Have the appropriate precautions been taken to obtain good quality machining?
8. What is the quality of the machined surface? Cuts per inch?
9. What is the pitch and depth of the cutter marks?
10. Are all the cutters cutting?
11. What is the amount of stock removal required in the sanding?
12. Is the sanding operation being asked to do what an efficient machining operation should have done previously?
13. Does the sanding include rectification of bad machining?
14. Has the sanding to remove dents, scratches, and fine cutter marks?
15. What pressure is applied during the sanding?
16. Is an open or closed coated abrasive used?
17. What is the speed of the sanding equipment? Revs. per minute? Surface feet per minute?
18. What are the recommended speeds for the type of equipment?
19. What sanded finish is to be produced?
20. By what standard is this quality to be determined?
21. Is sanding done prior to assembly and subsequently to the parts store?
22. Is sanding done prior to the parts store?
23. What type of abrasive is used for sanding? Garnet? Aluminium oxide? Silicon carbide? etc.
24. What abrasive size is used?
25. What backing is used? Paper? Cloth? What weight?
26. What flexibility is required of the backing?
27. What bonding agent is used to fix the abrasive to the backing?
28. What jointing and splicing is used?
29. What is the procedure for making the joint?
30. How is the abrasive stored?
31. Is it stored correctly?

The answers to these questions will provide a basis for an evaluation of the efficiency of the sanding process. This will furnish the methods analyst with a valuable means of improving the process method.

The Method Study Procedure of Critical Examination

The use of this procedure of examination demands that the methods situation be presented in terms of operations, but not necessarily in operation symbols. However, some methods problems are more conveniently presented by alternative means. Whilst it is possible to offer nearly all methods problems for analysis in this form there are some occasions when it would be inconvenient to do this simply for the sake of justifying the universal application of this procedure of examination. It is important to remember that where it is possible to present the problem in a form suitable for the application of this procedure, this should be done.

As this procedure is an extremely rigorous form of examination, its correct application makes considerable demands on the investigator. It requires that the questions posed are answered correctly and honestly. If the investigator is not satisfied with the answer to any one question, he should persevere with his inquiries until the correct information is considered to have been obtained, as the success obtained from such an analysis is dependent on the quality of these answers. If they are not obtained in a conscientious and accurate manner the purpose of this procedure of critical examination is defeated.

Before commencing the actual analysis, the operations that comprise the constituent parts of the method for review are classified into the following categories, the "make ready", the "do", and the "put away" operations. The "make ready" operations are those that are concerned with the preparation of material plant or equipment so that "do" activities can be carried out. "Do" operations are those which represent the actual performance of work on materials or with plant and equipment, which results in a change in the material or the production of products or components. The "put away" operations are those that are concerned with the clearing away and removal of material, components, or products after the "do" operations have been completed. When these three kinds of operation have been identified the "do" operations are marked, to separate them from the other two categories, and it is these that are then examined in the order of their importance.

The operations are examined in preference to transports and delays because if an operation is eliminated as a result of the analysis, the transports and delays preceding and subsequent to the operation will be automatically eliminated, thus the time for the analysis will be reduced.

The "do" operations are now subjected to a standard procedure and pattern of analysis. This examination is carried out in two parts. The first is concerned with the primary questions which are designed to obtain details about the operation and the reasons for it and the secondary questions which enable alternatives to be considered and indicate suitable possibilities for improvement. The primary questioning sequence is as follows:

(i) *Purpose. What is done? Why is it necessary?*
The activity is scrutinized for the purpose of determining whether the work will be incorporated in the new method. In considering what is done, the activity should be viewed in isolation, but at the same time remembering the subject of the recording. The reason given for its necessity may not be true, for present conditions may no longer be applicable.

(ii) *Place. Where is the work done? Why is it done there?*
Where the activity takes place should be indicated by reference to its location in the shop, the machine or bench number, and the distance from the previous and subsequent activity. The reason for the particular location and, if this is not known, any historical or original reasons for the location.

(iii) *Sequence. When is it done? Why is it done then?*
The answers to these questions will give the details of the previous and subsequent work, the time factors involved, and the frequency with which the work takes place. They will also indicate what determines the sequence and frequency of processing.

(iv) *Person. Who does it? Why does that person do it?*
Details of the operators, their number, grade, and whether skilled or unskilled, male or female. Method of employment, whether on day work or shift work. Wage scale and incentive scheme, if one is in operation. The reason for each of the above points.

(v) *Means. How is it done? Why is it done that way?*
The answers to these questions will indicate the procedure by which the activity was carried out. Special importance should be given to the materials and equipment used and the operator's method. The reasons for each of the items should also be stated.

These primary questions will provide all the basic information about the present method of performing the activity.

It is important during this questioning sequence not to confuse the questions and answers relating to "purpose" and "means". For instance, when considering the operation of fitting hinges to a furniture cabinet assembly, the question "What is done?" would receive the answer "A method for opening the cabinet door is fitted to the assembly" and not "A hinge is fitted to the cabinet". Similarly in applying these questions to the operation "Bore 3 × $\frac{3}{8}$ inch dowel holes in a wooden component" the question "What is done?" should receive the answer "Three dowel holes of $\frac{3}{8}$-in. diameter are bored in a wooden component". To the question "How is it done?" might come the answer "By boring with three high-speed Jennings bits using a one and a half horse-power horizontal wood boring machine".

It is important that the description beside the symbols, on the process chart, should be as accurately phrased as possible. The answers to each of the primary questions will demand that the investigator supplement the information on these charts by seeking fresh information to answer the questions.

The secondary questions enable the investigator to discover alternative avenues of development that are available for the improvement of the method.

What else could be done?
Where else could it be done?
When else could it be done?
Who else could do it?
How else could it be done?

From the answers to the above questions the most suitable alternatives will be indicated. The answers to these is never nothing. The alternatives that must be considered are the elimination or partial elimination of the activity, thereby avoiding the necessity for the operation. Whether the activity can be combined with another or excluded by changing the sequence in which the activity is performed, or whether the operation can be simplified.

What should be done?
Where should it be done?
When should it be done?
Who should do it?
How should it be done?

The answers to these questions will indicate the possibilities that exist for improvements. Both the primary and the secondary questions are used to analyse an individual "Do" operation before proceeding to the next.

Standard preprinted forms (Fig. 55) are available to the methods analyst which enable the questioning sequence to be carried out and the recording of the answers in the appropriate spaces allowed. Usually in

METHOD STUDY – CRITICAL EXAMINATION SHEET

Operation ○ Inspection □ Ref. No. ....
Page .... of ......

	THE PRESENT FACTS		POSSIBLE ALTERNATIVES	SELECTED ALTERNATIVES
PURPOSE	What is achieved ?	Is it necessary ? Why?	What else could be done ?	What should be done ?
PLACE	Where is it done ?	Why there ? Advantages: Disadvantages:	Where else could it be ? A: D:	Where should it be done ?
SEQUENCE	When is it done ? After: Before	Why then ? A: D:	When else could it be done ? A: D:	When should it be done ?
PERSON	Who does it ?	Why that person ? A: D:	Who else could do it? A: D:	Who should do it ?
MEANS	How is it done ?	Why that way ? A: D:	How else could it be done ? A: B:	How should it be done ?

Fig. 55. Critical examination sheet.

using these forms it is found that there is insufficient space on them in which to write the complete answers to the many questions, so that what is usually done in such circumstances is to record a reference in each of the spaces reserved for the answers and to write the details on foolscap sheets of plain paper attached to the standard form.

Heuristic Procedure of Analysis

The heuristic procedure of analysis is an approach to problem solving which belongs to the confines of logic. But whereas logic enables the results produced by thinking to be checked by supplying the forms and rules which enable this to be done, it does not study the process which is involved when a person is thinking. Logic only provides the means by which the validity of a conclusion may be tested or a reasoned argument assessed. It does not provide the means by which to establish the truth of a conclusion within the limits of a given problem area, or whether something is sensible or absurd. It cannot assist in the search, selection, or interpretation of the information required.

Heuristic analysis, however, simulates the detective's method of inquiry by using conclusions obtained by a questioning sequence at each stage of the investigation in order to obtain the next progression towards a solution. It is therefore based on induction and analogy.

The application of this procedure has found favour with methods investigators in their search for solutions to various kinds of industrial problem, amongst which may be mentioned problems associated with material utilization, product and component analysis, value analysis, production control, production line balancing, and aspects of operator training, to name only a few.

It is an alternative to the conventional procedure of critical analysis where the nature of the problem is such that this cannot be used. An important aspect of heuristic application is that its use enables the investigator to understand the process of solving problems, especially those mental operations used to obtain a solution. This provides not only a means of gaining experience in this essential activity but also a means of guiding others who may have to conduct similar forms of assignment.

It is often considered to be an extension of the method study procedure of critical examination, as it is found useful in the secondary questioning sequence, in certain applications.

The heuristic procedure provides a thought process for progressively clarifying problems too complex or too uncertain for the straightforward application of the procedure of critical analysis. For this reason it has been found useful in defining the method study assignment and the initial diagnosis of the problem. It supplies a means of approaching certain kinds of method investigation and the selection of the appropriate facet of the activity for analysis by the conventional method study techniques.

To apply this form of analysis successfully demands some experience not only in the conduct of method studies themselves but also in the use of the heuristic procedure. But when this has been obtained, its application tends to be more rigorous than the other methods of analysis. However, the investigator would do well to adhere to the conventional procedure until such time as this experience has been gained. Although heuristic problem solving is a very successful method of seeking a solution it would be wasteful and uneconomical to seek an answer by these means if a simpler method would suffice. For this reason it is only used for the solution of those methods problems which cannot conveniently be solved by the other procedures.

The nature of the direction given to a methods analyst using this procedure will have a considerable influence on the success of the investigation. It is for this reason customary therefore for an experienced investigator to be available to the person carrying out an analysis of this kind for the first time. When experience has been gained this direction may be reduced.

In the initial stages of such an investigation unrelated data is quite often collected. From these data inferences may possibly be drawn, but usually a working hypothesis or possible answer to each stage of the problem is made as a guide to the search for a solution. The validity of these hypotheses are constantly checked with the original data. If these are not valid they are rejected and another selected until finally a consistent set of conclusions emerge. These conclusions are then tested to determine whether they meet the conditions of the problem or whether they are acceptable.

The use of this analytical method demands that at the various stages of the investigation notes should be carefully written as a faithful record of the analysis reached at that point. This is done to organize the thoughts of the investigator at each stage and thus enables him to begin the assembly of results that look as though they will contribute to the solution of the whole problem. When another direction of inquiry and search is sought, and this particular approach is found to contribute no solution, because a record has been kept of the preceding stage, the investigation can be taken up again at a convenient point. Then another direction of investigation may proceed in much the same manner as a person seeking his way methodically through a maze.

There is no universal plan for the conduct of the heuristic procedure of analysis, though Polya has suggested a procedure, as also have Westaway and Hodnett. But these can only form the basis for an initial understanding of its use. A complete understanding of the appropriate plan of approach in all circumstances will come eventually with experience and practice. It would be unreasonable to expect a detective to work to a rigid plan in his investigation, likewise the methods analyst has a degree of freedom within the confines of a basic procedure.

Experience is best built up by carrying out investigations gradually over a period of time, progressing from quite simple problems to more complex examples and the examination of case studies with supervision and direction. In the training of method study investigators in this procedure the use of a tape recorder is frequently found an advantage, as it enables the instantaneous recording of the thought process of the student as he carries out the procedure in solving carefully prepared problems and describes each stage of his approach. These recordings can then be played back to the group for criticism and discussion. By the solution of a graduated sequence of such tasks the student soon acquires the skill which enables him to approach the heuristic procedure for solving problems of greater complexity with confidence.

The general characteristic of heuristic problem solving may be indicated by the following procedure which is based on that suggested by Polya. This has been particularly useful to methods investigators as a guide to this form of analysis. Although Polya, in describing the use of the procedure, uses examples taken largely from geometry, his principal aim is to teach a method of analysis which can be applied to the solution of other problems more or less of a technical nature, such as would confront the investigator in industry. This suggested approach is a constant regardless of the subject of the problem and is expressed in the following simple questions.

Heuristic Procedure

(a) *To become familiar with the problem*

State the problem. Review the situation.

What is to be determined?

Select the objectives? What improvements should be made?

What information is available?

Get the necessary information.

What are the terms of reference conditions or restraints that have to be observed in determining a solution to the problem?

Is it possible to satisfy these conditions?

Is it possible to solve this type of problem?

Is it possible to solve this type of problem within the terms of reference and conditions imposed on the solution?

Check the facts. Define and investigate significant factors.

Is sufficient information available with which to solve the problem?

Diagnose the cause of the present problem.

What information is required?

What information would be superfluous?

What information if obtained would contradict the problem?

Draw a diagram or construct a model of the problem.

Separate the various parts of the problem and the conditions.

What are the constant and the variable factors?

Reduce the elements of the problem to suitable symbols or notation.

(b) *Plan a method for the solution of the problem*

Has the problem been encountered before?

Has it been encountered in another form?

Is a similar problem known?

Are rules or procedures known that would be useful?

Look at the solution desired.

Is a problem known which produced the same desired solution?

Consider alternative lines of approach.

Restate the problem.

Is it possible to restate the problem?

Is it of any assistance to restate the problem?

Return to definitions.

Analyse and decide.

Can a plan for a method of solution be determined?

If not, plan the solution of a related problem, a more general problem, a special problem, or an analogous problem.

Can a solution of part of the problem be obtained by retaining only part of the condition and disregarding the other part?

As a result, how far is it possible to obtain a solution?

In what manner can the solution vary?

Can any useful results be obtained from the information collected?

Can other suitable information be an aid in obtaining a solution?

Is it possible to alter or rearrange the proposed solution to the problem, or the information, or both if required, so that the desired solution and the information are more compatible?

Has all the information been used to obtain the solution?

Have all the conditions been considered?

Have all the contingent considerations involved in the solution been examined? Select the best solution and act.

(c) *Implement the plan for the solution of the problem*

What action is to be taken? Who? When?

Carry out the proposals for a solution.

Check the results.

Is each step correct? Can it be proved that the step is correct?

Modify the solution if necessary.

(d) *Revision and examination*

Is it possible to check the solution?

Is it possible to check the argument and reasoning?

Prepare written description and instructions.

Is it possible to see the solution immediately?

Could a solution have been obtained differently?

Is it possible to use the solution or the method of obtaining the solution for other problems?

Selected References and Suggestions for Further Reading

Questionnaires and Check Lists

BATTERSBY, A., *A Guide to Stock Control*, Pitman, London, Appendix 1, pp. 104–5, Stock Control Questionnaire.

MORROW, R. L., *Time and Motion Economy with Procedures for Methods Improvement*, Ronald Press, New York, chapter 7, Analysis Techniques.

MUNDEL, M. E., *Motion and Time Study*, Prentice-Hall, Englewood Cliffs, N.J. and London.

NADLER, G., *Motion and Time Study*, McGraw-Hill, London and New York, chapter 13, Applying the Check List.

Critical Examination Procedure

CURRIE, R. M., *Outline of Work Study—Part II, Method Study*, British Institute of Management, London, chapter 8.

CURRIE, R. M., *Work Study*, Pitman, London, chapter 6.

CURRIE R. M., Machine efficiency in garment manufacture, *Work Study and Management*, vol. 7, No. 2, pp. 77–81, February 1963. Excellent example of the application of the procedure.

Heuristic Procedure

ARMSTRONG, H. E., *The Teaching of Scientific Method*, Macmillan, 1910, chapter xv, The Heuristic Method.

COHEN, M. R. and NAGEL, E., *An Introduction to Logic and Scientific Method*, Harcourt, Brace & Co., New York; Routledge and Kegan Paul, London.

HODNETT, E., *The Art of Problem Solving*, Harper, New York.

MINTER, A. L., Problem solving, *Work Study and Management*, vol. 7, No. 8, August 1963, pp. 362–5.

POLYA, G., *How to Solve It*, Doubleday Anchor Book, Doubleday & Co., New York.

SIMON, H. A. and NEWALL, A., Heuristic problem solving, *Journal of the Operations Research Society of America*, January–February 1958, pp. 1–10; May–June 1958, pp. 449–50.

SIMON, H. A., *Heuristic Problem Solving. The New Science of Management Decisions*, Harper, New York.

THOMSON, R., *The Psychology of Thinking*, chapter 3, Penguin Books.

WEBSTER, L. and KILBRIDGE, M. D., A heuristic method of assembly line balancing, *The Journal of Industrial Engineering* (*U.S.A.*), July–August 1961, pp. 292–8.

WEBSTER, L. and KILBRIDGE, M. D., Heuristic line balancing: a case, *The Journal of Industrial Engineering* (*U.S.A.*), May–June 1962, pp. 139–49.

WESTAWAY, F. W., *Scientific Method*, Blackie, London, chapter xl, The Heuristic Method.

WERTHEIMER, M., *Productive Thinking*, Harper, 1945.

CHAPTER 6

Development of the Proposed Method

IN THE process of making a critical examination of the recorded data the possibilities for improving the present method are indicated. It is these possibilities that are now used as a guide to the development of the improved method. In preparation for this examination the "do" operations and the inspections will have been isolated and if these were not subsequently eliminated, they will form the basis of the improved method. The "make ready" and "put away" activities associated with these operations that are retained will also be included. All these activities are now arranged in a sequence to form a basis for the most effective improvement. This rearrangement will frequently be made as a result of a compromise between a large number of considerations.

At this development stage the investigator will be required to use all the qualities of resourcefulness, ingenuity, and creative imagination, so that the best possible results may be obtained. The value of any hunches or bright ideas which may have been obtained during the critical examination should now be considered. It is also necessary to test the practicability of any ideas or suggestions by trial and error, or, if this is not appropriate, sometimes by simple experimental method. It may also be necessary to construct a simple array, model, or "mock up" to evaluate the possibilities of any proposed ideas, which may include the use of improvised equipment.

During this process of development, the results likely to be achieved by the study should always be appreciated as this is likely to suggest who and what is going to be subsequently affected by the results of the study, and will also indicate who is most suitable to approach, and to call upon to participate in the development. This will also ensure the maximum co-operation of all who are likely to contribute to the development, and enables the methods analyst to benefit from the knowledge of others, which may be valuable in the light it throws on past custom and historical practices and simplifies the evaluation of alternative lines of development.

In addition, by this consultation the subsequent acceptance and installation of the proposed method will be made much easier.

The purpose of the procedure of critical examination is to examine the information about the present method from all aspects, as a preparation for the development of improved methods. If this is done in a correct and conscientious manner, the ground will have been thoroughly prepared for the development stage. As much of the preparation for development will have already been made as a result of this, the purpose of this development is to determine and try out proposals which will achieve the particular objectives of the study, in the situations and circumstances in which they will have to operate. In the course of this, many improvements will be suggested that would answer the method problem; some of these will be eliminated by either being too costly or not being appropriate in the circumstances.

It is often useful when developing a new method to think of the ideal solution to the problem and modify this to suit the immediate requirements, resources, and conditions of the situation. If a clear specification of what is required can be made it is invariably found that by the careful analysis of this, an indication can be given as to how the present method may be improved. However, the development of new methods should never be expected to be a matter of routine.

The proposals for any method improvement may be further enhanced by giving attention to certain contingent considerations such as lighting, heating, colour, seating, ventilation, noise, safety, first aid, and fire precautions. It is of little use proposing a new method of work if bad conditions, relative to these factors, exist in the factory in the immediate environment of the workers. It will also be of little use expecting their co-operation for any proposals if they have been complaining for some time about conditions and nothing has been done to improve them. Although the introduction of improvements in the physical organization of an operation or procedure will produce measurable savings, the results that these contingent considerations can contribute to the improvement of the proposed method cannot always be measured in terms of cost savings or increased production, but it is known that attention to these aspects has a considerable effect on the attitude of personnel to the proposed methods. This, and what they think about the method, is obviously important, as their subsequent co-operation during the period of installation is essential.

The degree of success achieved in the development of a proposed method will frequently be indicated by the ready acceptance of the method by personnel, and also by the assessment previously determined at the commencement of the study. In this way it is possible to judge how effective the process of development has been and whether the predetermined objectives have been achieved.

The possible difficulties that are likely to be encountered in selling the results to personnel should be considered at all times, and the possibilities of obtaining their co-operation and assistance in the subsequent installation of the method. Improvements should also be considered that are not of immediate importance but which can be subsequently reviewed.

It should be remembered that there is always a better way. No activity should become a habit and be left unquestioned for any great length of time.

Ideas and suggestions from factory workers should at all times be received and considered carefully, for these workers are often in a position to suggest improvements to methods.

When the proposed method has been developed, it is recorded in the most appropriate manner. This recording is then subjected to a process of refinement which will involve the same degree of scrutiny as that made previously when reviewing the existing method. This will ensure that the proposed method will be logical and capable of withstanding future criticism.

Creative Thinking

In the process of developing a new method a considerable measure of creativity will have to be exercised by the person conducting this development. In order to achieve this creative approach it has been found beneficial to apply the procedures of creative thinking which have been developed by those persons who have suggested ways by which to obtain a more imaginative approach to the development of better methods.

The results obtained have proved themselves superior to the conventional groping for improvements that invariably occurs in this part of the method study procedure. Its application improves the ability of methods personnel to produce original and good quality ideas, and improves the fluency of these ideas rather than the practice of judicial thinking. It has been found easier to apply the procedure to methods development than to other areas of creativity.

In the development of better methods too much reliance is often placed on process knowledge, and the use of standard solutions. Methods personnel are too often content to go through the procedure of development without making any great personal contribution. Whilst this approach will often provide satisfactory proposals, acceptable to management, it will never provide the really imaginative answer.

Creative thinking is a procedure which enables the methods investigator to break away from the conventional thought process and think in a manner likely to engender the production of ideas for the development of better methods. In this way results are gradually assembled that contribute to an improvement. Many startling ideas, particularly those which involve little or no technical knowledge, have been developed in this way, but which most people given instruction could have created for themselves. As a result personnel are often tempted to ask "Why didn't I think of that?" The application of this type of thinking develops a positive outlook of "anything can be done". As all methods personnel frequently have to contend with expressions of "What's the use, it can't be done" or "it isn't done, it isn't practical, we've got no time for theories", and all the other unfortunate substitutes for hard thinking, this positive approach is most beneficial for the consideration of ideas.

Barriers to Creativity

Method study personnel during training often find it difficult to think in a creative and imaginative way, because they have not become aware of nor appreciate the barriers to creativity that exists in the individual, or of how it is possible to get rid of these influences. The various attitudes of mind that prevent the individual from exercising his creative potential to the full are numerous. The following indicate some of these attitudes, but the list cannot be considered to be in any way exhaustive. They are all habits and experiences that are barriers to the exercise of creative imagination. These barriers produce a blind conformity which frequently influences the person from trying any new approach: a non-perceptive mind and one that is unattentive and easily distracted; lack of mental aggressiveness and an attitude of presumption and acceptance of things as they exist; a complacent and timid attitude of mind possessing no confidence; a mind concerned with the unimportant instead of issues of greater significance; "cook book" thinking and an inability to think in abstract terms; lack of imagination and an inability to comprehend important relationships; lack of foresight and an inability to anticipate; allowing one's specialization to limit one's breadth of mental perception; too easily influenced by previous cases, examples, and experience; a negative attitude of mind, or one devoid of simplicity in thought, or without an objective attitude; a mind so concerned with perfection that alternatives of a lower standard but potentially valuable are not considered; being complaisant and agreeing with the opinions of others too easily; some committees have a retarding effect on creative thinking, because of their preoccupation with procedure and detail; dissipation of creative energies; tendency of allowing the search for truth to be influenced by vested rights or personal interests; reliance on authority because authority has said it should be done this way—in this situation individuals seldom give thought to alternative methods.

Creative thinking is thinking for ourselves and divorcing the creative activity from its environment and condition. The initial reaction to ideas should not be allowed to influence the person who has produced them into disregarding these ideas for method improvement.

Many persons are hampered by a burden of knowledge, much of which is useless because the ability of using it has never been impressed upon them, and self reliance has never been taught. Flexibility of mind and the ability of adapting oneself to new circumstances and conditions are the qualities that are required.

Procedure

The methodology of creativity has not as yet been brought together into a definite technique suitable for all situations. It is recognized as one of the fields of psychology requiring much further research. However, it possesses a procedure which has become useful to the methods investigator as a means of developing better methods. This procedure does not discount the possibility of inspiration, or any suggestion that a clearly defined procedure can in fact be laid down for all to apply. It is recognized that different individuals, once trained, have different ways of approaching the process of creative thinking. The primary abilities, however, can be developed in various ways, for instance by the solution of certain types of problem. Thinking for oneself can be a difficult process but it is an old maxim that a person learns to do by doing, so that to learn to develop an aptitude for creative thinking it is necessary to obtain plenty of experience and practice. In the process of obtaining this the mental reactions to difficult creative activity should be observed carefully as much can be learnt from the way they are approached. The use of case studies can provide the student with an excellent means of exercising his ability in this direction.

To make a creative approach to the development of a new method the information collected during the procedure of critical examination should be programmed to the mind in the correct sequence. What is required should be set down and what would be worth doing if it could be done should be stated. A period of incubation should be allowed to elapse after this, then subsequently the investigator should come back to the thought process again. All interested persons should be consulted in order to speed the process and exercise the mind. The basic ideas should be fitted together and refined and the investigator must be critical of the results and modify them where necessary. No attempts should be made to adhere to time limits. The mental activity involved in methods development will take its own time; if attempts are made to hasten this process unduly it will result in failure, or some commonplace or standard answer. But above all the individual should have faith in his ability to produce the right improvement. It should be remembered too that the initial suggestions for improvements can often be further simplified. In the production of ideas one should not be too influenced by the reactions of others to these proposals.

There is never a best solution to a creative development problem, but only one that has been obtained by thinking creatively to certain limits. If more effort is spent in probing more deeply into each aspect of the subject to be developed, a solution closer to that of a "perfect" one is more likely to be obtained. There is also no theoretical limit to the number of alternatives that may be listed, but it is recognized that there are practical limitations.

The quality of creativity that exists in a person is dependent on the individual's first-hand experience of life, and what he has gained by reading, training, and instruction. But creativity is only possible from those persons who have the ability and desire to carry out the necessary preparation for this activity, and the capacity to exercise the self-discipline that is required to produce original work. But however educated and trained a person may be, if any of the barriers to creativity are present very little creative imagination will be displayed by that person.

The following suggested procedure cannot supply a rigid structure for so dynamic a process as creative thinking, and this should be emphasized when this procedure is used. Although this provides no more than a helpful guide it cannot be considered to be inflexible.

Creative Procedure. Development of the Proposed Method

I. *Fact finding*

(a) What facts have been obtained about the method to be improved? List fact-finding questions, not judicial or creative ones. Disregard whether or not this information is obtained. If it is desired, raise the question.

(b) Where could the answers to these significant questions be obtained? List all conceivable sources of information.

(c) Using the best sources find the answers to the most significant of these questions.

II. *Problem finding*

List all the creative-type questions problems or challenges suggested by the method to be developed. Such as:

How might I . . .?
What ways might I . . .?
What ideas might I produce to . . .?

If problem finding or judicial-type questions occur convert them to creative type questions by stating them as:

How might I find out . . .?
How might I decide . . .?

How many problems of this type are suggested by the situation and the additional facts that have been gathered about the situation?

Stop for a moment and ask the following questions.

What is the real problem of improvement? Why?
What is the basic objective in the improvement? Why?
What do I want to accomplish by the improvement? Why?

As a result of these questions try to restate and broaden the problem.

Try to find problem questions that give the largest number of possible approaches.

Try restating the sense of the passage in other words.

Now that the problem has been broadened, what other creative aspects or approaches or sub-problems can be seen that were not listed earlier?

Now circle the best and the most promising statements indicating the avenues of method development for consideration.

Perhaps it is the one that would give the greatest opportunity, the largest number of approaches, or areas for exploration.

Select the one which is most significant to the particular method improvement problem. The one most in need of the creative approach.

It may at this stage be considered necessary to go back and carry out additional fact finding if this has not already been done.

Now that the problem has been restated the new wording may suggest many more facts which it may now be possible to list.

III. *Idea finding*

(a) State the problem. Be sure that the statement is clear and is as brief as possible. Be telegraphic in wording. Be sure that it starts with words as:

What way might I . . .?

(b) Collect ideas. These can be tentative approaches to the method solution obtained from deliberate idea finding. Use any of the sub-problems previously recorded as a means of approach to the production of ideas.

Other uses? Substitutes? Adapt? Modify? Maximize? Minimize? Rearrange? Combine? Reverse?

Now return and circle those ideas that seem to offer the best opportunities. Judgement is to be exercised at this stage.

IV. *Solution finding*

Evaluation. What are the methods of evaluation by which the effectiveness of each of the ideas may be mentally tested?

This is really a further measure of the sensitivity of the investigator to problems. These problems might be implicit in the changes that could be brought about by each idea.

Try to anticipate all the effects, repercussions, and consequences of these ideas.

Evaluate those ideas that have been circled as offering the best potential solution. For each of these ideas indicate a rating. G, good; F, fair; P, poor; DP, does not pertain, etc. Then make a decision regarding each of the circled ideas based on its rating.

V. *Acceptance finding*

The purpose of this stage is to assist, by the use of creative thinking, in preparing to put the idea into effect.

This procedure should be followed for each idea that has been selected for use.

Consider the ways of implementing, carrying out, accomplishing, gaining acceptance for, insuring the effectiveness of, the idea to be developed and its improvement.

Who, when, and/or where? How and/or why? To gain acceptance and enthusiasm of others for the idea.

Creative thinking is the production of ideas. It can almost be considered to be autistic thinking or day-dreaming. But the fact that a solution has been produced by the exercise of creative imagination, intuition, or autistic thinking or any other non-logical thought process, does not mean that the person who has produced these ideas may not have to defend his ideas by logical argument. A logical argument will have to be prepared and put forward to state why it is thought that the ideas will work. But in connection with this, it should be remembered that ideas are not offered for the approval of others until the investigator is prepared to defend them with a suitable argument.

Experimental Procedure

Often in the development of some aspect of a method improvement, considerable time is spent in trying something out to see what will happen. Because no definite procedure is used in such situations the results are often inconclusive, sometimes conflicting, and more often than not a failure. Whilst hit and miss methods satisfy the methods analyst's immediate curiosity, they are often time wasting, and make no valid contribution to the development of the proposed method. Most method study experiments are carried out by naturalistic observation, that is where the subject of the experiment must be studied as it occurs naturally. This makes it all the more necessary for the use of some experimental design and control, in order that reasonably valid conclusions may be obtained from the results. Not all types of method development will call for such forms of experimentation, but where it does, the following guidance will assist the investigator in obtaining reasonable results. It is not possible within the confines of this volume to discuss the procedures of experimental method at any great length nor would it be appropriate to do so, as there are available adequate and easily read publications on this subject to which the method study practitioner can go for practical information. But he should be familiar with the following basic procedure.

The problem that is to be solved by experimentation must first be defined. This definition should be phrased in the form of a hypothesis, which is a suggested answer to the problem, the proving or disproving of which will be the subject of the experiment. This hypothesis should be an adequate and simple answer to the specific problem that requires a solution, and should be stated in such a way as to allow it to be refuted. When a hypothesis is stated negatively it is called a null hypothesis. It may be that to pose a problem in this form may sometimes simplify the experimental procedure, as hypotheses that are tested by an experiment in which the results are finally evaluated statistically are best if stated in this form.

Next, the following factors associated with the subject of the experiment have to be determined. What is the independent variable? This is the factor that will be manipulated by the experimenter in the course of carrying out the experiment. What is the dependent variable? This will be the subject that will vary as the experimenter manipulates the independent variable. How the dependent variable or variables are to be measured will next have to be considered.

What controls are considered necessary? How will these be applied in the experiment and why are they considered necessary? For what reason will they be required? The methods of accomplishing the control of an experiment are numerous, as can be seen by reference to a standard textbook on simple experimental method such as that by Townsend. The experimenter should become familiar with these methods if the results to be obtained from any experiment are to be considered reliable and beyond doubt.

What procedure is to be followed in carrying out the experiment? This will depend on the particular experimental design selected. Normally in the simple experiments that have to be made in connection with certain kinds of method study the experimental procedures used are usually of a straightforward nature. The apparatus or equipment used in the experiment should be described not only by means of a written description, but also by suitable diagrams. An exact description of what is proposed to be done should be made and an explanation given on how the experimental results are to be analysed. The experimental design should then be reviewed and the following aspects considered. What results were they obtained would support or fail to support the hypothesis. When this has been clearly defined the experiment should be conducted. Throughout the procedure the presence of unplanned occurrences that may influence the results should be sought, as these could invalidate the findings. If an operator is used in the experiment, his reactions, remarks, and attitudes to the experiment should be noted.

When the experiment has been completed the experimental results should be summarized in the form of tables, graphs, or other clear means of presentation. When this has been done the results can then be interpreted. A description of the tables and graphs and any statistical analysis should be made from the point of view of proving or disproving the hypothesis. Then the conclusions obtained from this can be stated.

Numerous occasions arise in the development of improved methods when it is an advantage for simple experiments to be conducted. In such situations simple experimental procedures save time, give a more reliable indication as to the practicability of any proposals, and, more important still, provide the investigator, who has to sell the method proposals to other personnel, with a means of supporting his argument with facts.

Simulation

The procedure of simulation is a means by which an approximate evaluation of certain kinds of system, activity, or situation may be obtained through experiment. It is generally used in method study to solve those aspects of method development which depend in some way upon chance or probability, and where physical experimentation or trying something out would be impracticable, too costly, or too time consuming. It enables an element of probability to be artificially introduced into a proposed system at its development stage in order that some aspect of the method problem may be solved.

It is, however, no advantage to use this procedure in all methods development, only in connection with those problems where its use is appropriate. It is frequently desirable to know how a proposed method will behave when it is subjected to random influences and conditions which are inherent in the system. But it is a device that is only used as a last resort, where the methods problem cannot be solved by the use of the conventional analytical methods.

Simulation when combined with the heuristic procedure, makes it possible to obtain solutions to problems which would otherwise be difficult to solve. The amount of time usually spent in the application of the actual procedure of simulation is often small when compared with that expended during the preparation period in heuristic.

Although it is a relatively simple procedure when applied to problems of method study where its use is found to be necessary, it is a procedure that demands a capacity for clear thought on the part of the investigator, so that the influences and elements of a system or method under review may be correctly defined.

There are, of course, various means available for the simulation of a method situation. One of the simplest of these and one that is frequently used in methods study consists of listing all the variable conditions or elements in the proposed method, and then to determine what influences their change from one situation to another, and what effect each will have upon any proposals. Although this is no alternative to the correct procedure of simulation, it frequently results in the investigator discovering aspects of a method which were not previously foreseen in the system, and thus enables those elements of the problem which were considered of no significance to be eliminated. It also enables subsequent attention to be given to the more important facets of a proposed method.

The procedure of simulation consists of the unrestricted random sampling of an activity whereby the items from a population are selected in such a manner that each has an equal chance of being selected. By means of this the random nature of events can be applied to the components of a method. The use of the simulation procedure is not something that the methods analyst can commence without appreciating the demands that it will make on him. It will require the collection of a great quantity of data about the system, and the use of a certain amount of arithmetic. But it does provide a quick means of estimating the answers to some questions about the operation of a system which previously were often guessed by the methods investigator. Where this guesswork was previously practised, the investigator frequently provided for all contingencies by building into the proposed method too large a safety margin, thus making the subsequent methods proposals more expensive than they should be. The procedure for carrying out a simulation study is commenced by first defining the model of the system that it is desired to simulate, together with its boundaries or limits. This is done by the judgement of the investigator and the application of the heuristic procedure of analysis. This preliminary work can sometimes be difficult and only familiarity and practice in approaching such problems will enable the investigator to become more expert in this activity. A further aspect that will also have to be considered at this stage is how much detail to include in the study. To answer this question and appreciate its significance the following further details will have to be defined. The components of the system, and the state of each of the elements of the system, and the rules which influence the change from one situation to another. As a change will occur in the system under review in relation to time, the simulation will be made by reference to a clock or counter. This will provide the time interval between the simulations, and it is this interval that will have to be determined. After the plan of the simulation study has been prepared random numbers are selected from a table in order that the system may be simulated with reference to the intervals chosen.

An understanding of the procedure is best obtained by the examination of a simple example.

In a certain furniture factory it is decided to improve the method of issuing cutters, jigs, and fixtures to personnel in a large machine shop. The storeman who at present performs this function does so single-handed and it is suggested as part of the possible improvements that an extra person should be employed to assist him, as the storeman finds himself nearly always busy and many workers who come to the service counter to collect items frequently have to wait, and complain that they waste time because of this. On those occasions when the cause of the complaint is checked by a visit to the store there appears to be hardly any incidence of waiting by operators, and the storeman appeared to be underemployed. The factory management, realizing that there were many factors that could influence the efficiency of this activity, requested method study to check the feasibility of employing an extra service storeman, and whether an additional one was, in fact, sufficient, and at the same time make proposals and recommendations for the improvement of the present method.

The method study investigator assigned to the study realized that no results could be obtained by employing an extra storeman for a trial period to see what would happen, a. in situations of this kind extra staff could always be somehow justified; thus for this reason it was not considered to be the best possible way of approaching this method problem.

The investigator also realized that the frequency with which individual machinists or their assistants came to the service counter conformed to a reasonably constant pattern as batch production was in operation in the shop for a relatively constant product range, the size of each batch being determined by reference to the longest individual machine set-up time in the process sequence. Each of the set-up activities had been the subject of a method study and time standards for each had been determined.

These standards were adhered to and the methods by which they were performed were constantly maintained.

The investigator decided to carry out a simulation study of the present method of issuing items at the service counter as a means of evaluating the various aspects of the present conditions. He commenced by collecting data about the nature of the components of the method, namely the interval between the arrivals of operators and the length of the service times. This was done over a representative period of a number of days.

The information obtained was then presented in the form shown in Table 1(a) (b) and Table 2(a) (b). After this had been done a table of two-digit random numbers was obtained whose numbers range from 00 to 99. A correspondence was then made between these numbers and the percentage frequency of arrivals and service times as indicated. For example in the case of the frequency of arrivals, as the interval of one minute occurred 11 per cent of the time, Table 1, eleven two-digit numbers, namely 00 01 02 03 . . . 10, were taken to correspond to this interval between arrivals. The second interval of two minutes occurred 10 per cent of the time, thus in a similar manner a further ten consecutive two-digit numbers, namely 11 12 13 14 . . . 20, were taken to correspond to this interval. This process was continued until every one of the two-digit random numbers from 00 to 99 had been assigned to the observed time intervals of arrivals and the service times, and the correspondences shown in Table 1(c) and Table 2(c) had been obtained.

The methods investigator is now in a position to simulate arrival and service times. To do this recourse is made again to tables of two-digit random numbers; these are used in conjunction with the information already obtained. Let us assume that the first random number taken from the table is 38. According to Table 1 and the correspondence between the random numbers and the intervals between arrivals, this number corresponds to an interval of 5 minutes. Therefore if the start of the working day in the machine shop is 7.30 the first arrival will occur at 7.30 plus this time interval of five minutes, i.e. 7.35. The next random number selected from the tables is 22. This corresponds to an interval of three minutes (Table 1) and indicates that the next simulated arrival occurs at 7.35 plus 3, or 7.38. Proceeding in this manner successive arrival times are generated as shown in Table 3. These can then be used to try out and develop the various possible methods of operating the service counter, and to determine the possible waiting time, and duration of the service times, when sufficient have been simulated in both cases.

TABLE 1. DISTRIBUTION OF TIMES BETWEEN SUCCESSIVE ARRIVALS

(a) Time interval between arrivals	(b) Percentage of arrivals at each time interval	(c) Correspondence between random numbers and time intervals
1	11	00–10
2	10	11–20
3	9	21–29
4	7	30–36
5	5	37–41
6	4	42–45
7	3	46–48
8	3	49–51
9	3	52–54
10	3	55–57
11	3	58–60
12	3	61–63
13	2	64–65
14	2	66–67
15	2	68–69
16	2	70–71
17	2	72–73
18	2	74–75
19	2	76–77
20	2	78–79
21	2	80–81
22	2	82–83
23	2	84–85
24	2	86–87
25	2	88–89
26	2	90–91
27	2	92–93
28	2	94–95
29	1	96
30	1	97
31	1	98
32	1	99

Having simulated both these components of the present method, namely the intervals between arrivals and the duration of the service times, the information obtained from doing this is now presented in a manner indicated in Table 3. This presentation will differ in every simulation study according to the number of components in the system being studied. This data is now used to construct a simulation bar chart usually made on

TABLE 2. DISTRIBUTION OF SERVICE TIMES

(a) Service times in minutes	(b) Percentage frequency	(c) Assigned numbers
4	7	00–06
5	40	07–46
6	31	47–77
7	7	78–84
8	7	85–91
11	4	92–95
16	4	96–99

TABLE 3. SIMULATED ARRIVAL AND SERVICE TIMES

Simulated arrival times			Simulated service times	
Random number	Time (min)	Start 7.30	Random number	Time (min)
28	3	7.33	20	5
54	9	7.42	30	5
99	32	8.14	08	5
83	22	8.36	71	6
27	3	8.39	88	8
40	5	8.44	64	6
87	24	9.09	04	4
16	2	9.11	99	16
18	2	9.13	43	5
03	1	9.14	77	6
47	7	9.21	69	6
70	16	9.37	24	5
43	6	9.43	89	8
83	22	10.05	74	6
55	10	10.15	43	5
62	12	10.27	06	4
61	12	10.39	80	7
11	2	10.41	41	5
96	29	11.10	18	5
98	31	11.41	61	6
03	1	11.42	14	5
04	1	11.43	80	7
78	20	12.03	11	5
39	5	12.08	91	8
81	21	12.29	92	11
26	3	12.32	10	5

squared paper, to indicate the changes that will arise in the present method if the system is operated in the present manner. This will then form the basis for the evaluation of different possibilities for method improvement. It is often found helpful in constructing this chart to indicate the waiting time of the service storeman by a colour, and operator waiting time by a circle in which a number indicating the units of time are placed. An arrow indicates the start of an interval, or arrival, and the number that precedes it denotes the simulated time for this arrival.

A multiple activity chart of this kind (Fig. 56), when constructed, will indicate the practicability of the method proposals that are considered for development. In the example that is being reviewed the following are possible considerations:

(a) Continue to operate the service counter with a single storekeeper.
(b) The employment of an assistant storeman.
(c) The employment of two assistant storemen.

Having decided on these possible considerations it is necessary to decide on some rules for the issue of the items at the service counter, and to determine on what occasions the service time is the longest and what features of the service activity produces this increase. Suppose that an operator's impatience is represented by the rule that if there are more than two operators already waiting at the service counter, the arrival does not wait but goes off to attend to some other aspect of the set-up activity, or takes a rest period. As the majority of the items issued at the service counter are of different kinds, such as saws, cutter blocks, and drill bits, the time occupied in issuing these is reduced by their easy identification when they are required, and their location in the store relative to the service counter. On some occasions in addition to these items, a jig and fixture may also have to be issued with the tools, these are used in connection with the machining of certain components. These jigs are stored in racks further from the service counter than the tools previously mentioned, thus whenever they are collected they have a tendency to increase the time spent in issuing items at the service counter.

Notification of machine set-up requirements and a rough job sequence for each day would enable the storeman to anticipate the needs of each operation so that he could collect the items near to the service counter. If this was done the time for issuing the articles would be reduced. In the present conditions, however, it is not always possible to anticipate requirements.

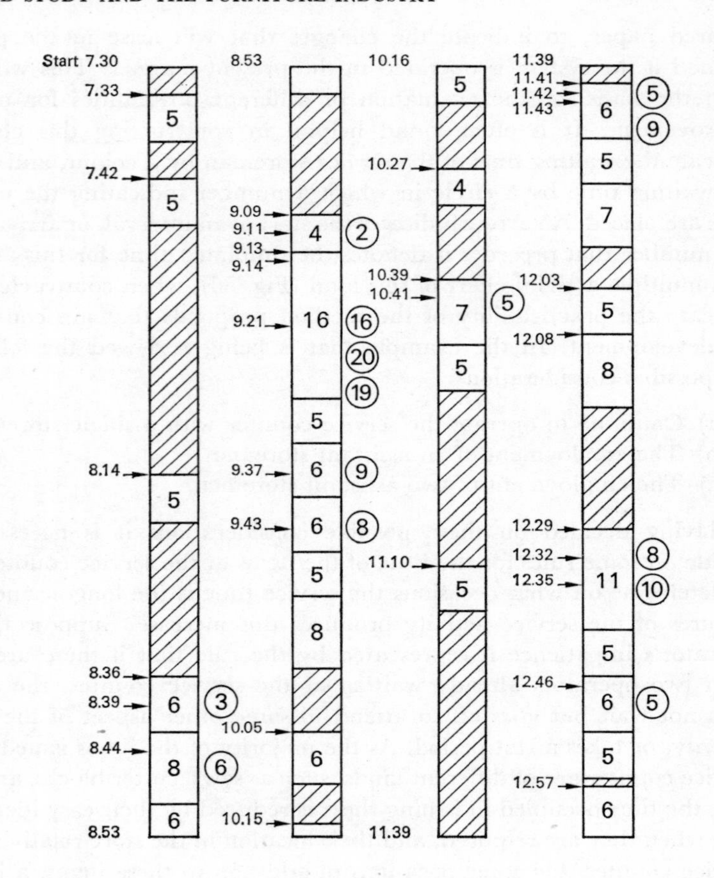

Fig. 56. Simulation—bar chart for single service operator.

For the purposes of dimensional control, accurate repetition, and correct maintenance, it is necessary to have all cutting tools and jigs returned to the stores. Many of the tools are also expensive and for this reason alone should receive careful maintenance. Because these tools are now no longer maintained by the individual operator, a standard form of cutter grinding and sharpening procedure can now be operated in conjunction with the tool room.

A simulation study made over a sufficiently long period will indicate the various values for the waiting time corresponding to the number of service facilities. When the cost and the effect of waiting time is compared with the increased cost of employing an extra service storeman or any other possible amendment, a suitable improvement in the method is invariably suggested. But often only an imperfect idea of what should be done in certain method development situations is obtainable. It is in such circumstances that the application of any procedure that may be helpful in developing an improved method, and which will result in a better understanding of the important aspect of a method problem, is justified at this stage.

It is probable that the methods used to record the initial details for the investigation would in certain circumstances have been sufficient to obtain an evaluation of the present situation, but it would not have been sufficient to form the basis of a development and assessment of the various methods possibilities, whose efficiency is affected by probabilistic influences. As is the case with the use of most method study techniques, it is possible that a problem could be solved by the use of a more appropriate procedure. But it should be appreciated that the simple example discussed has been used only as a means of explaining the basic principles of the procedure.

The duration of a simulation study is always determined by experiment, different simulation periods are selected and the results analysed to determine the significant differences between them and then to make sure that the results approximate to actual conditions. In the particular problem that has been discussed, if the service times are considered to be too long, a method study will be required to produce proposals which will reduce them to more suitable duration. However large the sample of simulations that are generated will be, this alone will not solve a methods problem. The investigator will have to supplement this simulation with efforts in various other directions and apply costs, as in any other methods development, in order to evaluate the possibilities that are being considered.

Submitting the Proposals and Recommendations

When the development of an improved method has been completed the proposals must be presented to management in the form of a report. The purpose of the report is to present a summary of the method study investigation and an explanation of those elements which form the basis of the conclusion and recommendations for the proposed method together with the reasoning on which these are based. This is done in order to obtain the approval of management for these proposals and as a preparation for their implementation.

The efficiency of the method study function in an organization is determined by the frequency with which proposed methods are accepted and implemented and not by the number of studies that are conducted. In view of the importance of this, good presentation should always be the aim of the investigator in preparing his report, as this has a considerable influence on those whose participation and assistance is required. Management may often be inclined to look more favourably on method proposals that are presented in an attractive manner, and if the presentation is of poor quality resulting in a poor management response, justice will not be done to the results obtained from an excellent investigation.

Before an actual report is written certain preparatory work has to be done. All the expected benefits that are to be obtained from the study should be listed in terms of the purpose and criteria of the study. The anticipated savings should be presented, as also should the estimated cost of the installation. If these things are done management is better able to evaluate the proposals. Many organizations have a standard method of writing and submitting the report; if this should be so, method study will be expected to conform to this standard. But it should be determined whether this is valid for the presentation of method study reports, as they are not always applicable, and adherence to these standards tends to have a limiting effect on an activity where the method of presentation is so important.

There are certain practices that should be avoided in the report if the contents are to be acceptable to personnel. Recrimination, for example, should be avoided, as this will destroy any desired participation on the part of personnel responsible for the present conditions. In this respect too the report should not be more of a post-mortem than is obviously necessary, for it should be remembered that the reason for the study was to rectify conditions which were already known to be suspect.

The report should be written clearly and without ambiguity, and jargon should be reduced to a minimum. Information should be presented in a logical order and clearly stated. Sentences and paragraphs should be kept as short as possible and important points should not be stated and restated too often. It is advisable not to survey too much, or too little, as there is a danger of missing the point of the report altogether. The reader of the report should never be asked to retrace the pattern of a long and weary investigation, it is sufficient just to state briefly the investigational procedure if this is considered necessary. The report should be self-supporting, any data that is referred to continuously throughout the report should be placed in the appendices, as this is the most convenient location for information that is continuously required to explain the text. When in doubt as to whether to put the item in the body of the text or not, the following rule may help to decide. If the chart or diagram is referred to frequently throughout the report it is more convenient to place it in the appendix, but if it is referred to once or twice only it can be placed close to the page on which it is quoted.

All the means that are available should be used to enhance the presentation of the information. All charts, photographs, and diagrams should be easily identified. The development of the proposed method should be described in some detail, as this will convey the reasoning upon which the proposals are based. Any alternative proposals which were considered and rejected should also be set out together with the reasoning for their rejection. If any experimental work was conducted during the development of the proposals, it should be clearly described and included in the report, if this forms part of the argument for the proposals. A correct appreciation of the situation should at all times be conveyed to management; the wrong impression should never be presented as misunderstandings can be inconvenient. The manner in which the various aspects of an organization are likely to be affected by the proposals should be indicated, and any probable difficulties which are likely to be encountered should be described with suggestions as to how these may be overcome. Any preliminary action that should be taken with respect to stores and purchasing should also be indicated.

The report should conclude with a full acknowledgement to the various people who have assisted in the investigation. As a result of this acknowledgement, participation is more likely to be assured, as the proposals contained in the report will be presented as a combined effort. A report that does not consider these important factors is likely to be inadequate, and will inevitably result in the subsequent loss of time at meetings called to discuss and implement the proposals contained in the report. On such occasions, where this is the situation, the investigator may have to retrace the facts of the investigation. This puts him at a disadvantage in a situation which is well known for its conflict of personalities, obstructions, lack of reasonableness, and misunderstandings. The logical presentation of a report, however, assists in the direction of such a meeting into areas where understanding and agreement can be obtained.

The report should be submitted through the appropriate channels and a copy sent to all those who are to be involved in the implementation of the proposals. Agreement should be obtained from management for a proposed circulation list before this is done.

After meetings and discussions have been held and agreement reached on the proposals, the results obtained at such gatherings should be recorded. This record should include any recommendations that were rejected, together with the reason why they were not accepted. These are valuable for future consideration as they may be subsequently reviewed and acceptable in the light of changed conditions.

Information should be given in the report that will provide the basis for any operating instructions which may have to be prepared before the installation of the new method. The responsibilities of everyone concerned in the introduction of the proposed method should be suggested as this will provide the basis for a management decision regarding this consideration before the actual installation of the method is commenced.

It is a misconception to assume that the longer the duration of a study, the longer and more complex the report will be. The length of any report is dependent on what essential information has to be imparted to management and personnel; if this can be done in a simple manner then the report will most probably be of minimum length. Various functional personnel on the circulation list will obviously be looking for different things in the report, because of this the requirements of these persons should be anticipated.

The report should be sufficiently condensed to allow it to be quickly read and understood. Senior management often only wish to know the main outline of the study in order to evaluate it in terms of improvements, financial expenditure, and savings, leaving the detailed study of the report for those who are to be responsible for the installation and implementation of its proposals. A summary should always be provided for this purpose as this when completed prior to the writing of the actual report can also form the basis of the complete presentation.

Whilst no rigid layout can be prescribed for all forms of method study report, it is generally accepted that the three-panel triptych layout is normally considered to be the most suitable. A report presented in this form will consist of one of two layouts:

(i) The body of the report is attached to a centre panel with appendices concerning the present method on the left hand and those concerning the proposed method on the right.

(ii) The evidence is fixed to the centre panel with the conclusions and recommendations to the left and also comments of the personnel to whom the report has been passed. The appendices in this form of layout are placed on the right-hand panel.

In both cases the top sheet of the centre panel should be the summary sheet, the back of the cover of the left-hand panel should carry the title and reference, and the back of the cover of the right-hand panel should contain the distribution list.

The outline of the report, it is suggested, should take the following form:

Title-page. This describes in as brief a way as possible the subject of the method study, and should contain a reference number in the top right-hand corner and the name of the investigator responsible for the study in the bottom right-hand corner.

The summary provides an overall review of the contents of the report and is, as previously stated, a précis of the contents. It will contain the following basic information:

By whom the study was initiated.
Report title and reference.
Purpose of the study.
Duration of study in terms of time and effort.
Procedure of the investigation.
Conclusions.
Recommendations.
Improvements that are likely to result from implementation of the proposals.
Cost savings.

An index will be placed on the next page to the summary and will indicate the breakdown of the report into the appropriate sections and where each may be found.

The terms of reference will indicate the boundaries of the inquiry. What the study proposed to do. What it did not propose to do, and any restrictions or limits that may have been imposed upon the scope of the investigations. These if present should be clearly defined.

The introduction should describe the area of the study and give the background information necessary for an appreciation of the investigation.

The procedure of the investigation should describe how the study was conducted, the techniques that were used, and the details of any experimental work.

The facts and conclusions that result from the study should be listed logically using a short and concise style. No statement should be placed in the conclusions unless it is supported by appropriate reasoning and evidence. It may be useful in this respect to determine what are the significant facts, and which facts have a bearing on each other. Are there any contradictions? Have sufficient facts been clearly and correctly established? Is the investigator sure of his facts? What do the facts indicate? What has been happening and why? What is likely to happen and what is to be done about it? Where does the organization stand in relation to others? Information on these various points of view should be collected and marshalled.

The recommendations should be presented in such a manner that the facts are balanced and an indication is given of how the inferences are drawn from them; what course of action is recommended. The short- and long-term implications of each possible recommendation should be considered. Statements are placed here that are inferred from the conclusions which also suggest the necessary action to be taken.

The appendix should contain those diagrams, charts and tables that will be referred to constantly throughout the report; these should be placed in consecutive order.

Selected References and Suggestions for Further Reading

Currie, R. M., *Work Study*, Pitman, London and New York, chapter 7.

Currie, R. M., *Outline of Work Study, Part II, Method Study*, British Institute of Management, London.

Currie, R. M., *Introduction to Work Study*, International Labour Office, Geneva, 1959, chapter 12.

Creative Thinking

Crawford, R. P., *The Techniques of Creative Thinking*, Hawthorn Books, New York, 1954.

Crawford, R. P., *How to Get Ideas*, University Associates, Lincoln, Nebraska, 1954.

Osborn, A. F., *Applied Imagination*, Charles Scribners Sons, New York, 1963.

PARNES, S. J., *Instructors Manual for Creative Problem Solving*, Creative Education Foundation, Buffalo 3, New York.

PARNES, S. J., *Student Workbook for Creative Problem Solving*, Creative Education Foundation, Buffalo 3, New York.

WHITING, C. S., *Creative Thinking*, Reinhold Publishing Corporation, New York, 1958.

Experimental Procedure

BROWNLEE, K. A., *Industrial Experimentation*, Her Majesty's Stationery Office, London; Reinhold Publishing Corporation, New York.

COHEN, M. R. and NAGEL, E., *An Introduction to Logic and Scientific Method*, Routledge and Kegan Paul, London.

TOWNSEND, J. C., *Introduction to Experimental Method*, McGraw-Hill, London and New York.

WESTAWAY, F. W., *Scientific Method*, Blackie, London.

Simulation

ANSON, C. J., Simulation of industrial operations, *Time and Motion Study*, July 1958, pp. 12–21.

BATTERSBY, A., Simulation—a new weapon, *The Manager*, part I, February 1963, pp. 29–33; part II, March 1963, pp. 48–51.

BATTERSBY, A., *Mathematics in Management*, Penguin Books, chapter 7, Simulation by Symbols.

MCCRACKEN, D. D., The Monte Carlo Method, *Scientific American*.

MEYER, H. A. (Ed.), *Symposium on Monte Carlo Methods*, John Wiley, London and New York.

TOCHER, K. D., *The Art of Simulation*, English Universities Press, London.

WELLS, J. W. and CARTER, L. R., *Simulation applied to a Loading Bay*, Industrial Operations Unit, Department of Scientific and Industrial Research, London.

Submitting the Proposals and Recommendations

COOPER, B. M., *Writing Technical Reports*, Penguin Books.

COOPER, B. M., *Report Writing*, British Association for Commercial and Industrial Education, London.

NELSON, J. R., *Writing the Technical Report*, McGraw-Hill, London and New York.

CHAPTER 7

Installation and Maintenance of the Proposed Method

THE duration of a method study is the period between the commencement of the investigation and the time when the satisfactory installation of the proposals can be said to have been completed. It is often not sufficiently realized that 75 per cent of this time is usually spent in the installation of the proposed method; sometimes this can be considerably longer depending on the magnitude of the assignment. For this reason alone the importance and critical nature of this part of the method study procedure should be appreciated, otherwise the duration of a study is likely to be unnecessarily prolonged and its introduction beset with unforeseen difficulties.

The correct timing of the introduction of the proposals is essential if the method is to have a fair trial. If it is introduced at an inconvenient time it may mean the difference between acceptance or rejection. It is for this reason that adequate preparation is made prior to the installation of the proposals.

If the preceding stages of the method study procedure have been made correctly, the participation of the personnel associated with the method improvement will have already been obtained. This prepares the way for the installation by establishing good relations during the study, and the development of a feeling that they have contributed to the success of the investigation.

The agreement to all the proposals that are to be introduced will have already been obtained prior to the commencement of the installation. This will have been achieved by seeing that the proposals and recommendations were circulated to all those who are likely to be affected by the study. The discussions concerning these will have included all those members of the organization who are to be associated with the installation.

The operating instructions and job specification for the new method should be prepared and agreement for these obtained not only from management but also from the union representatives in the particular shop where the improvements are to be introduced.

The circulation of the report and the subsequent meetings to discuss its contents will also have indicated clearly to personnel the part that each will have to take in the installation. An understanding of personal responsibilities will enable a plan of the installation to be devised in conjunction with these persons. The preparation necessary for the introduction of a method improvement will naturally depend on the kind of change it is intended to introduce.

The process of installation is divided into three stages: (i) devising a plan, (ii) organizing the arrangements, and (iii) conducting a rehearsal for the proposed installation.

A plan of the outline of the proposed installation should be prepared and agreement reached with the personnel associated with each stage. The responsibility for the installation should be given to one person only, as this will enable those who have problems associated with the installation to know who to approach. The person usually selected is the manager of the department in which the proposals are being introduced. The actual installation should take place in stages. These will be selected with reference to production commitments and responsibilities. A time-table should be prepared so that it is known by what date each stage of the installation is to be completed. It is often useful to construct a network diagram to determine the minimum time that it will take to carry out the installation, having regard to all the contributing factors.

In the preparation of the plan such considerations as the existing stock levels, the delivery of materials, and equipment required for the installation should be carefully examined. What effect normal maintenance, stock taking, and costing periods will have on the proposed plan should be considered. Periods when the organization is at its peak production, or when staff is depleted by holidays, is never an appropriate time for the installation of methods that involve either of these two factors.

In the arrangement and organization for the installation the proposed method should be checked to see that all equipment and services are available for the installation. Where equipment has been ordered, it should be checked that this will be available when required.

Old stocks are not likely to be used subsequent to the introduction of the proposed methods, because of this every effort should be made to reduce these. Stocks of materials required for the new method should be built up if necessary to the required level, and the availability and continuance of supplies and services should be assured. One of the factors often overlooked is the availability of clerical staff, for control and comparison during this period. If any change in the hours of working are considered necessary, arrangements for this should be made at this stage, and also the availability of the necessary auxiliary services, such as transport and canteen facilities.

Where workers have to operate the new method during a trial period these should be selected carefully with respect to what necessary skills are required, whether they have to be adaptable, whether they have the right attitude of mind, and, where teamwork is to be operated, whether the workers selected are compatible and are able to work together as a team. Consideration should also be given to those workers who were not selected, particularly if enthusiasm has been created for the method improvement, these should be told that they will have an opportunity of working on the new method after it has been successfully installed. Training should be provided for those workers who do not have the necessary skills. This is a most important consideration, particularly as problems may arise where unskilled workers are allowed to operate the new method. Their inability to reach the desired performance standards will frequently not be considered to be the result of their lack of skill, but due only to the unreasonable demands of the proposed method.

Wage payment problems associated with the installation should be anticipated and settled well in advance. As the costing, accounts, and wages departments are likely to be closely involved in the introduction of the new methods, they should be informed when the actual installation commences. The rehearsal for the installation will include a test of the new method. This should be made whilst the old method is still in operation, so that any difficulties that may arise will not interfere with production. If any experimenting is to be done in the shop, this should not take place during working hours, for workers will naturally be interested in the new method and if anything of an unfortunate nature should occur, their confidence in the new method may be disturbed. For this reason experimenting is best done outside production time.

It is important to see that all inspections have been allowed for, if they are a feature of the proposed method, and that the correct quality standards are known. When the actual rehearsal takes place, it is essential to see that all persons whose comments are required concerning the operation of the new method are in fact represented at the rehearsal.

After the details of the preparation and rehearsal have been made, the problems associated with the actual installation may now be considered. The time selected for this should be outside working hours so that production is not disrupted, and it should be appreciated that the first few days of the actual installation are critical. Many excellent methods have failed at this stage because supervision was not good enough, or the workers were not sufficiently familiar with the improved method and its requirements.

Any amendments to the method that are thought to be necessary, as a result of problems encountered in the installation, should be made, and at the same time the operating instructions or job specification should be amended.

Throughout the various stages of the installation a careful watch should be kept for any indication of possible bias or prejudice. Where the presence of this attitude is discovered the reason for this should be determined.

If extra periods of training are considered necessary these should be given. If certain workers do not measure up to the standards required after consideration of their individual circumstances they should be replaced. Where the work is a team activity and it is thought necessary to increase the number in the team, this should be done, but only after the reasons for this have been considered carefully.

A watchful eye should always be kept on the effect that the installation of the new method will have on the level of stocks, other departments, and similar areas of influence.

Throughout the installation the qualities of tact and restraint are continuously required. It is an often repeated statement by method study practitioners that the installation of a new method can only be considered complete when it is running effectively, and when the manager of the department concerned is prepared to accept it as satisfactory.

Instructing the Operator in the Proposed Method

The way an operator will be expected to perform an operation is usually shown in the recording which goes with the proposals. Although these are quite detailed and sometimes are accompanied by operating specifications they are no substitute for actual instruction. For this reason the method study practitioner will frequently be required to instruct selected personnel in the operation of the new method. This may consist of instructing the worker who is to carry out the task or showing the person who is actually going to do the instructing. It is important in the installation of the proposals that the worker is instructed correctly in the right method. If the instruction is not done in this way there is no guarantee that what the worker will learn will be the proposed method. To reduce delays and possible misunderstandings the right procedure of instruction should always be employed. In certain industrial organizations this instruction may be given by a special training department, particularly in those circumstances where the activities are complex, and the skills associated with them take some time to acquire. For these reasons an understanding of the principles of operator instruction and its requirements is an essential part of the training for method study application.

Before the commencement of any proposed training it is advisable to consider the possible deployment of personnel that may be necessary, and the changes that will be required, so that this can be done. It is also necessary to carefully check and define the performance standards that are to be required, with respect to production per hour, quality, and the operation of associated equipment or machines. A review should be made of the production requirements and the managerial commitments in respect of this. It is essential also to see that important activities have emergency safeguards, and whether it is desirable to deploy extra workers to these. The operators chosen for the training in the new method should be carefully selected. The best use should be made of each available operators ability. A date should also be selected when it is desired that this training should be completed. A training programme will be prepared which will indicate what is to be learnt and by what date. It is important that this should be kept up to date as also should the operation, instruction, and specification sheets.

Operator training associated with method study may be either of two kinds:

(i) Job instruction training.
(ii) Analytical training.

Job instruction is the kind of training which is used to impart the normal methods or skills to average workers. Analytical training is used for the analysis and instruction of complex and difficult skills to average operators with no particular aptitudes.

It is to be remembered that the services of men is one of the resources of the industrial enterprise, and productivity is affected just as much by better training as in the devising of better methods, which are to be the subject of the instruction.

Job Instruction

In preparing for the instruction of an operator in a new method, the task to be taught should be separated into elements of instruction. These are logical components of the complete operation in which something is done to advance the work. These elements are further reduced to well-defined stages, the contents of which are easily imparted to the operator in one demonstration. The important features of each of these stages should be emphasized. The factors of safety, quality, and the correct use of tools and equipment constitute some of these important aspects.

The instructor, in order to prepare himself for the instruction, should carry out the operation himself so that he will be familiar with every detail of the activity. Everything required for the purpose of the instruction, such as tools, equipment, materials, and supplies, should be available and correctly arranged in a manner that the operator will be expected to keep them in performing the task. Any aids that will enable the operator to grasp more quickly some difficult point in the instruction should be prepared. A plan of the instruction should also be made prior to the actual commencement of the training, irrespective of how well he may be familiar with the operation, or how skilled he may be in its performance. In preparing this, an instruction sheet of the kind shown in Fig. 57 is filled in; when this is completed, it will indicate the task broken down into stages, or logical elements of the operation, in which something is done to further the work. These stages are pieces of the overall operation which can be demonstrated and easily assimilated by the operator at any one time. By each of these stages will be indicated the key points, these are any directions or pieces of information that will assist in the correct performance of each stage safely and easily by the operator. The possession of an operational breakdown does not constitute a complete instructional plan, many other things are necessary as well. However, it is certain that if a task cannot be described in detail by a person, that person is not in a position to teach that job.

When the instruction sheet has been prepared, the procedure for carrying out the actual instruction should be considered. This will be done with reference to the four following stages.

(i) The preparation of the worker.
(ii) The presentation of the task.
(iii) The performance of the task by the worker.
(iv) Maintenance and evaluation of the instruction.

OPERATION BREAKDOWN FOR TRAINING

Steps in the operation	Key points
Step: A logical segment of the operation in which something is done to advance the work.	Key points: Any directions or bits of information that helps to perform the step correctly, safely, and easily.
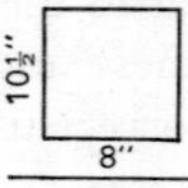 (10½" × 8") Place 8" x 10½" sheet of paper in front of you on flat surface.	1. Be sure surface is flat free of interfering objects.
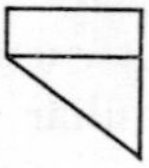 Fold lower left hand corner up.	2a. Line up the right hand edges. b. Make a sharp crease.
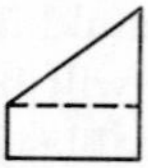 Turn paper over.	3a. Pick up lower right hand corner with right hand and place it at the top. b. Folded flap should now be underneath.
 Fold excess lower edge up.	4a. Line up right hand edges. b. Fold should line up with bottom edge. c. Make sharp crease.
 ("C" "A" "B") Fold lower left hand corner flush with edge "A".	5a. Keep edges "B" and "C" parallel. b. Hold bottom edge in the centre with finger while making fold.
 ("D") Fold upper corner to point "D".	6a. Hold cup firmly with left hand. b. Bring upper corner down with right hand.
 Separate lower right corner and fold back.	7a. Hold cup with left hand. b. Fold back with right hand. c. Make sharp creases.
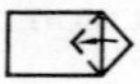 Turn cup over and fold remaining flap back.	8. Make sharp creases.
 Check cup to be sure it will hold water.	9. Open cup and look inside.

Fig. 57. Instruction sheet prepared for making a paper cup.

In the first stage of this procedure, the instructor will prepare the operator for the demonstration by putting him at his ease, and dispelling any anxiety that the operator may have about his capacity for learning the new method. This purpose is often made easier by personal knowledge of the operator. When a state of composure has been achieved, the instructor will define the subject of the instruction in as few words as possible, and find out if the operator has any knowledge of the task or a similar type of task to that in which instruction is to be given. If it is possible at this stage, an enthusiasm should be developed in the operator to learn the new method, and to get him interested and willing to absorb the details of the task. A knowledge of the individual will again enable the instructor to find means of doing this. It may be achieved by appealing to his present skills or interests, or the possible status that will go with having learnt the new method.

It is important at this stage also that the operator has the right attitude of mind towards the method in which he is about to be instructed. His position in relation to that of the instructor should be such that he can see all the instruction. The instructor should see that he places himself in this correct position.

In the second stage the task is presented to the operator. In doing this the instructor will demonstrate and describe one element of the operation at a time, stressing the important features of each. He should make certain that the instruction is understandable and unambiguous. Patience, tactfulness, and an ability of imparting the information at a suitable pace is important.

In the third stage the performance of the worker will be checked. The instructor will ask the operator to perform and explain each element of the task by himself, whilst being observed by the instructor. Any errors that may occur will be corrected, and it is important that the key points included in the task are understood as each element is performed. This procedure of verification is continued until the instructor is satisfied that the operator has understood the instruction.

In the fourth stage of the instructional procedure the quality of the instruction is evaluated, and the performance of the operator maintained. The instructor allows the operator to work at the task on his own, but before doing this he states clearly the operator's personal responsibilities with regard to the performance of the operation, and indicates the person, whether supervision or working chargehand, who will assist him if he should experience difficulty or have any problems. Before he is placed on his own the instructor will encourage him to ask questions about the task, and at the same time check again that he has learnt the method correctly. Frequent visits should be made to the operator to see that he is in fact performing the method as prescribed. During such visits extra advice and instruction may have to be given. In the course of time the extra instruction considered necessary and the required maintenance should be reduced.

It may seem hard on the instructor, but it is a frequently quoted saying that "If the worker hasn't learnt, the instructor hasn't taught". If operators are carefully selected there is no reason why this should not apply.

Analytical Training

Where workers have to be trained in tasks of a complex nature, certain detailed information about the activity is necessary before the training requirements can be determined. These complex tasks may in present circumstances demand long and expensive periods of training, and the nature of the task may be such that only exceptional workers in the past have been able to eventually perform the operation satisfactorily.

There may also be an urgent need for the services of workers who can perform these complex tasks.

Analytical training is a means of investigating these complex industrial tasks in order to make them easier to communicate to the average worker, and to reduce the period of training necessary for their accomplishment. Its use makes it possible to train average workers with no particular aptitudes in these tasks.

Where analytical training is introduced into an organization, it frequently falls to method study to provide the analysis of the task. This is often done from a micromotion or memomotion film of the particular operation. The analysis of the task provides the answers to the following two questions. What is it that the trainees will have to learn, and how can they be helped to learn the task quickly? In order to answer these two questions, it has been found appropriate to consider the operation in terms of three types of activity—sensory, mental, and physical—and to consider each of these separately.

Sensory activity involves the reception of information from the senses and its transmission to the brain. Apart from the five familiar senses, seeing, hearing, touching, smelling, and tasting, there is another important one known as the "kinaesthetic" sense through which information is transmitted to the brain from the nerve endings. By this sense knowledge is given of the position and speed of movement of a limb and the pressure exerted by the muscles.

Mental activity involves deciding what action to take as the result of having received information from the senses. Decisions fall approximately into two classes: "non-symbolic", in which the sensory information bears a direct relationship to the subsequent action, and "symbolic", in which the sensory information has to be translated in some way according to arbitrary rules which the operator has learnt.

The third type of activity to be considered is that of physical movement. Method study possesses a range of appropriate techniques for the study of this, and provides a means for the identification of such movements in terms of their basic divisions of accomplishment. The performance of any of these will involve various muscles which may work in a variety of combinations. It is the precise adjustment of this muscular action to the individual task that contributes to the skilled performance.

The stages in the learning of an industrial operation are the following:

(i) Learning the sequence in which the activities are to be performed. What is to be done? In what order?
(ii) Learning the method to be used for each element of the task.
(iii) Selecting the appropriate sensory channel to use for the control of each element of the motion pattern.
(iv) Modifying the sensory channel and organizing the information from it.
(v) Using this sensory information effectively.
(vi) Combining all the elements of the task into a complete activity.

It is the purpose of what are called "perception studies" to obtain much of the information required for the study of each of these stages.

The factor that will influence the speed of performing the activity, in relation to the amount of sensory information and decision making required to guide the action, is called the perceptual load of the task. This is the main cause of the difficulties experienced by workers in learning a new skill.

Just as the pattern of movement can be divided into distinct basic divisions of accomplishment, so it is useful to draw a distinction between the kinds of sensory and perceptual activity that make up the skilled worker's performance, because the purpose of these perceptual influences is to guide and control the performance of the operation.

There are three distinct elements of sensory and perceptual activity which can be easily recognized.

Plan The reception of the information making a decision and the preparation for an activity before it commences.

Control The direction of the activity while it is being performed.

Check Making certain that the objective of an operation has been obtained after it has been completed.

Two further elements can be used when a sensory signal for starting or stopping an activity is obtained from the nature of the work or its surroundings.

Start The initiation or commencement of an activity when a sensory signal is received.

Stop The termination or ending of an activity when a sensory signal is received.

Each of these elements requires information from the various sensory channels.

The difficulties associated with the production of speed in carrying out an operation are connected with the following:

Discrimination The difficulty experienced in the identification of the sensory signals which the task presents.

Choice The difficulty experienced in making a decision between different actions.

Control The difficulty experienced in accurately directing a movement.

Perception Study

The method of analysing an industrial operation as a preparation for the determination of training requirements is obtained by making a perception study. This is an analysis of the operation in question in terms of the elements previously described and the construction of a type of two-handed process chart called a sensorimotor process chart. This is a record of the sensory and perceptual elements of a manual operation, studied in relation to the pattern of movement of both the hands which they direct and control.

In organizations where perception studies are frequently made preprinted sensorimotor process chart forms are used (Fig. 58). These forms have a column for recording the physical actions of the left and right hands in terms of the basic divisions of accomplishment, and means of including the important measurements of length of distance travelled and weight carried. Alongside these columns there are others for recording the different sensory information obtained by vision, hearing, touch, and kinaesthesis. Between these two sets of columns is one for recording the mental decisions required in the performance of the task.

Left hand				Brain				Right hand				Notes
	K	T	Mot	Mem	Dec	Vis 1	Vis 2	Mot	T	K		Notes
Holding iron											Holding solder	Solder one joint
			—					—			—	Find next joint on list
To joint			M 6 in.					—			—	
Tip on wire			P					M 4 in.			To joint	
H			H					P			Solder on tip	
H			H					H			H	Wait for solder to melt then feed more on
H								M 1 in.			Feed solder	Avoid kinking and slipping. Stop when sufficient
Remove iron			M 1 in.					M 1 in.			Remove solder	Watch joint till surface changes from bright to filmy.
Await cooling			—								—	Observe junction with wire. Decide whether good joint
			—								—	and either repeat or look for next joint.

Symbols used in Sensorimotor Process Chart

Perceptual activities

Plan V
Control
Check Λ
Initiate o
Stop ●

Movement

Move M
Position P
Hold H

Operation: sub-chassis soldering

Sensorimotor Process Chart

Fig. 58. Sensorimotor process chart. (Reproduced by permission of the Controller of Her Majesty's Stationery Office.)

Entries are made in the appropriate columns whenever a movement is planned, guided, checked, started, or stopped. To simplify the recording of the perceptual elements five symbols have been devised. These are illustrated to the side of Fig. 58. Each of these represents the occurrence of a perceptual element. They may be connected by a thin line with the movement it governs.

When using this chart the observer first carefully records the pattern of the movement; this is usually done by the analysis of a film of the activity, but it can be done by eye observation in certain circumstances.

Then the manner in which planning, controlling, and checking of each of the recorded elements is determined is made in order to discover the ones that need attention. Many of the movements will be seen to be easy and require little or no perceptual help. However, the analyst should ask the following questions about each of the elements of movement.

(i) Does the objective of the movement change from occasion to occasion? If it does planning will be needed to redirect it on each occasion.
(ii) Must a given accuracy be attained or does the target alter its position during the motion? If the answer to each question is "yes", control will be required.
(iii) Is it at all likely to go wrong? If it is a check will be required.
(iv) Is it initiated or terminated in response to any outside signal? If it is a start or stop will be required.

By analysing the operation in this fashion the method analyst concentrates his attention on each section of the activity in turn, and constructs a mental picture of its training requirements. He can also estimate the relative difficulty of the complete task and its individual parts, and make an assessment of the degree of improvement likely to be achieved with practice, by having regard to the incidence of perceptual elements in the task.

Perceptual "bottlenecks" can by these means be discovered and the task improved by eliminating them, or by changing their sequence, and spreading the perceptual load over the whole task more evenly.

With regard to training requirements, the analysis will enable exercises and instructions to be developed to help the operator to obtain an effective relationship between perception and movement more quickly.

The example of the sensorimotor process chart (Fig. 58) describes the task of soldering a joint. A micromotion film study was made of this activity and the film was analysed, the details of the operation were then recorded in the form of a sensorimotor process chart. This analysis indicated that visual checking accounted for about one-quarter of the total time, and that the feeding of the solder was a difficult operation. Improvements were possible by simplifying the method of feeding the solder, and so eliminating the need for visually checking the joint.

It is important to remember that one way of making the task easier to learn is to make the task easier to perform. This method of recording enables the difficulties of an operation to be made more apparent, which greatly assists in the installation of a new method where the application of the technique is appropriate.

Maintaining the New Method

After a new method has been installed successfully, the benefits from such a method cannot be assumed to continue indefinitely. The conditions in the factory and the work environment have a tendency to change, for a number of valid reasons, and these have a serious effect on the methods of doing work.

It is possible that the assumptions on which the improved method was originally based may no longer be valid with reference to present circumstances. There may have been alterations in the amount of work inherent in the job, which have affected the balance of work in the job itself, or in the shop, and which have affected the amount of labour required. Moreover, alterations to a method will frequently arise through valid amendments to the specification, such as the result of operator suggestion schemes, or innovations by operators or supervision.

If a method which has been installed is to function correctly over a long period of time it must be maintained. To be able to maintain a method demands that a clear, detailed, and unambiguous method specification must have been prepared at the period of installation, wherein all the possible variables and aspects likely to be the subject of method change are clearly specified. If these specifications are not prepared correctly, it may be subsequently difficult, when reference is made to it, to determine whether a method change has in fact taken place. Correctly prepared specifications will enable periodical checks to be made to see that the method as installed is in fact being operated, and that a general drift away from prescribed methods is not taking place. The frequency with which this review is made will depend largely on the nature of the method and the work.

Where amendments have to be made to a method, a notification of all such modifications should be sent to the method study section, so that the necessity for the alteration can be appreciated and evaluated and so that the method specification may be amended. To obtain the correct operation of this procedure a good relationship must exist between supervision and the method study section. Where undesirable innovations are noticed and recognized, the method must revert to the prescribed practice. Undesirable practices which are often introduced frequently produce a deterioration in the quality of output, lowering of operating safety standards, and duplication of work.

In order that maintenance difficulties may be anticipated, notice should be taken of the reactions and comments of the operators in the work situation, to the method that is installed. These reactions invariably indicate possibilities for further improvement. This also stimulates a methods consciousness on the part of operatives and supervision, which will create the appropriate climate for further method study application.

Selected References and Suggestions for Further Reading

Installation and Maintenance

CURRIE, R. M., *Work Study*, Pitman, London and New York, chapter 8.

CURRIE, R. M., *Outline of Work Study—Part II, Method Study*, British Institute of Management, London, chapters 12 and 13.

CURRIE, R. M., *Introduction to Work Study*, International Labour Office, Geneva, chapter 12.

JUDSON, A. S., *A Manager's Guide to Making Changes*, John Wiley, 1966.

Operator Instruction

CROSSMAN, E. R. F. W., Perception study, a complement to motion study, *The Manager*, vol. 24, No. 2, February 1956, pp. 141–5.

CROSSMAN, E. R. F. W., *Training Made Easier*, Problems of Progress in Industry No. 6, Her Majesty's Stationery Office, 1960.

SEYMOUR, W. D., *Industrial Training for Manual Operations*, Pitman, London and New York

CHAPTER 8

Product Analysis

PRODUCT analysis is the application of the method study procedure to the detailed examination of the design and manufacture of a product. It is applied equally to either the present or proposed methods, and the product may consist of either a complete manufactured article or a single component. It can be regarded as a systematic approach to what would otherwise be a creative function, that of minimizing the cost of a product, service, or component without in any way impairing its function or appeal. It is an important aspect of method study application, as management are under continuous pressure to do two things: to reduce their manufacturing costs and to produce output of higher quality. This emphasis on the need for better quality for less cost is an expression of the necessity for better value. This has influenced the application of method study in this direction, for it has enabled the value of individual products to be improved.

The application of method study in this field develops and stimulates the best creative thinking within an organization for finding answers to product problems, and it ensures that any decision for the improvement of value, once made and accepted, is implemented. It frequently leads to the development of better uses for alternative materials, processes, and the services of specialized suppliers. It develops methods for obtaining equivalent performance for lower cost. It is not, however, a substitute for the conventional cost reduction procedures of the accountant, but can be considered to be complementary to them. Quite commonly a reduction of 15–25 per cent in manufacturing costs can be achieved, and often much more, by its effective application, frequently with no reductionin quality, safety, or the attractiveness of the article.

The objectives of product analysis may be stated as follows:

To determine the most economical methods of manufacturing the product, having regard to the available resources of material, labour, floor space, and the available plant and machinery. To reduce the manufacturing cost of the product and to improve its quality, value, and saleability.

Method study frequently reveals that excessive labour time is added to the basic manufacturing costs of a product by reason of defects in the design and specification of the product, inefficient methods of manufacture, and the performance of the operations. This is one of the reasons why many products do not pass, when subjected to close analysis, without disclosing unfortunate mistakes which only add to the cost of the product and increase the manufacturing time.

There are numerous advantages to be achieved by the application of the procedure of product analysis besides that of making better use of the organizations available resources. It produces a more competitive product, and if the factory has spent considerable time and money on product development it will be more able to remain competitive should some other manufacturer wish to copy their product. If this procedure of analysis has been conducted correctly the product can only be made by another manufacturer by a reduction in quality, standards, or at an uncompetitive price. Its application also prepares for other areas of method study, as it is difficult and even foolish to commence the development of tools, jigs, and fixtures, methods, layouts, and production control systems until the final and correct form and scope of a product has been determined. There is a tendency for the manufacturer to adhere to conventional methods of making a product, instead of being more adventurous and taking advantage of the results of research into new materials, processes, and equipment, which can often reduce the cost of manufacturing the product considerably. It is often the practice when a manufacturer is producing a totally new product to rely too much on its novelty as a means of obtaining sales, thus the product is manufactured by methods which are selected without much consideration. The result of this is that the product suffers initially from many disadvantages, among which will be a manufacturing cost higher than it should be. In the course of deciding on the method of manufacturing a product, it is realized that there are many methods to choose from, even within the limits of a factory's resources. How a product is to be made with these resources, will depend on the volume of production desired. A method appropriate for one quantity of output is not always suitable for another.

Another result that is likely to be obtained from product analysis is the influence it will have on those who are responsible for the preparation of the initial design brief. These persons will prepare subsequent briefing more carefully in future.

The monetary savings that can be obtained from the application of the procedure are considerable and are usually in excess of those likely to be obtained in other fields of method study application, but although the results obtained are large by comparison the application of product analysis is beset with many difficulties. It is therefore necessary for methods personnel to have regard to these problems particularly those associated with the human factor as it is a recognized hazard in this area of method study application.

Procedure

Frequently the method study function is requested to analyse some aspect of an existing product because for various reasons it has become too costly to make. Thus instead of an analysis of a prototype product it is an existing model that is the subject of the study. Whether the analysis is to be applied to an existing or prototype product the procedure of analysis will be the same.

So that it may not appear that method study is usurping the responsibilities of the design function, it should be made quite clear that it is not usual for method study to make an analysis of a complete product unless requested to do so. It is more usual for them only to analyse a component product or collection of components that exist in a sub-assembly or feature of the total product. If, however, a complete product is to be investigated, method study personnel experienced in this form of analysis are usually included as important members of a team consisting of various disciplines. However, it should be realized that the purpose of a product analysis is to make the best possible use of the available resources of production, whereas the purpose of the designer in applying his systematic design procedure is to obtain the best possible answer to his design problem within the terms of reference of his design brief.

The approach to the analysis of a product may be stated briefly as follows:

Record (a) Collection of the product data.

- (i) Operation process charts of the present or proposed method of manufacture.
- (ii) Part drawings.
- (iii) Tabulated information and cost data.
- (iv) Actual product or component.
- (v) Material specification sheets.

Examine (b) Analysis of the product with respect to:
- (i) Function.
- (ii) Features.
- (iii) Material.
- (iv) Process.
- (v) Operations and inspections.

Develop (c) Development of the proposed product with respect to:
- (i) Simplification.
- (ii) Variety reduction.
- (iii) Standardization.
- (iv) Specialization.
- (v) Simultation.

The collection of the product data is commenced by obtaining detailed and authoritative information about the proposed or present method of manufacturing the particular product. The product, if it is a collection of components, is broken down into its smallest components and operation process charts are constructed for the present or proposed methods of manufacturing each. The part drawings should be obtained as they will not only give the complete features, dimensions, and the limits and tolerances of the component, but also all the original instructions for the manufacture of the part. Information should also be collected and tabulated concerning all the features of the component in relation to other components of a similar kind and their relevant cost data. Where they are available it is useful to have examples of the actual product or component to hand so that they may be referred to when the occasion demands. The material specification sheets should also be obtained so that material costs may be supported by details of the form in which the material is purchased, the rough and machined finished sizes, and the quantity per component or product.

When all this information has been collected the analysis of the component may be said to have commenced. This analysis will be made not only for the individual component, but for the sub-assembly of which it is part in order to determine the relationship between them.

This examination of the data can be made by the use of the three procedures previously described. Product analysis questionnaires have been found useful for guiding the thought process along lines that are most profitable. The method study procedure of critical examination can be used conveniently for the analysis of the operation process charts, and the heuristic procedure for the consideration of the other aspects of the analysis.

The analysis will commence by the examination of the product or component function. This is achieved by the identification of the product function and the evaluation of this function by comparison. Subsequently the functional alternatives determined as a result will be reviewed. An example of the type of questionnaire that is used at this stage is indicated below.

Function Questionnaire

What is the functional purpose?
What are the functional requirements?
What are the functions of the individual parts and features?
What are the dimensional requirements? Length? Width? Thickness? etc.
Are there any safety factors to be observed?
Are there any physiological factors to be observed?
Are all the required functional design data available?
What alternative means can be suggested for meeting these functional requirements?

If the answers to these questions are obtained correctly this stage will have identified the functional requirements of the component and suggested possible alternatives. This will also give an indication whether these functions are being achieved at minimum cost, and whether the component provides this function. The various functional alternatives that have been indicated should be separated and classified according to their comparative cost, and those that suggest the best opportunities for further consideration should be marked. Details of the functional requirements with respect to the user are readily available in numerous books and publications concerned with ergonomics or human engineering.

After the functional aspects of the component or product have been examined, the next stage in the analysis is the examination of the features of the component with respect to their value and contribution to the product. This is conducted in the following manner, which for the purpose of explanation is indicated in the form of a check list:

Component Questionnaire

Is the component really necessary?

Can it be excluded?
Does it need all its features?
Is its cost proportionate to its usefulness?
Does it contribute value to the product?
Is there anything better for the intended use?
Can a useable part be made by a lower cost method?
Can a standard product be found which will serve the purpose?
Is it made by the appropriate process considering the quantities used?
Will another dependable supplier provide it for less?
Is anyone buying it for less?

Frequently, as a result of the examination of the component along these lines (Fig. 59), it is found to be unnecessary, often contributing nothing to the mechanical, structural, functional, or aesthetic purpose of the product, and it can often be excluded without affecting the total product in any way. Where it is not possible to exclude the component, it is often found that all its features are not required, this frequently makes it possible for the part to be made similar to an existing one. Sometimes it is seen that the cost of some quite small and unimportant part is excessive, and out of all proportion to its contribution to the total product. In cases such as this the analysis will result in a more appropriate manufacturing process being selected to produce it, in order to bring the manufacturing cost nearer to a desired standard. It is commonly found in various industries that components and component features contribute value to a product; where this is found to be the case these should only be discarded after considerable thought. However, as these preferences and standards of value are based on empirical data, conditions may easily change which would eliminate the necessity for their being included in the product on this account. There are often found to be enumerable alternatives to a component and its features—this is indicated by the considerable supply of research data which explains these alternatives in reasonably simple terms for the analyst to evaluate their advantages. These are quite frequently found to have properties superior to the old conditions. Often it is discovered that there are standard proprietary products which can be purchased from specialist suppliers which eliminate the necessity for the factory to make them.

It is constantly realized that the process for manufacturing a particular component is out of all proportion to its cost, considering the quantities used. If large or small quantities are required, an appropriate process is introduced to reduce the cost of the component. It is frequently being discovered by manufacturers that a supplier will provide the component for far less than it would cost the factory to make it, and give suitable delivery.

After the features of the component has been analysed the material from which it is made is then examined. This examination takes the form of the material specification questionnaire on pp. 110–11, Chapter 5.

Industry is fortunate in having available many alternative materials whose mechanical properties and uses vary, as does their price per unit quantity. The advantages that can be obtained by using them are not as well known as they should be, but in carrying out the examination of a component material the possibilities to be obtained from these alternatives should be appreciated. Much technical information is available on which to make a correct assessment of these alternatives. Also many advantages can be achieved in purchasing these in the correct form. The supplier is often in a position to perform additional work upon the material that either makes it more suitable for processing at little or no extra charge. In seeking the correct utilization of materials various techniques have been developed by method study in those industries where the cost of materials constitutes a major percentage of the product cost, an example of this is described by Creighton, Stump, and Hutchins.

In the next stage of the component analysis the process is reviewed. This may be done with reference to a process check list similar to that described on p. 114. But whatever the means by which this is done, the object of the investigation is to make the best possible use of the available process resources and at the same time improve the product or component.

The operations and the inspections for quality are next reviewed. The questions that are asked about these activities are indicated in the operation questionnaire and the inspection and quality questionnaire on p. 110. The operations for the manufacture of the component will have been recorded in terms of outline process charts and the questioning sequence will be made with the object of eliminating the operations and thereby reducing the labour cost of the component.

In the course of subjecting the component to a detailed analysis, with regard to inspections and quality, the question of limits and tolerances is not overlooked. It is upon the correct choice of these that the cost of manufacture and the type of machinery that can be used will depend, as not all machines will produce close limits. In practice it is found impossible to manufacture parts to an exact size as not only must unavoidable varia-

1. DOES ITS USE CONTRIBUTE VALUE ?

PART : Condenser used across contacts of a relay to provide arc suppression as contact opens

COST : 500,000 per year, at 10 cents each

When cobalt again became available after the war, an alnico magnet was used to provide snap action. Analysis was initiated to re-evaluate necessity of the condenser with this magnet. It was found that the condenser did not add value, and it was eliminated

SAVING : $50,000 per year : 100 per cent.

2. IS ITS COST PROPORTIONATE TO ITS USEFULNESS ?

PART : Spacer hub for mounting light aluminium disks

COST : $0.90 per unit

Considering its simple function in the assembly, this cost was not proportionate to its usefulness. Cost was high, due to undercutting to reduce weight, which was an important consideration. Value analysis study showed that by making the part of aluminium the undercutting could be eliminated and a resulting 20-cent part provided identical performance with still further reduced weight

SAVING : 70 cents per unit

3. DOES IT NEED ALL OF ITS FEATURES ?

PART : Stainless steel disk in dispensing machine

COST : 70,000 per year, at 18 cents each

These washers were formerly chamfered one side. Study developed that for the indicated use the chamfer made no contribution to value. By eliminating it the cost was reduced to 5 cents each

SAVING : 13 cents per unit : $9,100 per year : 72 per cent.

4. IS THERE ANYTHING BETTER FOR THE INTENDED USE ?

PART : Mica stack used for insulation

COST : $40 per M.

By changing to Micalex cost of $34 per M. was available and, due to the moulded contour of the Micalex, the parts of the assembly were more rigidly mounted

SAVING : 15 per cent. and a better assembly

5. CAN A USABLE PART BE MADE BY A LOWER COST METHOD ?

PART : Hub assembly

COST : $30 per M.

Formerly designed and made as a two-part riveted or staked assembly. Study showed that part could be made as a casting, eliminating assembly operation and simplifying production

SAVING : $20 per M. : 67 per cent.

Fig. 59. Component questionnaire. (By permission of the British Productivity Council.)

6. CAN A STANDARD PRODUCT BE FOUND WHICH WILL BE USABLE ?

PART : Stud contact
COST : $27 per M.

This part was made to special design. Search revealed that a standard stud contact was available at about half the cost, equally suitable and providing identical performance. Another case of a well-directed intensive purchasing search

SAVING : $13 per M. : 48 per cent.

7. IS IT MADE ON PROPER TOOLING, CONSIDERING QUANTITIES USED ?

PART : Stainless weld nipple
COST : 20 cents each

Because of relatively small quantities required, procedure had been established to purchase a standard stainless fitting and machine away a part of it to provide the desired weld embossing. Re-evaluation disclosed that production requirements had stepped up sufficiently that it was now economical to make it on an automatic screw machine. Cost by the latter method was reduced to 5 cents each

SAVING : 15 cents per unit : 75 per cent.

8. DO MATERIAL, REASONABLE LABOUR, OVERHEAD AND PROFIT TOTAL ITS COST ?

PART : Stainless dowel pin
COST : $3 per M. (50,000,000 a year)

This dowel pin is purchased according to special design and specifications. Value analysis indicated that the cosc was out of line with reasonable standards. Every detail of the specification, manufacturing process and inspection was studied with the vendor's manufacturing people. As a result, some wastes of material and labour were eliminated. The identical part, produced to identical tolerances, is now purchased at $2 per M.

SAVING : $1 per M. : $50,000 per year : 33 per cent.

9. WILL ANOTHER DEPENDABLE SUPPLIER PROVIDE IT FOR LESS ?

PART : Bushing
COST : $18 per M.

Examples similar to this are being developed by the dozen by the buyers in virtually every product classification. In this case an exploration of the market resulted in finding an equally reliable source of supply that would furnish the identical part at $13.50 per M.

SAVING : $4.50 per M. : 25 per cent.

10. IS ANYONE BUYING IT FOR LESS ?

PART : Button
COST : $2.50 per M. (used in large volume)

This phase of cost measurement draws no line of comparison whether within or outside of the company itself. The extensive purchasing activities of the GE organisation provide a ready means of comparison and are a logical starting point in considering this question. In this case, a similar button was being purchased in another GE high-production factory, at $1 per M., that would give identical performance in the application under study

SAVING : $1.50 per M. : 60 per cent.

FIG. 59 (*cont.*).

tions in the manufacturing processes be allowed for, but the inaccuracies of the measuring instruments must also be taken into account.

When reviewing the limits and tolerances the question of the type of assembly method to be used will also be considered. In interchangeable assembly the limits selected for the dimensions of the components enable the parts to be assembled together and function correctly when manufactured to the extreme sizes. This type of assembly frequently requires the use of fine tolerances and expensive machines and machining operations, but for quantity production and low labour cost in the assembly operations it is usually the most economical.

In selective assembly the manufacturing tolerances are coarser than those normally required, for satisfactory work the parts must be selected and grouped into sizes after they have been made. Selective assembly reduces the speed of production, and usually requires that a stock of parts be kept to ensure that there will be a sufficient selection of each range of sizes.

In fitting assembly considerable variations are likely to have occurred during the manufacture of the parts and it is often more economical for this reason to carry out machining operations during the assembly process. This procedure, however, is usually confined to relatively simple operations.

The analysis of the component has now been made with respect to its functions, features, material, processes, operations and inspections. This has enabled all the information to be collected about these aspects of the part as a preparation for the development of proposals for its improvement. This information is now reviewed and the possibilities for simplification, variety reduction, standardization, specialization, and simultation in the manufacture of the component is now considered.

Simplification

There is something most satisfying about being able to simplify a component, and obtain the previous objectives at a fraction of the previous cost. It is not sufficiently realized that the design of a product exerts a considerable influence on the potential productivity of the manufacturing resources of an organization. It is during the design process that the degree of simplicity or complexity of a product is determined. If the design function creates a product of higher complexity than is necessary for satisfactory performance, it lowers the productivity potential in its manufacture and thereby increases the manufacturing cost well above what it could be. It is invariably the case that a product is made more

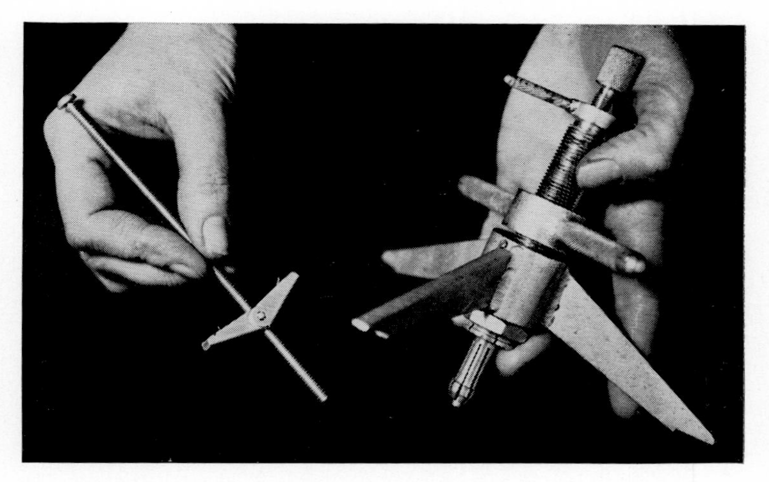

Fig. 60. Impellor assembly. Previous cost per assembly was £75. As a result of simplification assembly cost was reduced to 1*s*. 2*d*. (By permission of Value Engineering Ltd.)

complex than it should be, and there are many mitigating circumstances that absolve the designer from blame in this respect. This fact was recognized as far back as the eighteenth century by Adam Smith (1723–90), the celebrated Scottish political economist and writer, who once wrote as follows: "The machines that were first invented to perform any particular movement are always the most complex, and succeeding artists generally discovered that with fewer wheels, with fewer principles of motion than had originally been employed, the same effects may be more easily produced. . . ."

In order to speed this process of evolution and to determine what simplifications may be obtained in the component and its features, the answers to the previous questionnaires will have prepared the ground for this purpose. Industry is rich in examples of successful component simplification, which have not only solved manufacturing problems but have also had their influence on the solution of organizational problems as well. The example shown in Fig. 60 suggests the degree of simplification that can be obtained and the magnitude of the savings that are likely to be obtained. Many other examples could be quoted that show the same measure of results.

Variety Reduction

In the conduct of a product analysis it is frequently profitable to consider the individual component, which is the subject of the analysis, in relation to a complete range of similar parts manufactured by the organization. When a complete range of such components is listed and the differences in their common features tabulated, it is often seen that these individual differences are very small and difficult to justify. When this has been appreciated and the cost of each component compared it is seen that some are much cheaper to produce than others. If sales records are analysed it can also frequently be seen that 25 per cent of this range of components or products is responsible for 80 per cent of sales profit; this invariably leads the methods investigator to question why the other 75 per cent of the component range is being manufactured at all. If variety reduction through simplification can be achieved, this will possibly enable the complete range to be covered by 25 per cent of the existing components, thus achieving a considerable saving in money and resources.

Numerous examples can be quoted of successful variety reduction which indicate how frequently an unnecessary range is manufactured, and how easily it may be reduced.

A certain furniture manufacturer produced a component in seventy-six different forms; this produced difficulties in the control of production and the utilization of floor space. A method study was made which indicated to a surprised management that they were in fact doing this with a component which possessed six common features. This was nothing to their surprise when the proposals indicated that, by simplification, a reduction in the variety of this component could be made from seventy-six to three and still achieve the original purpose. The results that this had on stores, the utilization of floor space, and the production of the component was considerable.

The reduction in the variety of a particular component and its features will enable larger batch sizes to be produced, a greater spread of the set-up costs, a reduction in tooling, simpler inspection, cheaper stock and store control, and will indicate the possibilities for increased mechanization.

Reduction in variety does not necessarily signify restriction for its own sake, but a desirable restraint from increasing uneconomic diversity from the basic designs of the products and components.

Standardization

As a result of a reduction in the variety of products, components, and their features, and the better use of resources that it engenders, it is often considered desirable by management to see that this state is maintained. This desire results in management suggesting that specifications be devised for proposed standards. This naturally leads to the consideration of what standards should apply. When the correct answer to this question has been obtained, it will have been influenced by such considerations as what standard is indicated by past practice, what is indicated by anticipated future requirements, what would be considered an unnecessary restriction, what are the necessary reductions in variety that should be maintained, what are the cost factors of each proposed standard, and what is the technical basis on which a standard should be made. As a result of the consideration of these aspects of the problem, standards are devised from which management will not allow departure unless for a very good reason, and then only after consultation with senior management.

The design function may consider that standardization is an unnecessary restriction to their activities, but there are sufficient examples to prove that standardization can be successfully operated without taking away from the product any of its individuality. It is not sufficiently realized that the greatest scope in standardization is usually to be found in the more unobtrusive and often hidden components.

Specialization

It is now no longer economical for each manufacturer to attempt to produce all the parts or components in his own factory or from his own particular raw material. Parts and self-contained units which are in reasonably wide demand are now produced by organizations who specialize in their manufacture, and there is no doubt that considerable advantages are to be gained by purchasing these from such suppliers. The purchaser invariably benefits from the research and experience of the supplier at a nominal cost, and owing to the large quantities of the same pattern produced by them, the actual manufacturing costs are less than those of the manufacturer who attempts to make the product himself. Specialization enables the distribution of spare parts and deliveries to customers to be facilitated.

There are numerous products which have been so developed by specialist suppliers that it would not be economical for the individual manufacturer to attempt to produce them for his own use, even if an inferior article was acceptable. Such products are ball and roller bearings, wood screws, metal fasteners, to name only a few. Unless there are important reasons to the contrary, specialized articles can usually be incorporated to advantage by the designer into the product as a basis for an efficient and economical design.

The following five factors have to be considered when the decision as to whether to make or to buy is to be made:

(a) What is the cost of the product when purchased from a supplier?
(b) What is the total cost of making it oneself?
(c) What is the direct cost of making it, that is, the total cost less the fixed overhead?
(d) What is the relative profitability of producing other work?
(e) What is the available capacity in the factory?
(f) Is it profitable to manufacture the product when there is idle capacity?
(g) Is it profitable to manufacture the product when there is no idle capacity?

When there is idle capacity in the factory the following should be considered:

If the total cost of making the part is less than the supplier's price, it is better to consider making it than to purchase.

If the total cost of making the part is more than the supplier's price, it should only be made if the direct cost of making it is less than the supplier's price. The saving of the difference between the supplier's price and the direct cost will represent a contribution towards the factory overheads. When there is no idle capacity in the factory, consideration of whether to make or buy should only be made after the consideration of any detrimental effect this may have on customer goodwill due to late deliveries.

If the total cost of making the part is more than the supplier's price, the part should be purchased from the supplier as long as the capacity in the factory is employed on more profitable production.

If the total cost of making the part is less than the supplier's price, the profitability should be assessed in relation to the products that would normally be produced on basis of percentage profit to fixed overheads. If the part it is proposed to make shows a greater percentage of profit than some of the other products, the part should be made in preference to these products. Its profitability should be checked as any other product would be.

Simultation

It is E. P. Blanchard of the United States of America who can be given the credit for defining the principle and coining the word "simultation". It is the principle for governing the performance of multiple operations simultaneously. The minimum production time for a group of operations is obtained when the maximum overlapping or simultaneous performance of these operations is obtained. This demands a study of the possibilities for combining operations for economy of production and the manufacture of products. In the analysis of a component the possibilities of applying the principles of simultation to its manufacture are always considered, particularly if the component can be produced in sufficient quantities. Amendments to the features of the part in order to facilitate this purpose is also considered. With the increasing use and understanding of the principles of the simple devices for achieving multiple simultaneous operations, it is possible to construct such aids without a great amount of difficulty, within the factory, and with little or minor expenditure. These devices may always be translated into more sophisticated constructions, if this is subsequently desired and where expenditure is justified. But where this is considered appropriate care should be given to the simplification of the setting up of such apparatus, as experience has shown that where method study has not been applied this can be unnecessarily prolonged. Proprietary equipment and devices can be purchased which will make better use of an organization's available resources, by enabling the principles of simulation to be applied to a process or work situation. But in the majority of these cases the successful operations of these procedures will demand that the product or component will have been designed in a particular manner in order to achieve the successful operation of this equipment. It has always been one of the objectives of the design function to produce products and components that will conform to the demands of the particular process; it is now not only necessary and essential to consider this factor but the product or component should also be designed, so that advantage may be obtained in its production from applying the principles of simulation.

In the development of a proposed product or component subsequent to the product analysis, recourse will be made to all the pertinent information that will have been collected, and the free use of the qualities of creativity to develop the most profitable solution. Ideas and lines of approach, which the analysis will have suggested, and which will provide the most suitable opportunities for development, are now reviewed. In order to test those ideas the construction of a prototype of the proposed design may be required.

It is important that throughout the course of conducting a product analysis, all the necessary cost data should be obtained and reviewed, as without this information accurate decisions cannot be made to test the proposals.

It is essential to realize that product analysis is easier to apply at the drawing board stage than at any other, as the use of an indiarubber at the design stage is an easier method of making an amendment, than being confronted with the necessity for more complex remedial measures after the product has been put into production. Management often go to considerable lengths to reduce labour time of an operation by a few minutes but at the same time allow product development and the design function to add hours unnecessarily to the overall production time.

Selected References and Suggestions for Further Reading

ARCHER, B. L., *Systematic Method for Designers*, Council of Industrial Design publication, London.

ALLAN, D. H. W., *Statistical Quality Control, An Introduction for Management*, Reinhold, New York; Chapman & Hall, London.

"*Bädd Möbler mått och typer*", *Möbelfunktionsundersökningen*, Svenska Söljdföreningens Publikationsavdeling, Stockholm.

Design for Production, British Productivity Council, London.

Proceedings of a Conference on Ergonomics in Industry, 27–29 September 1960, Department of Scientific and Industrial Research, Her Majesty's Stationery Office, 1961.

CREIGHTON, J. W., STUMP, W. G. and HUTCHINS, W. F., Correlation of walnut furniture cutting requirements with grade yield, *Quarterly Bulletin of the Michigan Agricultural Experiment Station*, Michigan State College, vol. 35, No. 2, pp. 230–47, November 1952.

KOEPKE, C. A., *Plant Production Control*, John Wiley, New York; Chapman & Hall, London, chapter 9, Product Analysis.

KORIN, S. B., *Value Engineering and Analysis*, Industrial Education Institute, Boston 16, Massachusetts; Industrial Education International Ltd., London.

MARTIN, H. W., *Variety Reduction—Simplification Standardization Specialization*, The British Standards Institution and the Institution of Production Engineers, London.

Variety Reduction—Twelve Case Studies, British Productivity Council, London.

Value Analysis—Sixteen Case Studies, British Productivity Council, London.

MCCORMICK, E. J., *Human Engineering*, McGraw-Hill, London and New York.

MORGAN, C. T., CHAPANIS, A., COOK, J. S. and LUND, M. W., *Human Engineering Guide to Equipment Design*, McGraw-Hill, London and New York.

MILES, L. D., *Techniques of Value Analysis and Engineering*, McGraw-Hill, London and New York.

MUNDEL, M. E., *Motion and Time Study Principles and Practice*, Prentice-Hall, Englewood Cliffs, N. J., and London, chapter 5, Process Chart—Product Analysis.

OXENFELDT, A. R. and WATKINS, M. W., *Make or Buy, Consultant Reports*, McGraw-Hill, London and New York.

PITTMAN, H. B. and JOHNSON, E. S., *Cost Saving in Furniture Manufacture by Accurate Dimensional Control*, Southern Furniture Manufacturers Association, High Point, North Carolina.

WOODSON, W. E., *Human Engineering Guide for Equipment Designers*, University of California Press, Berkeley, Los Angeles.

Conference on Design Methods, Papers presented at the conference on systematic and intuitive methods in engineering industrial design, architecture and communications, London, September 1962, edited by JONES, J. C. and THOMLEY, D. G., Pergamon Press, 1963.

YOUNGER, J. and GESCHELIN, J., *Work Routing Scheduling and Dispatching in Production*, Ronald Press, New York, chapter 17, Simultation.

SCHERB, W. R., Designers Check List, *Product Engineering*, vol. 34, No. 13, 24 June 1963, pp. 74–5 (U.S.A.).

SHARP, H. J., *Engineering Materials Selection and Value Analysis*, Iliffe, London.

CHAPTER 9

Operation Analysis

OPERATION analysis is, as its name implies, the application of the method study procedure to the detailed examination of work performed at a single work place for the purpose of effecting improvements in the particular activity. Studies of this kind come within the field of what is called secondary analysis or the detailed study of an individual work location. This is always invariably preceded by primary analysis, or the study of all the factors that influence the individual operations and the flow of work through the factory or the office.

The variety of activity to which the procedure of operation analysis can be applied is diverse and can range from the setting up or operation of a machine or piece of equipment, the operation of a process by a worker, the assembly of a product, or a clerical activity such as filling in a form, to suggest only a few examples.

However, operations tend to fall into certain well-defined groups, and the standard approach to the analysis of each is modified according to the particular classification of the activity that is to be investigated. Those operations of a hand-controlled nature provide the best subjects for investigation, and will give the greatest opportunity for the application of the principles. But when all the other kinds of operation are studied by these means, considerable improvements are achieved. These improvements may consist of a reduction in labour time, increased production, making the operation easier to perform, reducing the incidence of operator fatigue associated with the task, or improved safety, to name only a few such possible results that could be obtained.

The procedures used for the recording of the present method of carrying out the operation, which has been selected for investigation, will depend on the category of the operation. For the purposes of method study industrial operations are generally classified into the following categories.

(a) Operations that consist of a single repeated cycle.

(b) Cyclic operations in which are included several subcycles which are performed with different frequency.
(c) Operations that vary from cycle to cycle.
(d) Operations with no regular cycle of activity.

Whilst the operations in categories (a) and (b) are generally studied by first recording the activities by two-handed process charts or micromotion film procedure, those in categories (c) and (d) are best recorded by the use of outline or flow process charts, activity sampling, or memomotion techniques.

The approach to the examination of an operation requires that the factors that come within the area of primary analysis, and which have a direct affect on the performance of an operation, should be considered in order that the possible limits of an investigation may be appreciated. These may be classified as follows:

(a) Design of the product.
(b) Nature and quality of the material used.
(c) Limits and tolerances.
(d) Skill of the worker.
(e) Working conditions.
(f) Machinery tools and equipment.
(g) Set-up and preparation.
(h) Jigs and fixtures.
(i) Method of production.
(j) Floor layout.
(k) Materials handling.

It is recognized that the purpose of method study is to make the best possible use of all available resources, and that these resources may not frequently allow the ideal to be considered. But it is necessary that the investigator should be aware of the influence of these considerations of primary analysis before a detailed study is made of the activity at an individual work location, as time spent in a detailed investigation of an operation can be wasted if these are not reviewed in the preliminary stages of the study. It is therefore always necessary that these be received before secondary analysis is commenced.

It is frequently possible for small amendments to the design of the product to be made, so that the process of manufacture and its associated operations can be simplified and reduced to a minimum. It is often a useful mental exercise when making a study of an operation to consider what alterations to the design and construction of a product would simplify the operation or eliminate the necessity for it altogether. Whilst management may not be prepared to consider or implement proposals of this nature, at the particular time, it may indicate possibilities for future methods improvement. At least this mental process will make the investigator appreciate the influence that design features can have on the performance of an operation.

Many materials are variable in their quality: this fact produces difficulties in the performance of an operation where these materials are used. Alternative materials at no greater cost may be simpler to use, and may eliminate these difficulties. Some operations in certain industries are of long duration because of the nature of the material being processed. When an alternative material is used and the most suitable form for its introduction into the process is considered, what was previously an operation of long duration can now be greatly reduced and frequently eliminated entirely. It is important that the investigator should consider whether a change in materials would simplify the operation and make it easier to perform.

The dimensional control of component parts of a product with respect to their limits and tolerances will influence the methods used to perform an operation. Many machines are incapable of providing the limits and tolerances sometimes required, and where certain limits are demanded this may restrict the choice of the machine that can be used to make a particular component. No limits should be demanded from equipment that is incapable of giving them, otherwise quality control problems will result, and it is to be remembered that an inspection procedure will not provide the required quality standard if the conditions necessary for it are not already present. The limits and tolerances selected will influence the method of assembly that can be used. Fitting, selective, and interchangeable methods of assembly all require different limits and tolerances, and if this aspect is not considered, the efficiency of an assembly operation will be greatly reduced.

The degree of skill of the workers that are to carry out the proposed method is also an important consideration, as it is of little use considering the introduction of improvements to an operation which assumes that the person who is to operate the method is a skilled worker if this is not the case. Either the proposed method that is to be developed will have to take this lack of skill into account, or before the proposed improvements to the method is installed, operator training will have to be considered.

The influence of the conditions in which operators have to work should never be disregarded, however preoccupied the investigator may be with the technical aspects of an operation. Bad working conditions such as poor lighting, dust, fumes, dirty conditions, humidity, dangerous conditions, machinery and equipment in disrepair, to name only a few possible conditions, can produce undue fatigue and other stresses which will invariably reduce the efficiency and production of a particular operation. The fact that it is not always possible to measure the results of a method improvement of this kind in terms of increased production should never be an argument for not making improvements to these aspects of the working conditions.

In many industrial situations that will confront the investigator, the machinery, tools, and equipment may be far from ideal, but it is to be realized that whatever their conditions they constitute the available resources of the factory. Whilst in the process of considering an operation it may be suggested, as part of the proposals for improvement, that a particular machine should be modified or replaced. However, management may not accept this proposal, in which case any proposed method will have to overcome the defects in the equipment as best it can, but it should not at the same time be expected to produce results which the equipment is incapable of obtaining. The limitations of machinery, tools, and equipment should therefore always be appreciated.

Every opportunity should be taken to reduce the time spent in set-up and preparation, as this is likely to affect the method of performing the subsequent operation. Activity that comes within this category is investigated and analysed in exactly the same way as for any other type of operation.

The time spent in this set-up activity will consist of time for clearing away after the last job, and the time to prepare for the next one. It will be of sufficient duration to allow for a correct set-up, and the activities that may be included in this time are such tasks as referring to any drawings, patterns, or instructions related to the manufacture of the item produced by the operation, and the checking of the first products or components both by the operator and supervision. The set-up will be completed only when supervision is satisfied that the first products produced are satisfactory. The number of good components or assemblies produced during the set-up are recorded by supervision before the operator commences the production of the batch quantity, so that these are not credited to the actual production operation.

It should be appreciated that the set-up activity for many operations will never be the same each time it has to be made, as certain aspects of a set-up may have been done in preparation for the previous operation. It is sometimes possible to take advantage of this by scheduling the sequence of work in order to reduce this set-up activity. In situations where the set-up may be variable as is the case with respect to certain machines an average set-up is used for the purposes of planning.

It is necessary to consider set-up activity carefully not only for the influence that it will have on the selection of the method to be used to perform an operation, but also because it is important that the time spent in the set-up activity is recovered in the production of the components or products. If this is not done the labour time for the operation will be greater than it need be. For this reason set-up time and operation time is always considered separately in order to exercise the necessary degree of control.

The time taken to perform one cycle of an operation to produce one component or product is called the unit standard time, it is frequently referred to also as floor-to-floor time. When a proportion of the set-up time is added to this unit standard time it then becomes the unit production time, and the difference between the two unit times is dependent on the number of products produced or batch quantity subsequent to the set-up. The formula for calculating the unit production time for various batch sizes is as follows:

$$UPT = \frac{SUT}{N} + UST,$$

where UPT = unit production time in minutes, SUT = set-up time in minutes, N = number of components or products in batch, UST = unit standard time in minutes.

Example. Determine the unit production time for a component produced by an operation where the quantity or batch of components produced is twelve, the set-up time is 60 min and the unit standard time is 2 min:

$$UPT = \frac{SUT}{N} + UST = \frac{60}{12} + 2 = 7 \text{ min.}$$

It can be appreciated that if more components are produced the unit production time will be reduced accordingly.

The proportion of the set-up time that is added to the unit standard time will vary according to the particular industry. In the furniture industry the unit standard time is increased by a maximum of 10 per cent to obtain the unit production time. It can be seen that after the proposed unit production time has been determined, as a direct result of the policy of management, this will suggest a batch quantity that it is necessary to produce, or if this is not possible the alternative method to be used for the performance of the operation. The quantity suggested may be below the batch quantity required for the use of a conventional method.

The formula for the determination of the minimum batch size for a known set-up time and a required unit production time is as follows:

$$B = \frac{SU}{UPT},$$

where B = minimum batch size, SU = set-up time, UPT = unit production time per component.

Example. Determine the minimum batch size for a manufacturing operation where the set-up is 82·5 min and the unit standard time is 0·25 min. The policy of the organization states that the maximum increase in the unit standard time as the result of the addition of a proportion of the set-up shall not exceed 10 per cent:

$$B = \frac{SU}{UPT} = \frac{82 \cdot 5}{0 \cdot 25 \times 10\%} = \frac{82 \cdot 5}{0 \cdot 0250} = 3300 \text{ components minimum}$$

batch quantity.

Where it is not considered appropriate to manufacture this quantity by the particular operation, the only alternative is to perform the operation by another method that requires a lower set-up time. The suitability of various methods may be compared by this approach, and the most economical method determined for various batch quantities.

It is frequently considered an advantage to introduce a jig or fixture into the operation method, in order to improve the performance and efficiency of the activity. It should be appreciated that their use has numerous advantages. A jig and fixture tends to reduce the set-up activity, and simplifies the performance of the operation, whether it happens to be a machine or an assembly operation. If it is a machine operation a jig and fixture will ensure the accurate repetitive production of the products of the operation. Each industry has its own particular technology concerned with jig and fixture design, and the areas of its application. The furniture industry is no exception, as they are used in all the processes and include procedures for machining and assembly. Operations in the latter category may frequently incorporate different methods for the heating of synthetic resin adhesives, so that subsequent to the operation the assembly will be immediately available for further processing.

Jigs and fixtures, however desirable they may be for the improvement of an operation, are expensive and this should be realized. The indiscriminate request for them is uneconomic, therefore before one is introduced into an operation a careful study should be made to determine how much the organization can afford to spend on a jig and fixture for a particular operation. The following formula assists the methods investigator to obtain an answer to this question:

$$\frac{C}{A} + (PT \times PY \times LR),$$

where C = cost of jig and fixture in £, A = amortization period (usually one or three years), PT = piece time or unit standard time for the proposed operation method in hours, PY = production per year of the component or product from the operation, LR = labour rate in £ per hour.

This formula is applied to each method that involves a proposed jig and fixture and the method that gives the lowest total result will be the most appropriate to use. By this procedure a reduction in the cost of a jig and fixture may frequently be achieved. This assumes that the method study procedure will have been applied to the design of this fixture prior to the use of this formula, in which case the procedure of product analysis will have been used.

Method of Production

A method suitable for one type of production will not necessarily be appropriate for another. The three kinds of production which will be encountered in a manufacturing organization are the following:

(a) Jobbing production.
(b) Batch production.
(c) Line production.

These should be considered with respect to the influence each will have on the proposals for the improvement of an operation.

Jobbing production is used where only one or two of a product is to be produced, because of this it is uneconomical to spend a great deal on expensive jigs and fixtures in the proposals for the improvement of an operation associated with this form of production. For the same reason the introduction of machines which require a noticeable amount of set-up time to prepare them for an operation is also not considered, as the result would be that the majority of the labour time would be spent in preparation and set-up when compared with that spent in actual production. As a result of these considerations, extensive use is made of hand tools and basic machinery in this form of production, as they require little or no set-up activity. Method studies on operations in jobbing production are frequently not as detailed as those in the other categories of production, because the individual operations are infinitely variable in the methods and procedures used, and often the only affinity between them will be the way the hand tools are used. This is not to suggest that method studies cannot be successfully conducted in these circumstances, or that another form of production should be introduced. Many case studies, however, indicate that considerable improvements can be made to operations and activities in this type of manufacturing. But investigations of any great duration are only justified if the results obtained can be used on other work either immediately or at some future occasion.

The workers who are usually employed in this kind of production are usually skilled workers who can work with a minimum of instruction and supervision. Because of the convenient nature of this arrangement, management are sometimes reluctant to consider a change to another form of production, even where conditions are appropriate for this. This may become apparent during the course of an investigation. If the products can be made in economic quantities then batch production should be operated so that the appropriate economies may be obtained.

Batch production is introduced where a minimum quantity or economic batch of a product can be manufactured at any given time. This is done so that high production machines may be used, and the labour time spent in the setting up of these machines may be recovered by producing a sufficient quantity of the product subsequent to the set-up. The set-up activity on the various machines for the production of a product will consist of different durations of time; in order to recover the set-up time the batch is determined on the basis of the longest individual set-up activity. Frequently time spent in set-up can be reduced by method study, and where batch production is introduced it is important to see that as much attention is given to the study of the set-up operations as is given to the individual manufacturing operations. The selection of an appropriate batch quantity will influence the economic aspects of any proposals for method improvement associated with an operation in the production sequence, and whether it is justified for a jig or fixture to be suggested as part of these improvements and how much can be reasonably spent on it.

Line production is said to operate where the product is transported from one operation to the next in a predetermined sequence, with a minimum of movement between these operations, and where the operation times are so balanced that there is a constant flow of production throughout the manufacturing sequence. This method of production can only be used where a standardized product is made by continuous production. It also demands conditions that will enable interchangeable assembly to be used. The use of this form of production requires extensive capital investment in machinery and equipment among which will be transfer machines and conveyers. Where conveyers are used, and they are usually associated with this form of production, a lack of flexibility in production is a natural result. However, production may be organized in this manner for certain aspects of a manufacturing process, without the total process being arranged in the same way. When an operation which is included in a manufacturing sequence of this kind is the subject of a method study, it cannot be considered in isolation but has to be viewed in relation to its group sequence in order that the balance between operations may be maintained, and the work shared equally between the stations. As the speed of processing is much greater sufficient manufacturing quantities of a product are necessary to justify this method of production. The manufacturing operations must be of a kind that may be broken down into activities that are sufficiently small to be learnt by the average operator in a short time, have cycle times of equal length, and be of a kind that will enable jigs and fixtures to be considered to ensure that each operation cycle is performed in exactly the same way. Line production should be flexible enough for small alterations to be made and should never be used if it cannot be operated continuously because of an insufficient demand for the product.

In an investigation it is frequently seen that the performance of an operation is made more complicated and unnecessarily protracted by the worker having to travel about in the course of the operation, due to the fixed position of items in the immediate vicinity of the activity. Unless otherwise instructed, in the terms of reference provided by management, the investigator will make proposals for reducing this travelling to a minimum, and any amendment that may be necessary in order to achieve this will be considered with reference to the type of production that is operated, and the importance of the operation in the production sequence.

One of the objectives of an investigation is to reduce, if not to eliminate, the amount of handling, fetching, and carrying done by the operator in the course of performing the operation, as this can often consist of a considerable percentage of the overall cycle time. The amount of handling associated with the average woodworking machine operation is on average 75 per cent of the total cycle time for the operation, 25 per cent of the time is occupied with the actual cutting operation, to suggest only one example. A study will indicate that operations performed in other parts of the factory process also include a considerable incidence of materials handling. The investigator, in examining an operation, is mindful of the influence that this can have on the efficiency of the operation, and consequently will eliminate the necessity for this by the various means at his disposal.

When these factors of primary analysis have been appreciated, they will provide the investigator with a means by which he will be able to assess the problems that are likely to be encountered in the examination of a particular operation, after the present method of performing the operation has been recorded.

The thought process behind this examination will follow a conventional sequence and in broad outline will take the following form. Prior to the commencement of the study it will have been determined whether it is economic to investigate the operation; if the answer to this question is in the affirmative time will have been allocated in order to do this. The object to be achieved by the proposed study will also have been defined. If the purpose of the study is to increase the production from the activity, the conditions or features of the operation that are likely to affect this are noted.

What is achieved by the operation will be carefully determined; it may be that what is done is to change the shape or condition of a material, or assemble a number of components, or perform an activity not strictly in the two above categories, such as, for example, filling in a form.

The necessity for the operation will then be questioned and the reasons for retaining it, and whether some other operation will more conveniently achieve the purpose of the activity. It is often found that an operation previously installed some years ago because conditions had suggested that the operation was then necessary, no longer applies; if this should be the case the possibility of eliminating the operation is indicated.

The operation may frequently be eliminated by the use of different materials, improved machinery, tools and equipment, or by improvements to the manufacturing process, or by a design change. It may be possible to partially eliminate certain features of an operation, or by dividing it into two or more short operations make it easier to perform. There may be occasions when two or more operations can be conveniently combined with others, as a result of the use of better methods, with no increase in labour time. The possibilities of combining operations and performing the activities simultaneously, or of carrying out an operation in multiple, should always be considered. A simple example is shown in Fig. 61 of an activity that was previously performed by a number of individual operations, but which, after analysis, was subsequently performed by a single operation.

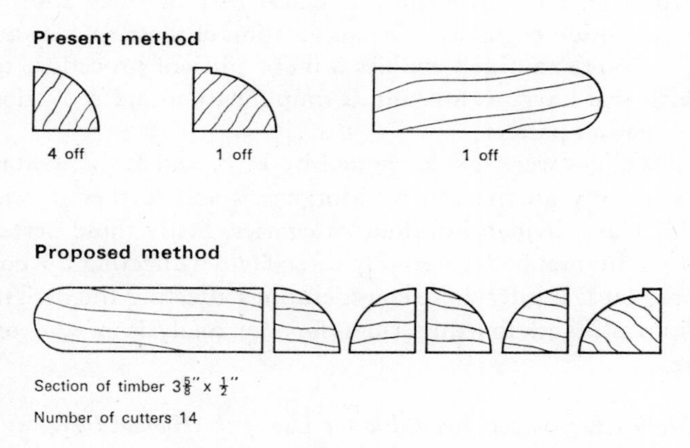

Fig. 61. The production of mouldings.

It is frequently found possible for an operation to be eliminated by a change in the sequence of a number of operations of which it is part.

When an attempt is made to eliminate the amount of movement that an operator makes during the course of an operation, it is frequently a useful mental exercise to consider what amendments to the layout of the operation area would have to be made if the operator was seated at his task in appropriate industrial seating. Consideration of this situation in relation to existing conditions will suggest amendments to the layout that will eliminate handling and generally improve the arrangement of the work area

It has long been recognized that most operations can be simplified, and when this is accomplished and the task made more convenient for the worker to perform, the lower will become the unit cost of the product produced and the higher the resultant quality.

F. B. Gilbreth, when investigating industrial activities, frequently paid special attention to the way overweight workers performed their operations, as he perceived that they invariably learnt to perform their task in a simple manner, and with quicker and less wasted motions.

The Principles of Motion Economy

In the process of the examination of an operation and the recording of the two-handed activity, not only is the procedure of critical examination available to effect improvements, but also certain rules known as the principles of motion economy. The application of these rules to an operation that is being examined enables a more efficient procedure to be devised, which will have, as a result, a simplification and reduction in the operator's motion pattern.

These principles were first suggested by F. B. and L. M. Gilbreth and were subsequently augmented by Morgensen and further developed by Barnes. They are divided into four categories, firstly those pertaining to the use of the human body, secondly those factors affecting the conditions of the work place, thirdly those considerations affecting the design of tools and equipment, and fourthly rules for the analysis of the operation procedure.

Rules of Motion Economy as Related to the Use of the Human Body

1. The motions of both the operator's hands should commence and finish at the same time. In this manner both hands will be productive and there will be no incidence of balance delay.
2. Both the hands should not be in delay except during a relaxation period. If for any reason this should take place during an operation, as, for example, in a machining operation, the hands should be given in cycle work to perform.
3. The motions of the arms should be simultaneous, symmetrical, and in opposite directions. A balance will thus be obtained between the activities of both hands.
4. The hand motions should be confined to the lowest classification of movement possible for achieving the purpose of the activity. This classification has been previously described in Chapter 3, p. 67. It can

be appreciated that if it is possible to use a lower rather than a higher class of movement to perform an operation, it would be less fatiguing for the operator and a more efficient operation.

5. Momentum should be employed in the movements of the hands whenever possible, as a smooth natural rhythm of performing an activity is easier and less fatiguing.
6. Parabolic or ballistic movements and smooth continuous motions should be employed, as these are easier for an operator to perform when compared with other motions.
7. The elements of an operation should be so arranged that an easy and natural rhythm of performing the task is possible. The manner in which the arrangement is made will be indicated by experience, but after some practice it is soon realized how this may be obtained.
8. The hands should be relieved of all work that can be done more conveniently by alternative means, such as by the use of a jig or fixture for holding an assembly or component instead of the hand, a foot-operated device for leaving the hands free for other productive activity, or an air-operated device actuated by the foot instead of the use of a hand-operated clamp. Where it is an advantage to introduce a foot-operated device consideration should be given to determine which is the most suitable device.

Rules of Motion Economy as Related to the Arrangement of the Work Place

1. All tools, materials, and controls should be pre-positioned in appropriate and recognized locations, and should be close to and directly in front of the operator. The proverbial "plumber's search" is a situation where this rule is not applied. It can be noticed that a skilled wood-carver arranges his many different hand-carving tools so that the type and size may be picked up for use when the particular occasion arises, and replaced in its appropriate location without hesitation. The work area of an operation should be arranged within the dimensions of the normal and maximum working areas in the horizontal and vertical planes, as indicated in Fig. 62. All tools, materials, and controls should always be positioned within this normal working area.
2. Whenever possible, gravity should be utilized to bring materials to the point of use, and also to eject and put aside the finished product. The application of this rule will eliminate the necessity for the operator to reach for each part when required, and to put aside when the operation is completed.

Normal working area horizontal plane

Finger, wrist and elbow movements

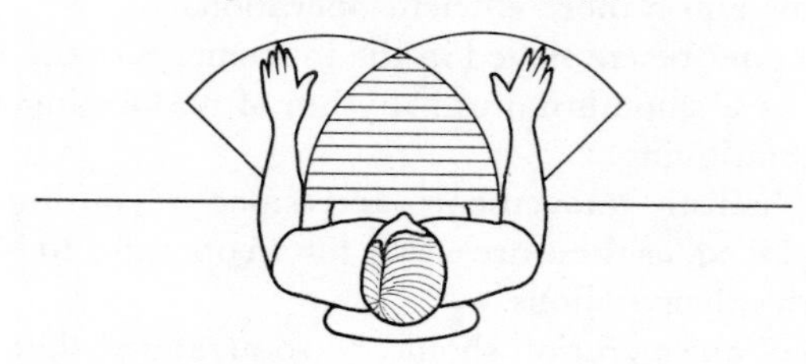

Maximum working area horizontal plane

Shoulder movements

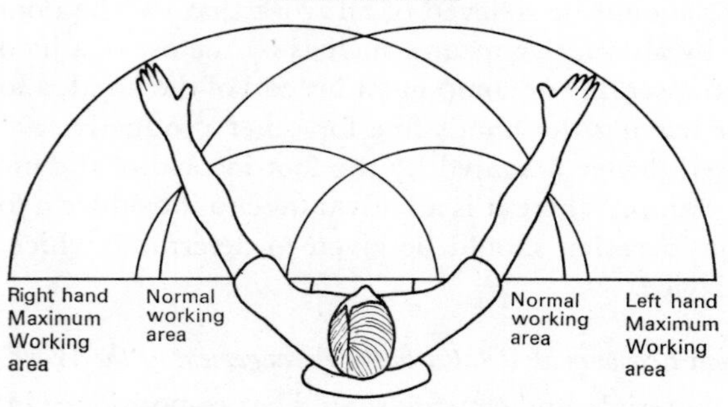

Normal and maximum working areas

FIG. 62. Normal and maximum working areas in the horizontal plane.

3. The tools, materials, and controls used in an operation should be arranged in such a manner that the best sequence of motions, and the minimum distance travelled by the hands in the course of these motions, is obtained (Fig. 63).
4. If the operator is to be seated during the performance of the operation the correct type of industrial seating should be provided. The height of the work bench and the seating provided should be of a kind that enables the operator to sit or stand during the operation, according to preference.
5. As an aid to the operator's correct visual perception appropriate lighting and colour at the work place should be introduced. Consideration should also be given to the provision of correct ventilation,

FIG. 63. Example of bench layout.

temperature, and humidity for the operator's comfort and health, as it is recognized in some process operations that these can have a considerable effect on the efficiency of an operation. An unfavourable climate of relations between management and workers will be created if the methods analyst concentrates on the motion sequence to the exclusion of the considerations of visual perception, health, and comfort.

Rules of Motion Economy as Related to the Design of Tools and Equipment

1. Whenever possible tools used in the operation should be combined, as this will reduce the number of separate tools required and simplify the question of their handling and location. Recourse to catalogues provided by tool suppliers will quickly indicate the possibilities that are likely to be achieved in this direction.
2. Where an activity or a piece of equipment is operated by the worker, the arrangement of this activity should be such that the work is evenly distributed between the fingers and limbs according to their capacity.
3. Correctly designed handles should be introduced for tools, levers, cross bars, and hand wheels so that the maximum mechanical advantage and an easier performance of the operation may be obtained by the worker.

Rules for the Analysis of the Operation Procedure

1. The cause of any hesitation noticed whilst the worker is carrying out the operation should be determined so that these can be eliminated.
2. Attention should be given to the number of basic divisions of accomplishment that are used to carry out an operation. It should be remembered that the best method of performing an operation is that which employs the lowest number of basic elements.
3. The best sequence of the basic divisions of accomplishment used to perform the operation should be used. This is usually a sequence in which the ineffective elements are absent.
4. Wherever a variation is seen to occur in the time required to perform an element of an operation, the cause of this should be determined. For the further study of these principles the student is recommended to refer to the selected literature contained in the bibliography at the end of the chapter and to Fig. 64.

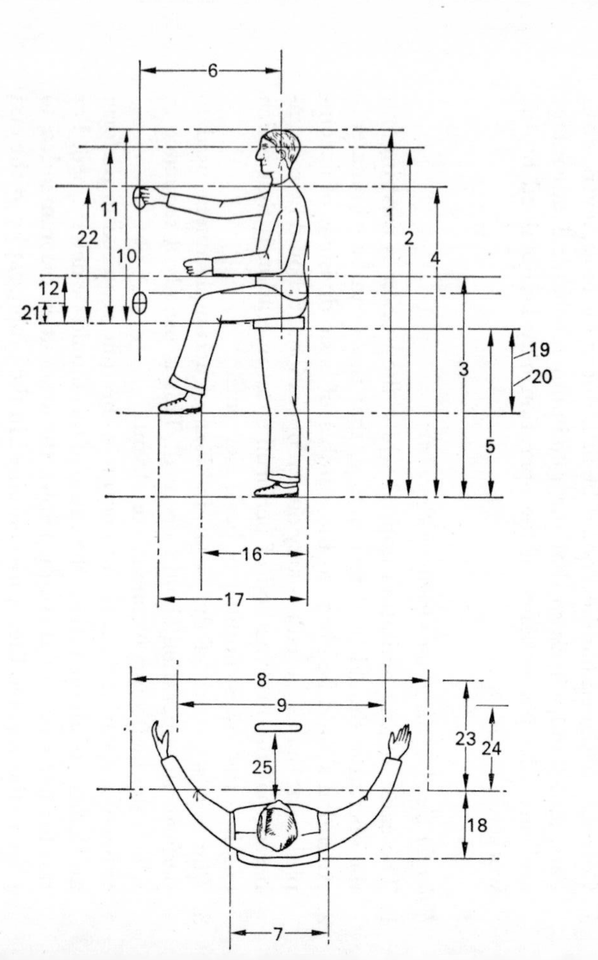

TABLE 1

	Male, in.	Female, in.	Range of adjust-ment, in.
1. Height	69	65	—
2. Eye level	65	61	5
3. Elbow height	42	40	3
4. Maximum height of controls (shoulder height)	56	52	—
5. Minimum height of controls (symphysis height) ..	35	33	—
6. Maximum distance of controls from centre line of body	18	14	—
7. Body width	19	17	—
8. Maximum span at working level	60	52	—
9. Normal span at working level	48	43	—
10. Sitting height above seat ..	36	34	—
11. Sitting eye-level above seat	32	30	4
12. Elbow height above seat ..	9	9	—
13. Seat length	16	15	—
14. Seat width	14—20		—
15. Depth of seat below work surface	7—9		—
16. Buttock to knee	24	22	—
17. Minimum leg room (back of seat to tip of toe)	34	32	—
18. Back of seat to front edge of bench	12—15		—
19. Seat height	17	15	4
20. When operator is seated at high bench, depth of foot-rest below seat	17	15	4
21. Minimum height of controls above seat	1	1	—
22. Maximum height of controls above seat	23	21	—
23. Maximum forward reach from front edge of bench	20	17	—
24. Normal forward reach from front edge of bench	13	11	—
25. Minimum distance of displays from eye	18	18	—
26. Maximum elevation of toe above horizontal	4½	4	Pivoted on heel
27. Normal elevation of toe above horizontal	3	3	
28. Normal depression of toe below horizontal	4½	4	
29. Maximum depression of toe below horizontal	6	5½	
30. Foot length	10½	9½	—

Methods Time Measurement

When it is necessary to make a detailed analysis of an operation, in order to evaluate the various methods by which it may be performed, the technique known as methods time measurement is a useful means of doing this. When all the other essential factors have been considered such as safety, fatigue, and whether asking the worker to perform an operation in a particular way is making an unreasonable request of him, the best method will invariably be the one that takes the least time.

This procedure also provides a precise way of recording and analysing an operation method, and a means of evaluating the relative merits of proposals at the development stage. It provides the means of supplying time values, expressed in time measurement units or T.M.U.s, for evaluating a proposed method of performing a task, which has already been expressed as the result of a motion analysis in terms of the basic divisions of accomplishment. A predetermined time standard is assigned to each motion; this will vary according to the nature of the motion, and the conditions in which it is made.

The procedure has been found to be particularly applicable to the comparison of assembly methods, and the feature of jig and fixture designs.

The information for the construction of the data was obtained by the frame by frame analysis of many hundreds of feet of cine film which had been made for a wide range of work; this was subsequently adjusted to the time that a normal operator would be required to perform each motion element, when working at an hourly rate of pay with no incentive payment. In practice it has been found that the data gave results a little above this performance standard.

These data were then tabulated and analysed to determine the influence of variable characteristics. Tables were then prepared which summarized these values (Fig. 65). It will be noticed that each basic motion is qualified by a time value in T.M.U.s, one T.M.U. being equal to 0·00001 hr, or 0·0006 min, or 0·036 sec. When a total T.M.U. value for a particular operation has been obtained, all that is necessary to convert the units to actual clock time is to multiply this total by either of the above conversion factors, according to the actual clock time units required.

The procedure to be followed in applying M.T.M. is first to analyse the operation in terms of all the motions required to perform the task for both the left and right hands. This is done on a methods analysis chart (Fig. 66). Then from the data tables the time for performing each basic element of

TABLE I—REACH—R

Distance Moved Inches	Time TMU A	Time TMU B	Time TMU C or D	Time TMU E	Hand In Motion A	Hand In Motion B
¾ or less	2.0	2.0	2.0	2.0	1.6	1.6
1	2.5	2.5	3.6	2.4	2.3	2.3
2	4.0	4.0	5.9	3.8	3.5	2.7
3	5.3	5.3	7.3	5.3	4.5	3.6
4	6.1	6.4	8.4	6.8	4.9	4.3
5	6.5	7.8	9.4	7.4	5.3	5.0
6	7.0	8.6	10.1	8.0	5.7	5.7
7	7.4	9.3	10.8	8.7	6.1	6.5
8	7.9	10.1	11.5	9.3	6.5	7.2
9	8.3	10.8	12.2	9.9	6.9	7.9
10	8.7	11.5	12.9	10.5	7.3	8.6
12	9.6	12.9	14.2	11.8	8.1	10.1
14	10.5	14.4	15.6	13.0	8.9	11.5
16	11.4	15.8	17.0	14.2	9.7	12.9
18	12.3	17.2	18.4	15.5	10.5	14.4
20	13.1	18.6	19.8	16.7	11.3	15.8
22	14.0	20.1	21.2	18.0	12.1	17.3
24	14.9	21.5	22.5	19.2	12.9	18.8
26	15.8	22.9	23.9	20.4	13.7	20.2
28	16.7	24.4	25.3	21.7	14.5	21.7
30	17.5	25.8	26.7	22.9	15.3	23.2

CASE AND DESCRIPTION
A Reach to object in fixed location, or to object in other hand or on which other hand rests.
B Reach to single object in location which may vary slightly from cycle to cycle.
C Reach to object jumbled with other objects in a group so that search and select occur.
D Reach to a very small object or where accurate grasp is required.
E Reach to indefinite location to get hand in position for body balance or next motion or out of way.

TABLE II—MOVE—M

Distance Moved Inches	Time TMU A	Time TMU B	Time TMU C	Hand in Motion B
¾ or less	2.0	2.0	2.0	1.7
1	2.5	2.9	3.4	2.3
2	3.6	4.6	5.2	2.9
3	4.9	5.7	6.7	3.6
4	6.1	6.9	8.0	4.3
5	7.3	8.0	9.2	5.0
6	8.1	8.9	10.3	5.7
7	8.9	9.7	11.1	6.5
8	9.7	10.6	11.8	7.2
9	10.5	11.5	12.7	7.9
10	11.3	12.2	13.5	8.6
12	12.9	13.4	15.2	10.0
14	14.4	14.6	16.9	11.4
16	16.0	15.8	18.7	12.8
18	17.6	17.0	20.4	14.2
20	19.2	18.2	22.1	15.6
22	20.8	19.4	23.8	17.0
24	22.4	20.6	25.5	18.4
26	24.0	21.8	27.3	19.8
28	25.5	23.1	29.0	21.2
30	27.1	24.3	30.7	22.7

Wt. Allowance: Wt. (lb.) Up to	Factor	Constant TMU
2.5	1.00	0
7.5	1.06	2.2
12.5	1.11	3.9
17.5	1.17	5.6
22.5	1.22	7.4
27.5	1.28	9.1
32.5	1.33	10.8
37.5	1.39	12.5
42.5	1.44	14.3
47.5	1.50	16.0

CASE AND DESCRIPTION
A Move object to other hand or against stop.
B Move object to approximate or indefinite location.
C Move object to exact location.

TABLE III—TURN AND APPLY PRESSURE—T AND AP

Weight	30°	45°	60°	75°	90°	105°	120°	135°	150°	165°	180°
	Time TMU for Degrees Turned										
Small— 0 to 2 Pounds	2.8	3.5	4.1	4.8	5.4	6.1	6.8	7.4	8.1	8.7	9.4
Medium—2.1 to 10 Pounds	4.4	5.5	6.5	7.5	8.5	9.6	10.6	11.6	12.7	13.7	14.8
Large— 10.1 to 35 Pounds	8.4	10.5	12.3	14.4	16.2	18.3	20.4	22.2	24.3	26.1	28.2

APPLY PRESSURE CASE 1—16.2 TMU. APPLY PRESSURE CASE 2—10.6 TMU

FIG. 65. Methods time measurement. Tables I–III, IV–VIII, IX–X. (By permission of MTM Association for Standards and Research.)

TABLE IV—GRASP—G

Case	Time TMU	DESCRIPTION
1A	2.0	**Pick Up Grasp**—Small, medium or large object by itself, easily grasped.
1B	3.5	Very small object or object lying close against a flat surface.
1C1	7.3	Interference with grasp on bottom and one side of nearly cylindrical object. Diameter larger than ½".
1C2	8.7	Interference with grasp on bottom and one side of nearly cylindrical object. Diameter ¼" to ½".
1C3	10.8	Interference with grasp on bottom and one side of nearly cylindrical object. Diameter less than ¼".
2	5.6	**Regrasp.**
3	5.6	**Transfer Grasp.**
4A	7.3	Object jumbled with other objects so search and select occur. Larger than 1" x 1" x 1".
4B	9.1	Object jumbled with other objects so search and select occur. ¼" x ¼" x ⅛" to 1" x 1" x 1".
4C	12.9	Object jumbled with other objects so search and select occur. Smaller than ¼" x ¼" x ⅛".
5	0	Contact, sliding or hook grasp.

TABLE V—POSITION*—P

CLASS OF FIT		Symmetry	Easy To Handle	Difficult To Handle
1—Loose	No pressure required	S	5.6	11.2
		SS	9.1	14.7
		NS	10.4	16.0
2—Close	Light pressure required	S	16.2	21.8
		SS	19.7	25.3
		NS	21.0	26.6
3—Exact	Heavy pressure required.	S	43.0	48.6
		SS	46.5	52.1
		NS	47.8	53.4

*Distance moved to engage—1" or less.

TABLE VI—RELEASE—RL

Case	Time TMU	DESCRIPTION
1	2.0	Normal release performed by opening fingers as independent motion.
2	0	Contact Release.

TABLE VII—DISENGAGE—D

CLASS OF FIT	Easy to Handle	Difficult to Handle
1—Loose—Very slight effort, blends with subsequent move.	4.0	5.7
2—Close — Normal effort, slight recoil.	7.5	11.8
3—Tight — Considerable effort, hand recoils markedly.	22.9	34.7

TABLE VIII—EYE TRAVEL TIME AND EYE FOCUS—ET AND EF

Eye Travel Time $= 15.2 \times \frac{T}{D}$ TMU, with a maximum value of 20 TMU.

where T = the distance between points from and to which the eye travels.
D = the perpendicular distance from the eye to the line of travel T.

Eye Focus Time = 7.3 TMU.

FIG. 65 (*cont.*).

TABLE IX—BODY, LEG AND FOOT MOTIONS

DESCRIPTION	SYMBOL	DISTANCE	TIME TMU
Foot Motion—Hinged at Ankle.	FM	Up to 4″	8.5
With heavy pressure.	FMP		19.1
Leg or Foreleg Motion.	LM —	Up to 6″	7.1
		Each add'l. inch	1.2
Sidestep—Case 1—Complete when leading leg contacts floor.	SS-C1	Less than 12″	Use REACH or MOVE Time
		12″	17.0
		Each add'l. inch	.6
Case 2—Lagging leg must contact floor before next motion can be made.	SS-C2	12″	34.1
		Each add'l. inch	1.1
Bend, Stoop, or Kneel on One Knee.	B,S,KOK		29.0
Arise.	AB,AS,AKOK		31.9
Kneel on Floor—Both Knees.	KBK		69.4
Arise.	AKBK		76.7
Sit.	SIT		34.7
Stand from Sitting Position.	STD		43.4
Turn Body 45 to 90 degrees—Case 1—Complete when leading leg contacts floor.	TBC1		18.6
Case 2—Lagging leg must contact floor before next motion can be made.	TBC2		37.2
Walk.	W-FT.	Per Foot	5.3
Walk.	W-P	Per Pace	15.0

TABLE X—SIMULTANEOUS MOTIONS

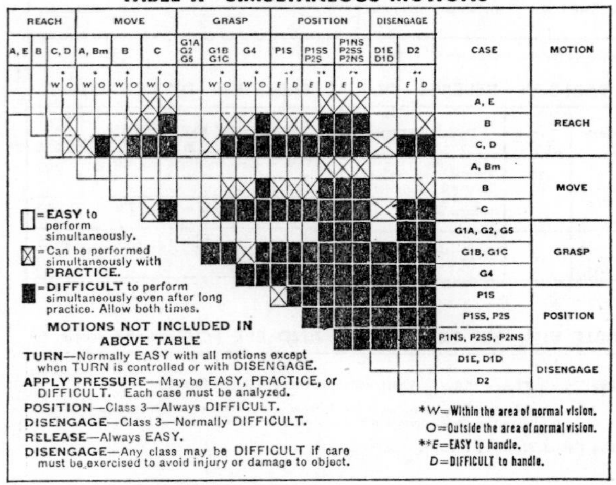

FIG. 65 (*cont.*).

METHODS ANALYSIS CHART

Part: ________ Dept: ________ DWG ________ Term ________

Operation ________ Date ________

Description - Left hand	No.	Class	T.M.U.	Class	No.	Description - Right hand

Fig. 66. Methods analysis chart.

the operation is determined in terms of T.M.U.s. The time for each of these basic elements will depend on a number of independent variables. For example with reference to the basic motion element "Reach", the variables that will influence the time for this will be the length of the motion, whether the hand is moving at the beginning or at the end of the motion, and the degree of control required in carrying it out. The M.T.M. system has procedures for assessing these variables and symbols are used to indicate these differences. For example when the following is recorded, MR18B, the length of the motion reach is indicated by 18, which signifies 18 in., whether the hand is moving at the beginning is signified by M, and the degree of control is indicated by one of five letters A, B, C, D, or E, which is placed immediately after the number of inches moved. In the particular example shown, B indicates that it is a "Reach" to a single object in a location that may vary slightly from cycle to cycle as indicated in Table I (see Fig. 65).

If, for example, in a two-handed activity the right-hand made a "Reach" of 14 in. to pick up an object in a box, the symbol that would be used to record this would be R14C, and consulting Table I it is seen that the value for this is 15·6 T.M.U.s. If at the same time the left-hand reaches 7 in. also to pick up an object in a box, the symbol would be R7C, and its value would be 10·8 T.M.U.s. In this instance the right-handed activity would be the limiting factor and 10·8 unit value for the left-hand activity would not be used in calculating the overall duration of the operation. This non-limiting motion should be circled or deleted, as only the limiting motion will be required to determine the time required to perform the operation by that method.

To appreciate the degree of detail necessary for the analysis of an operation, and the application of M.T.M., it should be remembered that an element of an operation may often be of only a few seconds' duration, but may on analysis contain as many as fifty basic motions. But in the training of method study practitioners, this degree of analysis produces a conciousness and appreciation of method differences, which are frequently the cause of increased time. But as far as method study is concerned the time determined for the carrying out of an operation is not necessarily that which an operation would take when performed by a worker. M.T.M. provides only a means of measurement by which operations may be analysed and compared; no attempt should be made to apply it in any way, unless the proper application of the data is understood. This word of caution is given to prevent difficulties that will invariably result from the misapplication of the procedure. Those methods analysts who wish to understand this useful method study technique more thoroughly are referred to the standard textbook on the subject. This provides a rigorous treatment of the subject with many examples of its application.

The hand and arm motion elements which are indicated in the tables are defined as follows:

Reach which is indicated by the symbol R in Table I, is the basic element employed when the predominant purpose is to move the hand to a destination or general location, and whose time is affected by the length of the reach, destination, and relative position.

(i) Length is the distance in inches travelled by the knuckle of the forefinger.

(ii) Destination is classified into five categories A, B, C, D, and E as defined in the tables.

(iii) Relative position of the hand before and after the work element. Separate reach times are listed for categories A and B, when the hand is in motion either at the beginning or at the end of the element.

Move, which is indicated by the symbol M in Table II, is the basic element employed when the predominant purpose is to transport an object to a destination. The time for a move is determined by:

(i) Length measured in inches as for Reach.
(ii) Destination, categories of which are described in the table.
(iii) Weight of object moved.

Turn, which is indicated by the symbol T in Table III, is a movement that rotates the hand, wrist, and forearm, and is affected by the following considerations:

(i) Angle of turning estimated to the nearest 15 degrees by observing the movement of the thumb knuckle. The symbol used is T30°, T45°.
(ii) The weight measured in pounds is the resistance of the object handled.

Apply pressure, which is indicated by the symbol AP in Table III, is the element employed whenever pressure is applied; this is denoted by the following:

(i) AP1 when pressure is applied by the hand when employing a squeeze motion.
(ii) AP2 when pressure is applied by the arms and body against the resistance of an object that is to be moved.

Grasp, which is indicated by the symbol G in Table IV, is an element involving the use of the hand and fingers; it is employed when an object is required for further operations. The time values for this element depend on the dimensions of the part to be grasped.

Position, which is indicated by the symbol P in Table V, is the basic element employed to align, orient, and engage one object with another whenever the motions used are so minor that they do not justify classification as other basic elements. Alignment and orientation cover the movement involved in bringing the two objects together into a position where they may be engaged and assembled. The time for the element Position is affected by the class of fit (three such classes are described in the table) and the state of symmetry, which is classified into the following categories:

S Symmetrical, when an object can be positioned in an infinite number of ways about an axis which coincides with the direction of travel.

SS Semi-symmetrical, when an object can be positioned in several ways about an axis which coincides with the direction of travel.

NS Non-symmetrical, when an object can be positioned in only one way about an axis which coincides with the direction of travel.

Release, which is indicated by the symbol RL in Table VI, is the basic element employed to relinquish control of an object by the fingers or the hands.

Disengage, which is indicated by the symbol D in Table VII, is the basic element employed to break contact between objects, the time value for this being affected by the class of fit. Three classes of fit are described in the table and the handling is classified into:

(i) DE. Easy to handle when the parts may be grasped securely and disengaged without bending.
(ii) DD. Difficult to handle when there is obstruction in separating objects or when damage to the part or injury to fingers may occur.

Eye Travel and *Eye Focus* are indicated by the symbols ET and EF in Table VIII.

Body, leg, and foot motions, as indicated in Table IX, are represented by various symbols according to the motion. Where simultaneous motions are performed by two or more body members at the same time these combinations are shown in Table X and are classified as:

(i) Those that are easy to perform simultaneously.
(ii) Those that can be performed simultaneously with practice.
(iii) Those that are difficult to perform simultaneously even after long practice.

It should be noted that if two or more motions are combined or overlapped, all can be performed in the time required to perform the one demanding the greatest amount of time.

Selected References and Suggestions for Further Reading

MAYNARD, B. M. and STEGMERTEN, G. J., *Operation Analysis*, McGraw-Hill, London and New York.

NORDHOFF, W. A., *Machine Shop Estimating*, McGraw-Hill, London and New York.

Principles of Motion Economy

BARNES, R. M., *Motion and Time Study*, John Wiley, London and New York, chapters 15, 16, 17.

BARNES, R. M., *Motion and Time Study Applications*, John Wiley, London and New York.

MORROW, R. L., *Time Study and Motion Economy with procedures for method improvement*, Ronald Press, New York, chapter 5, How to do More Work with Less Effort.

MURRELL, K. F. H., *Ergonomics—Man in his working environment*, Chapman & Hall, London.

Methods Time Measurement

MAYNARD, H. B., *Methods Time Measurement*, McGraw-Hill, London and New York.

CURRIE, R. M., *Simplified P.M.T.S.*, A manual for practitioners and trainers, British Institute of Management, London.

CHAPTER 10

Plant Layout Analysis

PLANT layout is the physical arrangement of the resources of production within a proposed or existing area of the factory, in order to make the best possible use of the available resources of floor space and buildings, and to reduce the time spent by personnel in travelling between the different production locations.

In factories where no attention is given to these considerations, management is invariably seeking ways of obtaining more floor space to reduce the congestion which is all too frequently apparent in their shops. In their endeavours to overcome this problem management is often too hastily influenced into considering an expensive building programme for an extension, whilst a method study would show that half of the existing factory floor space is probably used ineffectively, and that the majority of the time of productive workers is spent in the movement of materials and other unproductive activity because everything appears to be in the most inconvenient place.

Why such a situation arises in an organization is primarily due to its natural growth; as extra equipment is introduced it is placed in the most convenient and available location, buildings are added to the parent structure with very little consideration to any factor other than whether there is available space to build an extension. It is only when there is no further opportunity of obtaining extra floor space, and congested conditions make it practically impossible to operate the plant efficiently, or where management is finally faced with considerable capital expenditure for a building programme to overcome these difficulties, that method study is considered. In such a situation the investigator is requested to determine whether the organization is making the best possible use of its present resources of floor space and buildings, before the proposed extension is considered.

Opinions as to what constitutes an efficient factory layout have undergone a considerable change as a result of the application of method study.

Fig. 67. Mid-nineteenth-century machine shop layout. (Crown Copyright Science Museum, London.)

In the past little attention was paid to the layout of factories, machines were often arranged in rows, due to the use of belt drives from a line shaft running the length of the shop (Fig. 67). Benches and other equipment were placed wherever there was available space, and the general appearance of these shops was crowded, the movement of operators and materials were often difficult, and materials travelled up and down the length of the shop in a haphazard manner.

Whilst the principles of factory layout are similar for most industries, there are certain considerations that have to be remembered when approaching the layout of factories for certain manufacturing processes; these are particular to an individual industry, and are likely to present problems if they are not remembered.

Before any layout study is commenced, a definition has to be made of the proposed objectives. The object of a layout study is primarily to arrange the resources of production in such a manner that maximum efficiency is achieved at minimum cost. In attempting to accomplish this objective many factors have to be considered, some of which can only be improved at the expense of the others. It is therefore useful to decide which of these factors have the highest priority, so that undue emphasis is not given to those aspects that are of lesser importance. As a result of making this review it is soon realized that the solution to most layout problems is a compromise between these factors.

After the objectives of the layout study have been defined, a decision as to what kind of product is to be manufactured, and how it is to be processed, then has to be made. What quantity of the products can be sold then has to be determined. When these questions have been answered, the cost in direct labour, materials, and overheads for manufacturing the product in the agreed manner then has to be determined. In doing this it is to be remembered that in many industries various methods of manufacturing and processing are available, each having different direct labour, material costs, and overheads.

The question whether sales are steady or seasonal has also to be considered, for if seasonal, what maximum monthly production will be required, and to achieve this production whether materials are available as needed, or have they to be purchased in advance and stored in order to maintain a constant output.

Having decided on these important considerations, the details of the proposed method will be determined to accommodate these factors.

It should be appreciated that given a particular product or range of products to manufacture, there are different methods by which they may be made, each requiring a different labour force and floor area. With the vast amount of technical data which has been supplied by research now available, it is no longer necessary to manufacture a particular product in the old and conventional way. As long as there is complete satisfaction with the results the selection of a new process may indicate a means of producing the product to the limits and conditions previously considered desirable.

After the method of manufacture has been selected for the lowest labour cost, the floor space required for carrying out the manufacturing procedure in this manner is next considered. The minimum floor area required for each department will be determined, whilst in doing this it will be remembered that certain processes have recognized bottlenecks which often hold up production in the shops where they occur, because additional processed materials are not available from the area of the bottleneck. Any incidence of this wastes capital invested in the shop, because materials cannot be obtained in sufficient quantities. After these decisions have been made the actual layout may be commenced.

The layout of the floor area of a factory may be made in any one of three different ways.

(i) Layout by fixed position.
(ii) Process layout.
(iii) Product layout.

In the method of layout by fixed position the materials or components remain in a fixed location, and the tools, men, and machines are brought to it. The assembly of a heavy piece of machinery frequently comes within this category.

Process layout consists of grouping together all machinery and equipment for a given process in one shop or area. This type of layout has many advantages amongst the most important are that all operators doing a certain kind of work are together so that supervision is made easier, new workers can observe experienced operators and thus learn by observation and thus gradually assimilate process knowledge in course of time. This method enables materials and services to be kept in a nearby location and made easily accessible to the process. These advantages made process layout a procedure to be favoured until recent times. The disadvantages of the procedure, however, became more apparent as method studies were made of this type of layout. These studies indicated that the handling of materials was complicated, as the machines and equipment were not placed in the order in which they were to be used. Because of this disadvantage a different type of layout procedure was developed known as product layout. This method became popular, and was practised in those factories where a single standard type of product or range of products was manufactured. These products were frequently based on diversification from a single standard product incorporating standard components and sub-assemblies. As the equipment was arranged in the order in which it was to be used, the advantages were self-evident, but factories manufacturing a variety of products did not appreciate the full possibilities of product grouping until later, when some factories who were manufacturing individual products in large quantities, in order to reduce costs separated these products from the miscellaneous work by means of a product layout, primarily to set up separate cost centres.

When a single product is separated from the main production and the equipment for producing it is organized in a special area, product grouping is practised. The advantage to be achieved from doing this were so favourable that the possibilities of doing the same for other products were sought. On miscellaneous work, however, product grouping was found to be impractical, and process grouping had to be used, but even in such cases it was possible with the aid of suitable materials handling equipment to make layouts that obtained many of the advantages of a product layout.

It is a relatively simple matter to produce an efficient layout if the principles for making one are clearly understood, and complete information is available. Ideally, factory layouts are generally a combination of product and process layout, as certain of the processes have been found to operate more conveniently in the latter type of layout.

There are certain aspects of the problem that must be observed in a layout study which will not only influence the quality of the proposals but also the evaluation of the results.

The proposed layout should be one that achieves a minimum labour cost in its operation, for if the worker has been engaged to perform a particular task he should be able to devote the maximum time to it. Minimum labour costs are frequently obtained by the introduction of the following measures. The layout of the individual work benches, machines, and departments should be so arranged that a minimum time is taken in the movement from one location to another. The arrangement should be such that the effectiveness of the materials handling and the flow of materials throughout the production will be improved and the distances travelled by the materials and the number of individual handling operations will be reduced to a minimum. Attention should be given to the location of welfare facilities, such as canteens and lavatories, in order to reduce the unnecessary movement of workers.

The best use of available floor space can be obtained by allowing for the minimum of floor area for each process, within which it is possible to perform the manufacturing operations efficiently. Maximum machine utilization should be planned for, so that the available floor space need not be occupied by a large number of similar machines, whose individual utilization is low.

Finally, the proposed layout must be one that provides sufficient flexibility to enable alterations to be made quickly and without too much inconvenience to production.

The procedure for conducting a methods analysis of a layout problem, whilst it conforms to the basic method study procedure, has certain additional characteristics that have to be observed.

The objective of the study having been defined by the terms of reference provided by management, information is collected and recorded of a selected range of operations and work in the form of flow process charts. Information concerning the available floor space is also obtained; this will indicate how much floor area management can provide for a process. The expected yearly and monthly production is determined, and in doing this consideration is always given to the possibilities of greater production in the future, and the proposed layout must be made to accommodate these possibilities. The time required to perform each operation must be determined carefully, and also the number of work stations that must be provided to achieve the required daily production.

A plan of the available floor space should be obtained, to the suitable scale; this should not include any information other than those fixed features which are an integral part of the factory building, such as columns, lifts, washrooms, and lavatories. All other data necessary for the development of the proposed layout should be presented in a convenient manner for easy reference. The layout data form (Fig. 68) is a convenient way of presenting this and is used for this purpose. This data form is used to record the essential information concerning the process operations for making a component. Details are included of the present and anticipated production. Information about the operations, their process time, the machines or equipment, number of machines required to balance the flow of production, the dimensions of the floor space, or operations area of each machine and activity are all entered on it. Machine coupling data concerning the operator time and the machine time is also obtained. This last item of information is useful if it is desired to operate a number of machines in series with transfer equipment between them.

Each operation is considered in the order in which it is to be performed, together with the number of work stations that are required to balance the production at the particular location. The floor space occupied by each operation is also determined and recorded in the appropriate place on the layout form. Templates representing the plan silhouette of each machine, bench, or load of material that is to be included in the layout is

LAYOUT DATA FORM

Component ______________ Product ______________

Present production ______________

Anticipated production ______________

Operation	Allowed time	Machine	Number of machines reqd.	Floor space each machine	Machine coupling data	
					Man time	Machine time

Fig. 68. Layout data form.

made to the scale of the floor plan. Light, stiff cardboard is used for this purpose, different coloured card may be used to indicate different processes or equipment, and as proposals for different methods of handling may be developed during the course of the layout, the use of colour can be made to indicate a distinction between space occupied by equipment which is not subject to change, and space occupied by material. If only a minor revision to a layout is contemplated, present equipment and flow of materials can be indicated by lines drawn between the machines and equipment or by the use of a string diagram.

When the best possible layout has been made, it should be checked in detail so that all aspects of the problem can be seen to have been satisfied. Where a large number of products have to be considered, and the percentage movement between locations and departments is to be determined, the use of a travel chart will simplify this task.

If the silhouette of a machine used in the production of a component is marked, and the output per hour obtainable from it is indicated, a clear picture of the material flow will be obtained so that possible difficulties caused by machines being out of balance may be foreseen. Bottlenecks may be recognized more easily by this method and eliminated by the improvement of methods or by providing additional equipment. If these cannot be eliminated by this action, sufficient floor space will have to be allowed to hold the maximum amount of material that is likely to accumulate ahead of each work station. It is the practice in some industries not to make a machine a permanent fixture by bolting it down until after a few trial runs have been made in the proposed layout, most equipment will operate satisfactorily for a while in this condition. But if this is not considered, alternative methods of fixing machines to the floor should be reviewed, such as is obtained by resin-impregnated mats; these will give greater flexibility for the subsequent movement of a machine should an amendment to the layout be considered necessary.

When a final decision has to be made as to the best solution that is obtainable within the terms of reference and the objectives of the layout study, it will almost certainly indicate that a compromise will have been obtained.

A record of the proposed layout should always be kept for reference and possible revision at some future date, if this is considered necessary.

It should also be appreciated that the adoption or rejection of a proposed layout may frequently depend upon the clearness with which the proposals have been presented to other personnel.

A good layout is never the result of guesswork and hunches, but is obtained by a detailed analysis of the facts of the situation and the application of method study.

Office Layout Studies

In the process of making a method study of the layout of office space, considerable time is invariably wasted by delays and misunderstandings, which seem to be a feature of such studies. A procedure has been developed that provides a systematic approach to studies concerned with the layout of office space. It has been found useful as an additional aid to the conventional approach to layout problems, particularly at the development stage. This procedure, being systematic in its approach to the problem, reduces the possibility of these misunderstandings. It is essentially a procedure for solving small layout problems, such as are frequently encountered in offices, and should not be used for the solution of complex problems of this type.

The procedure consists of a set of six parts by which the three basic fundamentals of any layout planning project is achieved.

(i) The relationship between the various functions, activities, or work stations.
(ii) The space, its amount, and type for each activity.
(iii) The adjustment of the relationships and spaces in order to obtain a satisfactory layout.

The six parts of the procedure are as follows:

(i) Construct a relationship chart.
(ii) Determine floor space requirements in square feet, and any physical features that may be demanded by the subjects to be located in the floor area.
(iii) Connect the activities at the different locations, and indicate their relationship.
(iv) Prepare a proposed layout.

These six steps form a logical procedure which conforms to the method study approach, yet takes the planner from the basic data to a workable layout plan. Each stage of the procedure has its own chart, which is completed before proceeding to the next one.

First of all the activities, departments, or working groups, which are to be the subject of the layout are defined and their individual location relative to each other is determined. A particular closeness rating is assigned to each which is entered on the relationship chart (Fig. 69). This, when completed, records these results in an organized way. A vowel letter is used to represent each of the closeness ratings, A, E, I, O, U, in descending order of value, and X is used to indicate an undesirable relationship. In addition, the reason for each is indicated by a number code, each individual number being explained at the bottom of the form (Fig. 70).

In the second step a network relationship diagram is constructed (Fig. 71). In this, circles are used to represent the activities that are to be located in the layout, each of these are numbered for identification and

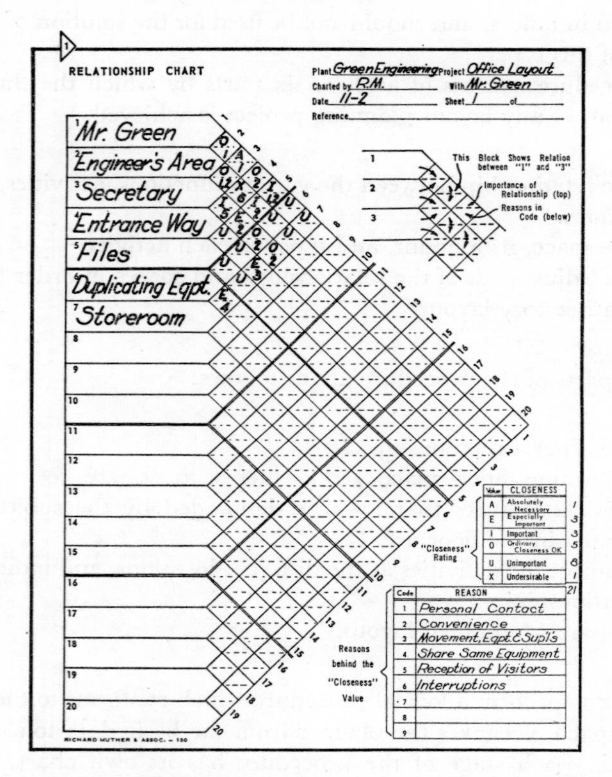

FIG. 69. Relationship chart. (From *Simplified Systematic Layout Planning*, Management and Industrial Research Publications, by permission of Richard Muther & Associates.)

connected by parallel lines corresponding to the ratings on the relationship chart in stage one of the procedure.

A ════ Absolutely necessary
E ════ Especially important
I ═══ Important
O ——— Ordinary closeness
U – – – – Unimportant
X ╲╱╲╱╲╱ Undesirable

2

ACTIVITIES AREA & FEATURES SHEET

Plant *Green Engineering* Project *Office Layout* By *R.M.* With *Mr. Green* Date *11-2* Page ___ of ___

Physical Features Required — Enter Unit and Required Amount under each (columns 1–5) / Relative Importance of Features: A – Absolutely Necessary, E – Especially Important, I – Important, O – Ordinary Importance, — Not Required (columns 6–13)

No.	Activity Name	Area in *Sq. Ft.* Total: *500*	O'Head Clearance (*Ft.*)	Max. Overhead Supported Load	Max. Floor Loading	Min. Column Spacing		Water & Drains	Steam	Compressed Air	Foundations or Pits	Fire or Explosion Hazard	Special Ventilation	Special Electrification	*Window Light*	Requirements for Shape or Configuration of Area (Space) — Enter Requirements for Shape or Configuration and Reasons therefore
1.	*Mr. Green* (a)	*125*	*9*	*–*	*–*	*–*		*–*	*–*	*–*	*–*	*–*	*Air Conditioned*	*–*	*E*	*Private Office; Appr. Square*
2.	*Engineer's Area* (b)	*120*	*9*	*–*	*–*	*–*		*–*	*–*	*–*	*–*	*–*		*–*	*I*	*Semi-Private Space*
3.	*Secretary* (c)	*65*	*9*	*–*	*–*	*–*		*–*	*–*	*–*	*–*	*–*		*–*	*O.*	
4.	*Entrance Way*	*50*	*9*	*–*	*–*	*–*		*–*	*–*	*–*	*–*	*–*		*–*	*–*	
5.	*Files (5 Ltr. Files)*	*40*	*9*	*–*	*–*	*–*		*–*	*–*	*–*	*–*	*–*		*–*	*–*	
6.	*Duplicating Eqpt.*	*20*	*9*	*–*	*–*	*–*		*–*	*–*	*–*	*–*	*–*		*–*	*–*	
7.	*Storeroom* (d)	*80*	*9*	*–*	*–*	*–*		*–*	*–*	*–*	*–*	*–*		*–*	*–*	
8.																
9.																
10.																
11.																
12.																
13.																
14.																
15.																

(Sub-Activities or Areas)

Notation References:
a *Desk, Table, Display Case, Dictating Mach. on Stand, Ltr. File, 3 Chairs*
b *2 Tables, Bookcase, 2 Chairs*
c *Desk w. Typewriter Pullout, Dictating Mach. on Stand, Cabinet, Chair*
d *Table, Stand, 2 Stock Racks*

RICHARD MUTHER & ASSOCIATES – 150 No. ____ Activity ____ Sheet ____ of ____

FIG. 70. Activities, area, and features form. (From *Simplified Systematic Layout Planning*, Management and Industrial Research Publications, by permission of Richard Muther & Associates.)

The object is to place the activities with the highest proximity rating nearest to each other, and lower ratings farther away. When the best arrangement has been obtained, the required floor area for each activity is entered on the diagrams beside each circle. When this diagram is completed, it represents the theoretical ideal arrangement of the activities, without physical consideration of the actual space involved for each activity. When this is done correctly it represents the most important step in the whole procedure.

So far the relationship between the items that are the subjects of the layout and the space that they have to occupy have been considered; next the diagram is adjusted to form a suitable layout. This preliminary layout is drawn on a single sheet of graph paper, and the space required for each activity is blocked in, at the same time maintaining the proximity relationship established in step three. This layout may need some modifications to allow for various other factors, such as individual site considerations and management procedures.

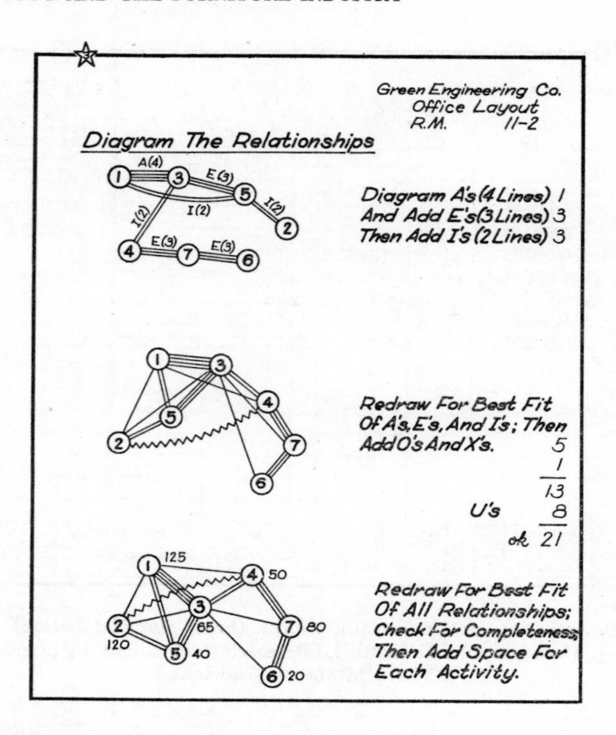

FIG. 71. Diagram of relationships. (From *Simplified Systematic Layout Planning*, Management and Industrial Research Publications, by permission of Richard Muther & Associates.)

Several layouts are usually made (Fig. 72) and the best of these is selected for further study. An evaluation procedure is used to assess the relative value of the different layouts, and the one with the highest rating is considered to be the best.

The final step is to redraw the layout to scale, at the same time identifying the areas and indicating any major features and equipment that may be an important consideration in the layout. This is then reviewed, and finally the plans are ready for the installation of the proposals (Figs. 73 and 74).

This simplified procedure is an approach to the solution of small layout problems and as such is appropriate for the investigation of the utilization and layout of office space.

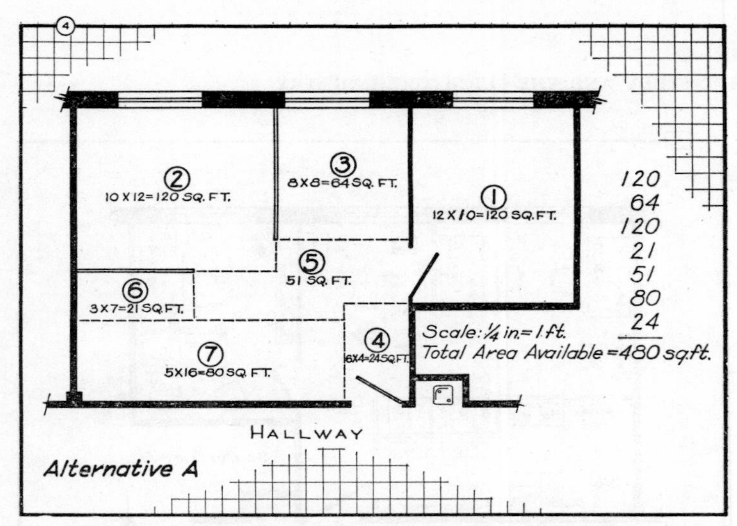

Fig. 72. Alternative solutions form. (From *Simplified Systematic Layout Planning*, Management and Industrial Research Publications, by permission of Richard Muther & Associates.)

5

EVALUATING ALTERNATIVES

Plant/Area Green Engineering Co. Project Office Layout Date 11-2

Description of Alternatives: A. Mr. Green in upper right

B. Mr. Green in upper left C.

D. E.

Weight set by Mr. Green and R.M. Ratings by R.M. Tally by R.M.

	FACTOR/CONSIDERATION	WT.	A	B	C	D	E	COMMENTS
			RATINGS AND WEIGHTED RATINGS					
1	Flexibility	8	E 24	I 16				
2	Convenience of Personnel	10	E 30	I 20				
3	Disruption, Interruption	6	E 18	O 6				
4	Cost of Partitions and Installation	6	I 12	I 12				
5	Best Fit in Space	4	I 8	O 4				
6	Use of Natural Light	5	E 15	I 10				
7	Movement of Eqpt. & Supplies	5	E 15	E 15				
8	Reception of Visitors	3	E 9	O 3				
9								
10								
11								
12								
13								
14								
	TOTALS		131	86				

NOTES

RICHARD MUTHER & ASSOCIATES – 171

Fig. 73. Evaluating alternatives form. (From *Simplified Systematic Layout Planning*, Management and Industrial Research Publications, by permission of Richard Muther & Associates.)

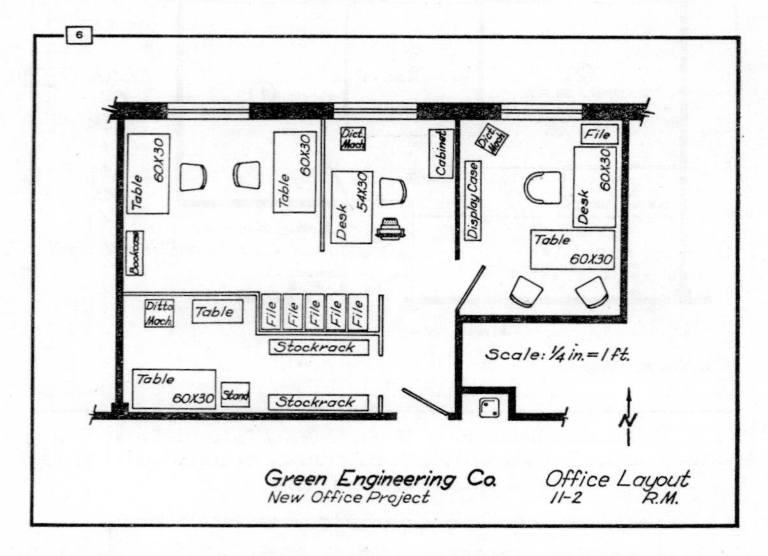

FIG. 74. Proposed office layout. (From *Simplified Systematic Layout Planning*, Management and Industrial Research Publications, by permission of Richard Muther & Associates.)

The Layout of Furniture Factories

It is a feature of most furniture factories that various shops could produce more if supplies from the preceding department were available; for example it frequently occurs that a machine shop is capable of producing more machined components if additional timber could be seasoned in the kilns. It is understandable that production bottlenecks occur, but they are invariably associated with certain shops and processes, such as kilns, sanding, and finishing processes, but they could occur in any shop in the factory. The difficulties encountered in the layout of a furniture factory are primarily due to a lack of appreciation of those factors that influence the layout of each of the shops of the factory, and the areas of process activity.

The timber yard, where the timber is stored and stacked for air drying, must be laid out for the particular type of handling equipment that has been chosen for use; this equipment is usually associated with certain space requirements necessary for its efficient operation. This is especially important with reference to the width of aisles between the stacks of timber and their height; these dimensions are selected according to the type of equipment used. When the method of handling to be employed in the timber yard has been selected, the area should be laid out for this. By comparing the space requirements of different equipment, it can be seen that each will require a different yard layout. It is uneconomical to operate the timber yard without the most suitable equipment, and with inadequate and poorly arranged yard space.

The drying kilns are another important aspect of the layout of a furniture factory. If timber drying kilns are to be included in the proposals for a plant layout, an appropriate allowance of space should be made for adequate kiln drying capacity. This is invariably underestimated, and where the possibilities of an increase in future production is concerned this may result in a production bottleneck.

It is sometimes convenient, in order to economize in the use of existing kiln space, to plan on the basis of high kiln bunks, the extra height produces extra kilned timber from the same ground space. The speeding up of the kiln drying schedule of operations is not the solution to this problem, as this only increases the timber waste from warping, checking, and case hardening. Sufficient kiln capacity should always be allowed so that the speeding up of the drying schedule will not be necessary. In old factories it is often difficult to obtain additional ground space suitable for the location of extra kilns. The following methods are often used in such circumstances to increase the output from existing kilns by reducing the duration of the kilning operation, or enabling a greater quantity of timber to be placed in the existing kiln.

(a) Air-dry timber longer in the yard before kilning.
(b) Laminate thick timber for a particular component instead of making if from one piece.
(c) Plane the kiln stickers or dividers to $\frac{3}{4}$ in. as this makes it possible to pile a few more layers of timber on the kiln load.
(d) Forced circulation in the kiln should be used as this quickens the drying process.
(e) Enough storage space should be provided so that the kilns may be emptied and refilled immediately the timber has completed its drying schedule. Kilns should never be used as a dry timber store for timber that has undergone the kilning process.
(f) Enough humidity should be used during the drying process to avoid case hardening, which seriously slows down the drying process.

Adequate space should be provided for the storage of kiln-dried timber, the amount of ground space to provide for this depending on the quantity of dried timber it is necessary to hold. It has been found correct practice to try and carry ten days' supply in dry storage. It is a good arrangement sometimes to equip this storage area with tracks to fit the kiln cars, so that the loads, immediately they are removed from the kiln, can be routed into this store without breaking down the load. It is desirable to have some heat and humidity in this store as in the shop.

In the rough mill and conversion shop it is often found that insufficient ripsaws have been provided to obtain the desired production. To overcome this deficiency it has been found impractical to have these machines working at maximum speed all the time. Fast-feed ripsaws, however, can be introduced to obtain the required production, if it is not found appropriate due to lack of floor space to have extra rip sawing machines in the proposed layout.

The layout of the rough mill and conversion shop will depend on the sequence and details of the process selected for operation in this shop. The selection of particular features of the process will be influenced by the type of timber that is used, the form in which it is received, and the kind of furniture produced. It may be considered necessary to rough plane timber before it is crosscut or ripped, this often being necessary on certain kinds of timber in order to detect the flaws that are usually present so that maximum utilization of a unit quantity is obtained. If this is required is it to be the first operation to come subsequent to crosscutting and ripping? Should the timber be surfaced or faced flat before rough planing? Should the crosscutting operation take place first or the ripping operation? Should one kind or class of timber be routed one way and another in a different direction? Where solid timber construction is used in the manufacture of a furniture product, will this timber be glued up directly from a straight line ripsaw, or will joints be prepared on an automatic glue jointer, or alternative equipment? It may be that gang ripsaws could be used to advantage; if this should be the case it must be remembered that they can be purchased in various forms, each requiring a different amount of floor area. How many different lengths and widths are to be cut at the same time on the crosscut and the ripsaws? Will the rough mill offcuts and scrap be processed by a reclaiming section, or put through a chopper to reduce it to a form that is more easily transported to the furnace?

The answers to all the questions mentioned above will influence the nature of the proposals made for the layout of the rough mill, and if a conveyor is not a feature of these proposals, it is essential to have adequate delay areas between the operations where loads of timber and work in progress may be located. The removal of scrap from the floor area should also not be overlooked, as scrap and offcuts have a tendency to collect in large quantities quickly, due to the speed of the process, and work is generally done more efficiently where scrap is absent.

High-production machines with a fast rate of feed will provide more output per square foot of floor space, at a lower labour cost, than slower equipment, but it has been found that a suitable production control system is required to achieve the desired economies.

The edge gluing shop, where small widths of timber are made up into wide boards, should be given careful consideration if this process is to be part of the manufacturing sequence. The appropriate gluing process that is to be used should be carefully considered, as there are various processes from which to choose, and each requires a different floor area for its operation. What kind of glue should be used? Should the gluing process require heat? The glue room must be as self-contained as possible for easy heating. The type of clamping equipment that is installed will influence space requirements in this area. If a problem should arise in connection with floor space for equipment, and the provision of delay areas, consideration should be given to the methods of heating used for curing and setting glues and adhesives. It should also be emphasized that what ever particular process is operated, labour costs and quality control are important factors in this department.

When considering the layout of a machine shop, adequate space should be allowed for a delay area to accommodate work in progress and material coming from the rough mill and the gluing shop. It is important to see that stock from the gluing shop is held for a sufficient period of time to reduce the possibility of sunken joints after planing.

The movement of timber from the rough mill and the gluing shop into the machine shop will probably not synchronize with the speed at which the quantities are required for routing to the shop. To reduce the problems that are likely to occur from this a suitable production control system will help to overcome the difficulties. In certain circumstances it is often found convenient to have floor space available to hold timber so that it can be organized into economical batches for the machining process.

When woodworking machinery is arranged in a proposed layout, it is essential to see that each item of equipment is placed in the available floor area to the best advantage. The exact position for each machine will be dependent on a number of considerations, among which will be the following:

The type of machine.
The appropriate position of a machine relative to walls, aisles, and the considerations of safety and convenience.
The direction from which the light will come relative to machine and the operator.
The working area of the machine such as the distance from the outfeed and infeed tables, and clearance either side of the machine to allow for the lengths of timber that will be processed.

If this information is tabulated for each machine, it can be seen that each has a different floor space requirement and this consideration may be further influenced by the type of work that is being done, and the quality of the lighting in the shop.

Throughout the machine shop some delay areas will be required at convenient locations, but the size of these should be carefully calculated as too much floor space can easily be allocated for this purpose. The production in the machine shop always has a tendency of not running smoothly even in the most well-organized factories. As congestion occurs as a result of this, hold-ups will occur; for this reason delay areas will be required if some machines are not to be idle.

It is an important rule and necessary condition for the successful organization of an assembly shop to see that all components are available before the assembly process is commenced. If the machine shop for some reason has not produced all the parts required, assembly cannot commence. It is important to have adequate space for storing parts until the last item has been made and assembly can commence. It is not good practice or convenient to have these components in delay areas in the assembly shop. Many factories make use of parts stores as a solution to this problem, and it is the most satisfactory answer particularly if only a small batch of a product is assembled at any one time. It should be remembered, however, that the storing of components in a store is an expensive procedure, but it is preferable if floor space for storage in the assembly shop is not available. Considerable labour time can be consumed in placing components into racks and removing them again, and each time the particular component is handled it is exposed to the possibility of receiving dents, scratches, or other forms of damage. It is sometimes convenient to plan for various sub-assemblies proceeding to a final assembly, but in doing this the process time must be carefully considered, as the adhesive has to be given time to set before the sub-assembly or assembly is subsequently handled. To do this requires additional floor space, but it is an advantage if radio frequency and low voltage heating methods can reduce this, and enable sub-assemblies or assemblies to be immediately available for routing to the next operation.

Before making a layout of an assembly shop, the possibilities of introducing assembly aids should be considered, as for most assembly problems there is the one best method and this is invariably quite often associated with the use of specialized assembly aids.

In considering floor space requirements for the treatment of the final assembly, it is essential to remember that the important tasks in the assembly shop are sanding, cleaning up, and the preparation of the surface for finishing. It has been found to be good practice to machine sand the show wood or exposed parts before they are assembled, but it is appreciated that on some furniture constructions a sanding operation after assembly is necessary. Caution should be exercised in the choice of the method of sanding and cleaning up, as this can result in a considerable waste of process time if the right method is not selected, and a greater area of floor space will have to be allowed.

It is essential to see that parts are assembled and routed to the finishing shop as quickly as possible, to avoid any possibility of the grain on the wood surface rising before the finish has been applied. A day or two will be sufficient for this but components should never be sanded weeks ahead of the finishing process, as the labour time spent in this sanding activity will be wasted.

For the purpose of obtaining an efficient assembly shop layout the sanding process should be situated between the parts store and the assembly shop. Extra storage space should not be provided in the assembly shop, as any of this floor area that is unused will only fill up with rejects, scrap, and odds and ends, and not only be a waste of floor space but complicate the maintenance of order and tidiness.

The controlling consideration in preparing proposals for the layout of a finishing shop is the process time. All the elements of the finishing process, such as staining, filling, and lacquers, must have the required time to dry before the item proceeds to the next operation. To disregard this factor will only cause difficulties with the maintenance of quality standards and rework costs.

The influence and merits of the different finishing processes, as far as they affect the utilization of floor space, should be considered before proceeding to a draft of the layout proposals. Dipping of furniture components can often reduce the amount of finishing material used, without increasing in any way the labour costs or floor space requirements.

If forced drying methods are incorporated in the proposals, this will reduce to a minimum the amount of floor space that is required for items of furniture that cannot be routed to the next process until the surface finish from a particular stage of the process has been dried.

In those areas where the activities of packing, warehousing, and the loading of the vans take place, the conditions are very much alike in most industries. The aspect of the activities that has to be controlled in these locations is the labour, as much of this is occupied in handling. The floor space required in this area will depend on the total number of items that are to be available in store, and the total number of different items that are to be stocked. Different items should not be mixed in the same pile or location, as this practice invariably leads to the rehandling of the items, extra labour cost, and the possibility of damage to the particular items themselves.

Loading space should be set aside where van loads can be assembled prior to loading on a van; this will enable a complete van to be loaded at once. This space for the collection and preparation of the loads should be reasonably near the loading point or truck ramp.

In old factory buildings, if such a shop is to be the subject of a reorganization it may have an adequate total floor area, but this, due to the nature of the building, may be poorly arranged. In such situations the introduction of fast-feed, high-production machines will eliminate any incidence of conegstion in the rough mill and machine shop. Such machines will produce as much as two or three old-fashioned ones.

Another method for relieving congestion is to consider the introduction of an appropriate and carefully considered production control system, which should be operated by a competent clerk with the willing cooperation of all factory personnel. This interest and participation is important if it is to achieve what it sets out to do. Too much timber and too many components are frequently seen to be in process, and when this does not flow through the factory fast enough, it can take up much needed floor space and becomes uneconomical.

Those areas of the factory where this is likely to occur should be occasionally checked and the presence of all materials in delay should be questioned. If stillage loads of timber and parts have a heavy layer of dust on top of them, it can be inferred that the work in progress is not flowing through the shops in the correct manner. Over-runs from the rough mill should never be allowed to accumulate unused for too long, and if possible should always be prevented, but if they occur the timber should be reintroduced into the rough mill to be recut for current production, or the excess components that are produced as a result of an over-run should be accepted into the parts store.

Scrap and off-cuts should also not be allowed to accumulate in the rough mill, but should be either treated similarly to over-runs and recut or burnt as fuel depending on the value of the scrap. Many well-organized rough mills allocate floor space for reworking scrap. All that is required to organize a reclaiming section of this kind is a dimension saw bench, a ripsaw bench, and a thickness planer. Cutting lists are provided for standard part sizes of short or narrow kind, or for parts that permit sound defects, and the duty of the reclaim operator will be to get the longest and widest component within the range of standard sizes given from the scrap. This reclaiming section will occupy valuable floor space but if it is correctly operated it will considerably reduce timber waste in these circumstances.

Selected References and Suggestions for Further Reading

IMMER, J. R., *Layout Planning Techniques*, McGraw-Hill, London and New York.

MALLICK, R. W. and GAUDREAU, A. T., *Plant Layout: Planning and Practice*, John Wiley, London and New York.

MUTHER, R., *Practical Plant Layout*, McGraw-Hill, London and New York.

MUTHER, R., *Systematic Layout Planning*, Industrial Education Institute, Boston, Mass.; Industrial Education International, London.

MUTHER, R. and WHEELER, J. D., *Simplified Systematic Layout Planning*, Management and Research Publications, Kansas City, Missouri; Industrial Education International, London.

ROBICHAUD, B., *Selecting Planning and Managing Office Space*, McGraw-Hill, London and New York.

CHAPTER 11

Materials Handling Analysis

THE study of materials handling is concerned with the movement of materials throughout an organization and the way in which this is done. This movement not only includes the handling of finished products, sub-assemblies, and components but also paper controls and office paper-work. It should be realized that paper-work also has to be obtained and carried, and the effect of this on the efficiency of production is often forgotten in materials handling studies.

Materials handling in an industrial concern is the movement of materials from the supplier to the organizations stores, then through the different manufacturing processes for conversion into the finished products, and then to the warehouse where the products remain until they are required for dispatch to the customer. However, the investigation of materials handling is not confined only to the process and production aspects of the organization or the confines of the factory itself.

The study of materials handling provides one of the biggest single opportunities for increasing production and reducing overall costs that is available to the methods analyst. The following figures support this and indicate its importance and the economies that can be made. Approximately 90 per cent of all manufacturing time is spent in handling or holding materials and only 10 per cent in actual processing. In a materials handling study carried out by the author in an assembly shop of a furniture factory, three-fifths of the operator's time was consumed in fetching and carrying and two-fifths in actual production. The assembly shop had all the outward appearance of being highly productive and efficient, but the management in this particular factory was paying five days' wages for two days' actual productive work.

Other figures relating to industry generally give some further indication of the need for the study of materials handling.

For every ton of finished products dispatched, approximately 50 tons of material is handled in the course of their manufacture. The cost of handling or holding materials in temporary storage is never less than 15 per cent and in some instances as high as 85 per cent of total production costs, most of which is all too frequently classified and obscured or lost under such headings as "Overheads", "Indirect labour", or "General Plant and Equipment". The average is estimated to be about 25 per cent.

The reported lost time resulting from accidents during handling or carrying articles used in the course of manufacture amounts to 28 per cent of the total. This figure excludes accidents resulting from power-driven handling machines, and some indication of the loss to industry may be obtained from the estimate that industrial accidents cost the United Kingdom approximately £70 million a year.

These figures indicate the magnitude of the possible savings that could be obtained by improving materials handling, but it is to be recognized that these will vary according to the particular industry examined.

The purpose and objectives of the study of materials handling may be defined as follows. To eliminate handling altogether if possible, or reduce its occurrence to a minimum. To reduce the time spent in handling and increase the better utilization of transport equipment, and the services of labour. To make the operation of stores more efficient by reducing storage areas, improving the capacity of existing space, and the methods of storing and stacking of materials. To increase productivity by better movement of materials between production processes and departments, reduce overall production time, and increase the utilization of plant and equipment. To reduce the damage to materials, components, and products, and the incidence of accidents that occur as a result of materials handling. To improve the working conditions of factory personnel by reducing the incidence of operator fatigue and improve the use of skilled workers.

Poor handling effectiveness is by no means unrecognizable as it may be indicated by the following symptoms, if the cause is not due to other factors such as the shortcomings of management or production control.

When departments are crowded with materials or work in progress, aisles are congested, and movement is difficult. When stores are crowded and overhead space is unused. When materials, components, or articles are lost or damaged, or collection in delay areas is uncontrolled. When accidents, incurred through handling, are frequent. When complaints of late or non-delivery are frequently received from customers, departmental managers, or supervision. When the paperwork associated with materials handling is complicated and inconvenient. When skilled operators are employed in handling.

A number of factors have to be considered in the process of studying the materials handling in a factory; this is done in order to simplify the approach to the problem. When commencing the study, the materials handling is divided into three basic divisions of activity.

(i) Handling associated with the receipt, storage, and issue of incoming materials.
(ii) Handling during the process of manufacture.
(iii) Handling associated with the packaging, storage, and dispatch of the product.

These divisions follow the normal costing practice of dividing the organization into supply and stores, production, and distribution, for costing purposes. Cost figures alone will in no way solve a materials handling problem, but they will accentuate the items of major expenditure, and indicate where improved control is necessary, and where the greatest returns are likely to be obtained from a proposed materials handling study.

These divisions of handling activity are made for the convenience of the investigator, because each of the categories concerns itself with different objectives. For example the first concerns itself with how, and by what means, materials are handled from the supplier of the materials to the factory, in what quantity they arrive, and in what units or containers. The objective to be obtained by a study in this area of handling is to see that the materials arrive and go to the first process, with the minimum of preparation and handling. This is an area of materials handling that is not only likely to be influenced by detailed method study, but also with aspects of purchasing procedure, and stock and store control. The suitability of the packaging and the manner in which the materials arrive at the factory, will influence the quality of the handling up to the first process. The form in which the materials arrive at the factory may demand a large number of handling operations which could be reduced if the materials were delivered in another form. The materials may require inconvenient and time-consuming operations of unpacking before they are available for the manufacturing process.

The object to be achieved in the second division of handling is to obtain a minimum amount of materials handling from the first to the last process.

An investigation in this area of application will be concerned with the provision of suitable delay areas for work or materials in process at appropriate locations throughout the production sequence. The provision of suitable materials handling equipment, which may range from the consideration of hand-operated trucks or trolleys, transfer machines, or conveyor systems. A review of those features of the factory layout that permit the best possible use of the handling system selected for use.

The third division of a factories handling activity is concerned with the methods whereby the finished products get to the customer. As this can be an extremely expensive activity the methods selected for achieving this purpose should be such that the handling is reduced to a minimum. The solution to problems of this kind may require the co-operation of customers, to determine the most appropriate form the proposed methods should take.

Some general considerations which are useful to bear in mind when making a study of handling problems are as follows.

Always attempt to keep materials as close to the operator as possible, and at the same height at which they are to be worked upon. Never have materials placed on the floor, always on a pallet or platform, for when movement is required they will not have to be picked up individually. If materials are placed on the floor, they have a tendency to remain there and accumulate, instead of moving through the process. Always attempt to keep the distance over which the handling is to take place as short as possible. Always attempt to use gravity, at every possible occasion, to let materials roll or slide down chutes to the next operation or work station, instead of pushing or carrying them. Always handle materials or components in bulk over distance instead of handling small quantities or one at a time. A sufficient number of pallets, stillages, or platforms should always be available in suitable locations adjacent to the work areas, so that the operator is never without one and in order that he will always be able to place a finished product or component on the empty stillage after work has been performed on it. When the stillage is found to contain the appropriate quantity of products or a unit load, it is then taken to the next operation. Skilled operators should not be allowed to do their own servicing, as their efforts and skills are required for production, any handling that is required should be done by special service men. Gangways and aisles should always be kept clear, so that materials may be moved by a recognized route without hindrance or obstruction. If expensive handling equipment has been purchased, its utilization should not be reduced by its inability to move about the shop or factory area.

The procedure for conducting a materials handling study conforms to the accepted method study procedure. The area for investigation having been carefully selected, flow process charts are prepared, and these may be supplemented by information obtained as a result of activity sampling studies, if this is considered necessary to determine the percentage time consumed in undesirable handling activities. In addition, where it is required to show the relationship of the handling between departments, a travel chart or string diagrams may be constructed to indicate this, according to requirements.

When the necessary information has been collected it is often found convenient to present it in a form suitable for analysis. The manner in which this is done is shown in Fig. 75, and is called a materials handling study chart. This is constructed for each component of the product which consists of the subject of the materials handling study. It is a graphic form of presenting the sequence of the activities associated with the movement of materials in a given area. It provides a description of the handling activities, the number of men required to perform the handling, the distance moved in feet by the material, the type of equipment used to perform this handling, if any is used, and the load capacity of the equipment in pounds. The characteristics of the load, in terms of shape, length, width, and height, are also recorded on this form, together with the number of units, components, or products in the load. The weight of the load is also indicated, together with the frequency with which the particular handling operation occurs, and its cost per year in pence.

Some of the information entered on this form is obtained from plant layout drawings, flow process charts, and string diagrams, and this is often checked by visual observation. Additional data for the other entries, relating to the nature of the materials handling equipment used, and the personnel employed in using it, are collected at the same time. This information is then subjected to the method study procedure of critical analysis and an improved handling method is developed subsequent to this, with due regard to the considerations of costs. In connection with this it is to be remembered that the solution of a materials handling problem is obtained largely as a result of critically examining the present method and not by the purchase of proprietary handling equipment.

Considerable savings can be obtained by the careful study of the handling of materials, but to achieve these savings and a satisfactory solution to a particular problem, a systematic approach to the problem is necessary. Method study provides the means of obtaining this approach. Inevitably

Component *DRAW SLIPS* **MATERIALS HANDLING CHART**

Description of activity	○ □ ⇨ D ▽	No. of men reqd.	Dist. moved (ft.)	Time reqd. (min)	Type of equipment used	Load capacity of equipt. (lbs)	Load characteristics				No. of units in load	Wght of load (lbs)	Frequency	Cost/ annum in pence
							Shape	lgth.	wdth.	hgth.				
Move from S. L. E. to T. Store	1	1	8	0·75	Collins pallet truck	1120	Cradle	3'6"	2'6"	5'	1500	312	30	14·4
Temporary storage	1													
Move to 4 Cutter	2	1	25	1·3	Collins pallet truck	1120	Cradle	3'6"	2'6"	5'	1500	312	30	25·8
Move to Temp. storage	3	1	18	1	Collins pallet truck	1120	Cradle	3'6"	2'6"	5'	1500	312	30	19·3
Temporary storage	2													
Move to dimn. saw	4	1	198	7	Collins pallet truck	1120	Cradle	3'6"	2'6"	5'	1500	312	30	135
Tie in bundles	1	1			Manual						100	21	30	
Move from shop	5	1	60	2·5	Collins pallet truck	1120	Cradle	3'6"	2'6"	5'	15 bundles	312	30	48

Total £1. 0s. 2½d.

FIG. 75. Materials handling study chart.

during the development of proposed handling methods, the question of the selection of the most suitable equipment arises. But as the information about most of the various kinds of equipment is readily available to the investigator, this can easily be reviewed. The selection of suitable equipment should be done with due regard to the functional requirements of such equipment and the overall cost as this in certain circumstances may include the consideration of maintenance costs as well as the purchase price.

The satisfactory solution to most materials handling problems is often of a kind that requires little or no capital expenditure; it is also often of a kind that a person with the right attitude of mind can develop for himself. The furniture industry is rich in examples of such solutions, which range over the whole of the handling activity associated with the processes. However, the importance of materials handling in the furniture industry has generally not been fully appreciated. When the time usually spent in handling a piece of timber during its conversion into a furniture component is considered and compared with the process time, it is immediately apparent that time spent in handling is the greater item. In most conventional wood machining operations the time spent in actually machining the wood is small, when compared with the time spent in handling and positioning the part. In such operations it can be easily seen that the cutting time is between 20 and 30 per cent of the total operation cycle time. Whereas in the engineering industry the actual cutting of the metal takes much longer than the time taken to handle it.

Materials handling is an important consideration in the furniture industry, because materials and products are large and bulky and the individual operations are performed at a fast pace, for example a machine operator will often process many kiln car loads of timber in one day.

In considering the possibilities of reducing the incidence of materials handling throughout the furniture factory, the problem has to be examined in relation to the various process areas as each has certain considerations that require a different approach either because of the nature of the process or the items that have to be handled.

In the timber yard where the cost of handling can frequently be excessive, the use of the "package" method of handling is often found to reduce this considerably, but it is not always possible to operate this method. This procedure consists in unloading the timber on its arrival at the factory by means of a fork-lift truck in loads of standard width and height, the timber having been prepared in this form by the supplier when loading his lorry. If a sufficient quantity of timber is handled in this manner a fork-lift truck can be justified. Handling timber in this manner enables the supplier's lorry to be unloaded quickly, and only the operator of the fork-lift need be required for this operation. If the timber is to be kiln dried, each board can be stock-piled immediately it is unloaded from the supplier's lorry into a "package" and thus made up into a kiln bunk load on delivery. Each package of this kind is one-third of the height of a standard kiln compartment. With a simple elevating fork-lift truck, these packages can be stacked in the timber yard for air drying until required for kilning. Subsequently a fork-lift truck can take these packages from the timber yard and make them up into a kiln load by placing one on top of the other. If this handling procedure is followed correctly, each board is handled only once, namely when it is stock-piled into a kiln package.

If it is decided that a fork-lift should not be used in the timber yard, the excessive handling occasioned by activity in this area of the manufacturing process can still be avoided by stock-piling kiln loads on roller kiln trucks at the point of unloading from the timber supplier's truck, and these can then be moved to the storage area in the timber yard. The unloading point, storage area, and drying kilns can be served by one or more transfer cars where circumstances are appropriate.

When these loads are required for the rough mill, they should enter the shop and be positioned for preference on a timber lift which will enable the top layer of the timber to be always at a convenient height for the cross-cut saw operator and his assistant. When the load of timber has been converted, the truck can be returned to the yard with the stickers or dividers.

It is possible to reduce the amount of materials handling at the rough cross-cut sawing operation by giving the operator a cutting order for a diversity of lengths, so that random lengths or offcuts need not be laid back for later rework.

As the production in the rough mill is usually uniform in its sequence, handling can be done with connecting slides or conveyors from one machine to another. Such arrangements are quite common even with certain of the conventional machines.

When arrangements such as this are considered, it should be remembered that a proportion of the timber coming off a machine has defects in it, and this is the time to put aside such defective parts before more expensive machining operations are performed on them and while they are still in a form that can be reclaimed. A correctly trained off-bearer is primarily an inspector, his materials handling function being a minor activity and incidental to that of inspection.

Materials handling problems are easier to solve in the rough mill than in the machine shop, because the route taken by the timber from one machine to the next is fairly uniform. The timber can be handled from one operator to another by various pieces of equipment whose selection will depend on the product being made and the form of the material from which it is cut.

In the machine shop, in order to reduce the materials handling to a minimum, the distance between the delay areas and the individual machines should be as small as possible. The operation area for each machine should include sufficient space for the location of at least two stillages of work in progress depending on the machine speed of processing, in order that these may be positioned as near as possible to the point of processing. An adequate delay area near each group of machines should be arranged so that individual operators know where their next job can be found, and where their finished work has to go. It is sometimes convenient to have a hand-operated trolley for the movement of stillages to and from these work areas in a central position to a group of machines or operators, so that when a worker in such a group wishes to remove or obtain a stillage of material, the trolley will always be available. When an arrangement of this kind has been made it is often found convenient to lay down a rule that no one other than members of the group will use this trolley. In order that the trolley may be identified with the particular group, it is often painted a distinctive colour to indicate this.

In areas of the country where the furniture factory has difficulty in obtaining sufficient labourers, and where the number that would be required to service the operators would be excessive due to the speed of processing, it is often more convenient to have operators doing their own servicing where the methods introduced reduce this handling to a minimum.

Where suitable opportunities present themselves, individual machines should be joined by transfer machines or similar equipment. The furniture industry has numerous process situations where this has been done most effectively.

On some machines it is sometimes more economical to reduce the output from a machine and let one operator run it, than to increase the output and have two operators work it. Alternatively hopper feeds and mechanical off-bearers can often increase the output from one operator, without either reducing the processing speed of the machine or the need for extra handling.

When organizing a machine operation without an off-bearer or helper, on equipment that usually demands one, the reduction in output will mean that less is produced but the labour costs will be lower, and as production with a helper is nowhere double that of a single operator, working with a hopper feed and special off-bearing equipment has its advantages. This type of equipment is readily available for this purpose, as are such attachments as live rolls, or conveyor belts, which can be positioned at the outfeed of a machine so that as soon as the component is machined it will fall on to the roll or belt and be carried away faster than a helper could remove it.

The possibilities of machining in multiple, or of performing a series of operations simultaneously, should be considered. It is also possible sometimes to introduce an additional operation and in so doing to double or treble the output of components from an operation sequence, and at the same time eliminate the attendant materials handling. In most machine shops it is not practical to install any extensive form of conveyor between machines, as the flow of materials from one machine to another may not adhere to a standard sequence.

Handling in the parts store can be considerable because of the labour that is occupied in putting components into racks and removing them for issue to the assembly shop, but although this can be done in conjunction with an inspection activity, this is usually unnecessary if correct quality control procedures are operated in the machine shop. Further, each time components are handled in this location they are subject to being dented, scratched, or otherwise damaged; these dents and scratches must be removed and sanded out in the assembly shop with a further waste of labour and an increase in handling.

The ideal procedure for reducing the handling in the parts store to a minimum is to leave the components on the stillages or pallets just as they leave the last machine operation, but this requires a large amount of floor space. But if the principle of unit loads or pallets containing a standard quantity of components is introduced this can relieve this condition. However, if space is a critical consideration stake-type pallets can be used so that these can be stacked three or four high by means of pedestrian-type elevating fork trucks, and by this method a component put down at the last machine operation is not handled singly again until it is required at the assembly operation.

Materials handling in the assembly shop is a subject that is broad in its ramifications. The solution of most materials handling problems in this shop where conveyor systems and lift trucks are introduced has been well covered in various publications and literature, but the basic consideration of those factors that influence the actual picking up and putting down of the material during the course of the rapid and accurate assembly of parts has not been fully appreciated.

Most furniture assembly operations lend themselves to conveyorized operation, and generally for any one particular assembly problem there is the one best conveyor solution. However, there are various methods of assembly, in some the whole product can be assembled conveniently in one operation, whereas in others the complete job is divided into a number of sub-assembly operations, each of these having different process advantages and demanding various amounts of materials handling.

When considering the reduction of materials handling in assembly work, the important considerations are whether it is necessary to place the assembly or sub-assembly in a clamp for pressing and squaring up or whether the assembly operation can be completed without having to remove the assembly from the clamp, whether the assembly is of sufficient strength to remove it from the clamp immediately the assembly operation is completed, and if this is done to be able to ensure that it will remain square until the adhesive sets. An operator who has to contend with all these considerations, and still keeps the handling to a minimum, reduces the incidence of damage, and sees that the assemblies are not out of square, has to possess considerable skill.

Numerous methods are used to overcome these difficulties and reduce the necessity for control and handling. The appropriate method of furniture construction is selected for the particular process that it is intended to operate, so that ease of assembly is obtained and the necessity for making right- and left-hand components is obviated. This practice simplifies not only the supply of components but also the handling of these parts and the reduction of over or under runs.

A number of methods have been conveniently used for getting the components to the point of assembly; among these may be mentioned the use of hopper feed systems which have sometimes been used in conjunction with glue applicators so that the adhesive may be applied in the right quantity at the right place on being removed from the hopper. This method of glue application ensures that the surface of the components will not be smeared by the glue other than in the appropriate place, thus eliminating the cleaning-up process that is usually present in most assembly work and which can involve considerable handling. Previously the practice of glue application has always been to apply the adhesive with either a brush or round stick but with this method the correct quantity of glue was not always applied and it was impossible to maintain a proper control of the glue application. The introduction of glue applicators has eliminated these problems for all types of assembly work and with little skill the operator is able to apply correctly the right amount of glue to the assembly. Where dowel construction is used a dowel driver and gluer may be introduced to eliminate this handling but it should be remembered that the successful operation of this type of equipment in the assembly process depends upon a strict control being exercised of the quality and accuracy of the machine borings. If the quality of the machinery can be controlled within appropriate limits of accuracy, automatic furniture assembly methods can conveniently be used in certain operations where constructional methods allow this, and the introduction of such methods will further reduce the incidence of materials handling associated with the assembly process.

Materials handling in the finishing shop can represent a considerable percentage of total labour time if measures are not taken to reduce it to a minimum. Much can be done to reduce this handling, but any improvements in methods that are introduced have been found to depend on a detailed appreciation of the particular features of the finishing process at the time of the investigation. For instance where there is a considerable amount of handling associated with the sanding process, subsequent to staining, and this happens to be a critical factor, it is profitable to introduce non-graining raising stains as an alternative to the conventional stains, for by this means the complete sanding process is eliminated. Another example, where a dulling process requires a large labour force with pumice powder, linseed oil, and brushes, and considerable handling of the furniture product, this can be eliminated by the application of the dulling process or matt surface in the final coat of spray finish.

If the ideal is to be considered it should be remembered that furniture finishing operations are the easiest to conveyorize and one of the most profitable, but this can only be done after detailed method study. High-speed furniture finishing with materials handling reduced to a minimum can only be met by the installation of a conveyorized system in conjunction with a forced drying system, in order that the process times can be accurately controlled. The introduction of such an installation invariably doubles the output almost immediately without any increase in labour cost, or the use of extra floor space. The installation can also be designed to include all the aspects of the finishing process.

Where such methods are installed labour is not used in moving items around, and it is no longer necessary for spray operators to lift these itemst on and off the turn-tables to apply the finish. The conveyor arrangemen is frequently devised so that a certain degree of flexibility is achieved, and subsequent modifications may be introduced to satisfy new and increased production requirements. This is possible without excessive expenditure, but it should be remembered that floor space should be provided near the productive sections of the conveyor in order that auxiliary or special equipment, which may be required in the future as a result of such modifications, may be positioned.

Any system that is introduced to eliminate the materials handling should be able to accommodate various finishing schedules without the necessity for any major readjustment of the system, and be flexible enough to handle all kinds of furniture that may come within a reasonable product range. This is necessary in order that changes may be made from the smallest to the largest item without difficulty.

The main feature of a conveyorized system is that there is a continuous performance of all the operations, but it should be expected that furniture items may have to be removed for repair operations.

Successful solutions to materials handling problems in the furniture industry have been those where the opportunities afforded by a change in the process, construction, or design of the furniture product, have been appreciated. But in the development of proposed methods of handling it is an advantage to think of the ideal solution and then modify this according to circumstances or resources.

Selected References and Suggestions for Further Reading

IMMER, J. R., *Materials Handling*, McGraw-Hill, London and New York.

GILMOUR-BROWN, A., *Materials Handling in the Furniture Industry, Method Study*, Report No. 1, Furniture Development Council, Stevenage, Hertfordshire, England.

CHAPTER 12

Control and Systems Analysis

THE remaining area of method study application that has to be discussed is that of the analysis of production control procedures and systems. The term "production" is used here to mean the creation of goods or services whether in the factory or the office.

It has been understood for some time that the only sound basis for a control system is adequate method study, as more systems have failed as a result of disregarding this factor than for any other reason.

Formerly, management thought that the solution to most of the problems of production control was the introduction of a proprietary system into the factory or office. After considerable sums of money had been spent on such systems, it was found that they were not exercising the degree of control that it was suggested they could achieve. Experiences of this kind have made management realize the truth of the rule, that production control procedures, to be successful, must be tailored to the requirements of the individual productive unit.

Often in their attempts to discover the reasons for the failure of the proprietary system, management found that personnel in the factory had been using alternative systems of their own creation and completely disregarding the official system. Frequently also they discovered to their mortification that the unofficial system was successful and a simpler procedure. As a result of numerous examples and case studies of this kind, it has been realized that the participation of and willing acceptance of a system by all personnel is more important than the features of the system itself. A fact that the method study practitioner has considered self-evident in connection with the development and installation of all proposed methods.

Some form of control is obviously necessary in most production activities, whether these activities are concerned with products, services, or the processing of paper-work, in order to prevent the use of methods that leave the efficiency of production to chance. This element of control is usually made by watching for departures from correct standards and procedures after the appropriate standards have been determined by method study for the work concerned.

A control procedure enables a person responsible for an activity to be able to exercise the necessary control over it, without having to carry everything in his head, or have recourse only to the medium of verbal instructions. Although in the smaller organization it has been customary to control in this manner, it has been found that it places too much of a physical burden on the individual responsible for this control, particularly if he was a productive worker as well.

There are, of course, many other reasons why a production control system is desirable. Amongst some of these can be considered the fact that delivery dates can be carefully calculated, not only from one section of the factory to another but from the factory to the customer, and the fact that supervision in charge of the actual processes are able to obtain a clear understanding of the objectives required to carry out this production. Information is available on which to determine the quantities of materials required by production, and a calculation of the storage requirements. These data can contribute to the best use of available resources of production, whether these are machinery and equipment, floor space, or labour, to increase the productivity of the factory.

The need for an adequate production control system is invariably indicated by a number of common symptoms, such as the inability to quote delivery dates either to the customer or to the various shops in the factory, or where delivery dates are quoted, they are out of all proportion to the work content of the product. Arrears in delivery invariably indicate a lack of control, as well as certain inefficiences in the shops. These are usually due to the fact that supervision has difficulty in controlling production in their departments for various common reasons, and the fact that dispatch and sales are always wanting the particular item that the shop is not producing. Other factors that indicate a need for an investigation into present control procedures is apparent when the following symptoms cannot be traced to other areas of method study application. Such features as bottlenecks in production, too much work in progress, variations in quality, incidence of waiting time, excessive overtime, delivery dates not adherred to, high rejection rates at inspection, and waste of materials all indicate that the quality of the control procedure leaves much to be desired.

Where a good system has been introduced it will reduce the frequency with which these symptoms occur, if not eliminate them entirely. The result will be greater speed of production throughout the factory, no disorganization, or financial loss. However, it should be appreciated that whatever the merits of a system may be, its ultimate success will be influenced largely by the quality of the personnel operating it, and the measure of participation shown by all concerned in operating the system. If this is obtained, however, a production control system will reduce the indirect labour associated with materials handling, the space required, particularly storage space both on the shop floor and in efficient stores, and will reduce the capital tied up in such stores. It will also produce an orderliness which will have a favourable effect on employee relationships. Where, in order to save floor space, high production machines are installed, these will be operated to the best advantage if a suitable control system is introduced, otherwise too high a proportion of the machine time will be spent in set-up activity or idleness.

The purpose of a production control system is to enable the manufacturing methods and procedures, determined and installed with the aid of method study, to be operated and maintained correctly. A system is not a "cure all" and the introduction of any system is not necessarily going to solve production problems, any more than the introduction of a quality control system, based upon appropriate procedures of inspection, is going to inspect quality into a product. But however good a proposed system may be considered it will prove a failure if the willing participation of personnel, previously mentioned, is not obtained.

A system suitable for one type of production is not necessarily suitable for another, and this fact should always be recognized, as well as the point that a system is usually tailored to the production and organization into which it is to be introduced. That is why, when a control system operating successfully in another factory is copied in detail and installed in another, it is seldom the answer to the problem.

However, within the limits of a proposed system it may be found that certain standard or proprietary-type control procedures are suitable, but method study should be used to evaluate their worth in the given situation and determine in what circumstances they could be applicable but only after the basic requirements of the proposed system have been determined. The investigator who is likely to be associated with this area of method study application should make himself familiar with these various standard aids and systems.

Management, in order to determine the kind of control system that would be appropriate in a given situation, has recourse to the services of the methods investigator, because he has been trained in the procedures of investigation and can present in a convenient manner the existing method of control for examination with respect to the desired controls, what clerical personnel will be required, and in what manner it would be most convenient to achieve the requirements. The results obtained from this examination will form the basis of the proposals for an improved procedure.

Management also found that in order to determine the most appropriate control system to use in a given situation, preparatory work had to be made in the other areas of method study application, commencing with the analysis of the product and subsequently proceeding to the consideration of the operations, the layout of the floor space, and the materials handling, in order to determine standards for the basis of the control. It was found as a result of experience gained in such investigations, that studies concerned with control procedures and systems were more time-consuming and costly, if done correctly, than those in the other areas of methods analysis. It was also appreciated that an adequate control system could not be developed until this essential information had been obtained.

The consideration of these other areas of method study application will provide the basis by which an evaluation of the present system may be made, and the proposed procedures developed. However, as in all the other areas of methods analysis, the terms of reference given to the investigator may possibly preclude the consideration of certain of these aspects, but unlike the other types of method study, the results obtained from control studies will be seriously affected if all the essential aspects of the situation are not considered.

The consideration of what is the correct system to install in a given situation is dependent on a large number of factors. Unfortunately it has been too often associated with the introduction of some form of paper control procedure, which has been developed and installed without prior method study of the conditions in which it was to be operated. In situations of this kind, such a procedure was found more likely to aggravate an already difficult situation than contribute to the alleviation of the symptoms. Management also frequently discovered that their energies were dissipated in justifying a system whose contribution to actual control was questionable.

Method study having indicated the outline of the proposed control system, the number of form and records contained in it should be kept to a minimum, and the clerical work associated with them should be centralized as far as possible. The foreman should be left with a reasonable degree of flexibility with regard to methods that he can employ within the permissible limits allowed by planning, for this purpose alternative operations should be indicated in the job specifications, where it is considered convenient. Finally the proposed system must provide management with returns at selected intervals of time, in order for them to be able to exercise the necessary control should there be a deviation from standard.

It is essential, once a control system has been installed, to see that it is in fact exercising the degree of control that is required, as the only result that may have been obtained is the employment of extra clerical staff. It should be realized in connection with this that it does not necessarily follow that because a paper-work system has been installed a degree of control has been obtained.

Methods naturally have to be maintained for the reasons that make this an important part of the method study procedure. An appropriate control system can contribute to this maintenance, but it is also true that without this element of control, the results of a method study will almost certainly be denied the opportunity of maintenance.

After the objectives of a control system have been defined, the various individuals and departments in the organization who are involved in the present system are listed. In doing this care must be exercised to see that everyone is in fact included, as at this stage it is often possible to omit some person who is subsequently found to play an important part in the system and whose influence on its operation may be considerable.

When this has been done the contribution of each of these individuals to the present system is recorded, and this is sometimes presented in the form of a network pattern so that the sequential relationship of these individuals' contributions may be indicated. This is often made to indicate, as well as who they contact, by what means this is done, whether by verbal instructions, telephone, communication forms, or paper-work, how this is done in relation to time, and where and by whom the contact is initiated.

When this information has been obtained, it is presented in the form of the special type of flow diagram illustrated in Chapter 4 (Fig. 41) which shows the movement of the control materials, whether they are paper-work or verbal instructions, between the various departments and persons associated with the system. Across the top of this type of flow diagram from left to right the different departments and individuals in the system are indicated, and the surface area of the chart is then divided by vertical lines into areas associated with these locations. Down the left-hand side of this chart a suitable scale is sometimes constructed to indicate the change in the system in relation to time when this is considered necessary. Colour may also be used where appropriate, to indicate the different kinds of clerical operation or methods of communication.

Where it is necessary to show a part of a system in relation to a series of procedure records, in order to indicate the movement of the data from one form to another throughout the system, the forms themselves become the stations of the flow diagram and the flow of data or entries from one piece of paper-work to another is indicated by the simple means of pasting the forms on a large piece of paper and constructing a flow diagram with flow process chart symbols and specimen entries to indicate the movement of information from form to form.

The variations in the manner of presenting this type of chart are often considerable, and for those who wish to proceed to a more detailed understanding of this kind of procedure presentation, various standard literature is available for this purpose.

When a communication flow diagram has been constructed, because the information has been presented in this manner, some of the defects of the system under review may appear obvious, but it is invariably appreciated that without a recording of this kind these obvious defects would almost certainly not have been quite so apparent.

The fixed and variable aspects of the procedure are next determined. Most control systems which are the subject of method study investigations are usually found to contain elements that are constant in duration and method, although there may be some elements that have variable aspects for some reason or another. It is particularly important to do this so that the investigator can be assured that the correct details of the present method have been obtained.

The flow diagram is checked to see that the method presented is a true picture of each part of the system, and whether the features of the present situation are given in sufficient detail.

As an aid to the more detailed presentation and examination of a procedure another type of presentation may be used, called a "yes–no" flow diagram. This type of diagram follows the control activity from its commencement to its end, indicating all the possibilities and alternative aspects of the procedure that may occur so that a better appreciation of the present procedural situation is obtained. The presentation of a system in this form enables the procedure to be reduced to the most important basic decisions and activities which are inherent in such a system, and contributes to the subsequent critical examination of the situation.

A simple example of such a flow diagram is shown in Fig. 76. The action or operation is distinguished from the question which demands a decision by the use of different symbols. Actions or operations are represented by a rectangular shape, a question with two possible answers by a diamond

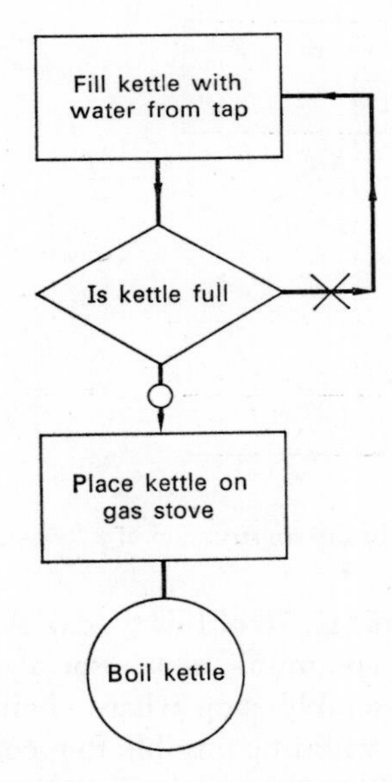

FIG. 76. Simple example of a "yes–no" flow diagram.

shape, and a state by a circular symbol (Fig. 77). Where the operator of a procedure has to choose between more than two possibilities, it is found easier to come to a decision if these are considered in pairs until they are eliminated one by one.

In the course of the construction of this type of flow diagram a clearness of thought must be exercised so that the system may be reduced to the three kinds of element associated with such a recording, namely "state", "action", and "question". In order to ensure that the description of each of these elements shall be as concise as possible the use of the minimum number of words is necessary.

When constructing this diagram care must also be taken to see that no fact is forgotten which might invalidate the whole thought and decision sequence.

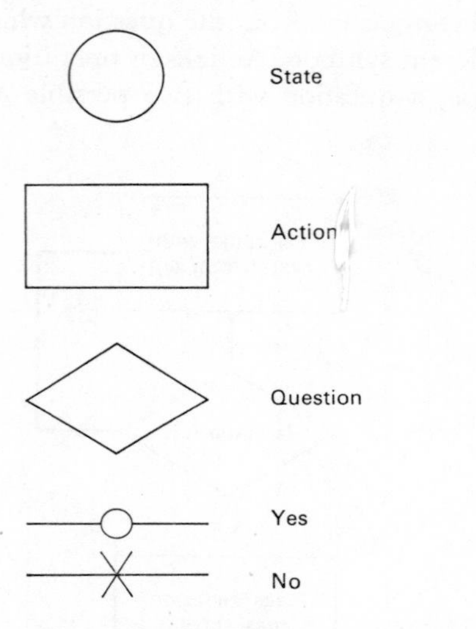

FIG. 77. Symbols used in the construction of a "yes–no" flow diagram.

An example is given in Fig. 78 of this type of flow diagram constructed for a present method of communication associated with the control procedure of a furniture assembly shop where chairs are produced. It can be seen from this that it would be possible to record this procedure in the form of an operation or flow process chart, but remembering the purpose of the present recording it is more convenient to present the information in the manner indicated.

The analysis of this type of diagram will be made by using the procedure of critical examination in the same manner as for the other methods of recording and the faults in the system determined as a result.

These faults should be examined to determine whether they are of a standard kind, for if they are, their rectification may be possible by recourse to the use of standard solutions, which have been found appropriate for the solution of such control problems.

The study of control procedures and systems can be reduced to the collection and recording of the details of the communication pattern and the number of ways that each element can be performed, followed by an

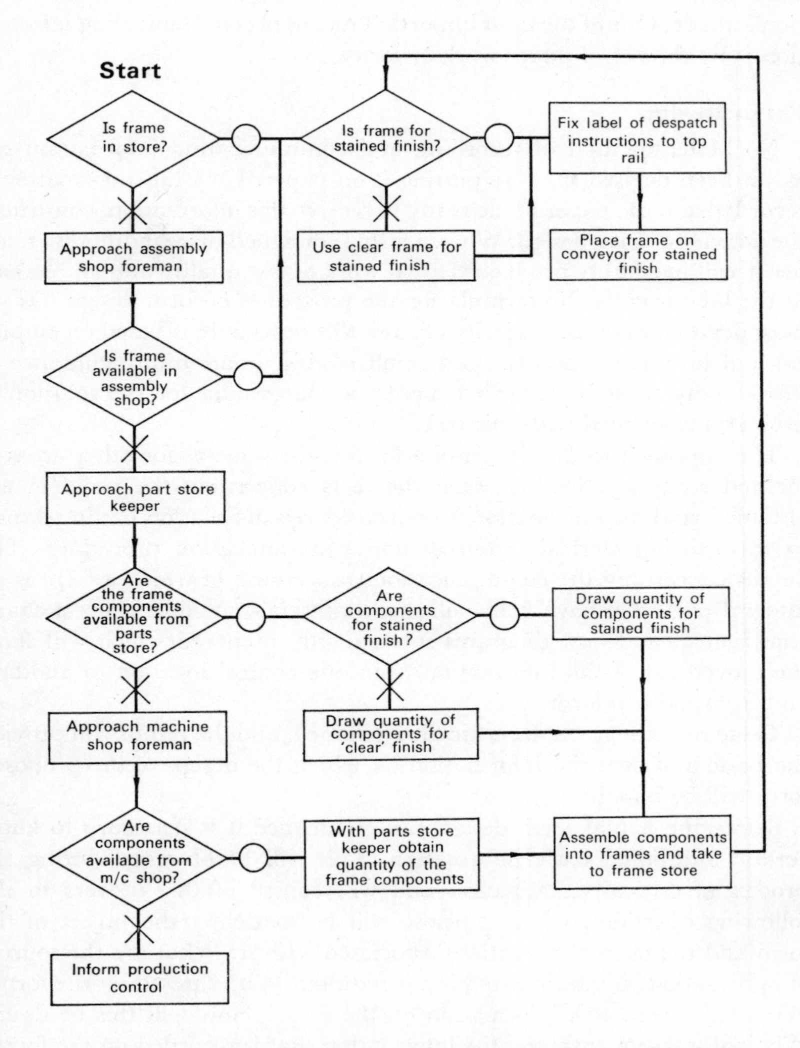

Fig. 78. "Yes–no" flow diagram for control procedure in assembly shop.

examination of the actual purpose and means by which the communication is made. One of the most important means of communicating information is by the use of paper-work or forms.

Form Design

No better method of recording and communicating information has as yet been devised than by putting it on paper. How this information is recorded and the paper made ready to receive this information, constitutes the activity of form design. When a form is designed in an indifferent manner it will inevitably produce clerical work of low quality and an increase in the labour costs. No formula for the procedure of form design has yet been devised, as in the majority of cases this procedure is based on empirical and intuitive concepts. As a result of this situation any guidance in this activity must be regarded merely as suggestions for the solution of problems associated with this task.

The approach to the design of a form is the same as for other areas of method study application. First the facts concerning the problem are obtained, and the information is not considered in isolation but in relation to the existing clerical resources and communication procedure. The details concerning the communications procedure, of which a form is an integral part, will have been collected, material-type flow process charts constructed, and flow diagrams subsequently prepared which will show the movement of the information from one control location to another, and from form to form.

These recordings will be critically examined, and the results will provide the basic and essential information on which the design of the proposed form will be based.

Before the actual form design can commence it is necessary to know certain additional basic information. This will be obtained during the process of critical examination and will consist of the answers to the following questions, whose purpose will be to define the object of the form and the clerical operations associated with it: What are the sources of information? What information is required to be entered on the form? Who will record this information on the form? How will this be done? Who will subsequently use the information that is recorded on the form? In connection with what activity will this recording be done? How will the entries on the form be made? What relationship exists between the proposed form and others in use? What are the working conditions of those who will be likely to use the form?

After the answers to the above questions have been obtained the design of the form can be commenced relative to two considerations, firstly the use of the form, and secondly its production.

At the initial stages of the method study it will have been determined whether a form is really necessary, and what information is to be entered on it; whether this information is of sufficient importance to justify a form, and whether an existing one can supply the same information or achieve the same purpose. It is frequently possible for the number of forms to be reduced to a minimum by being combined with others or relating them to other forms or documents.

The size and completion of the entry spaces are next considered as these will influence the size of the proposed form and its use. How entries are to be made on the proposed form is an important basis of the form design. The entry spaces should be designed and arranged to accommodate a number of considerations. They may be arranged so that they can conform to another form, from which the information will be obtained in a similar manner and sequence. But whatever the circumstances may be, the most natural order for making entries should be considered, as the possibility of grouping related entries may be obtained. Where the information falls into well-defined categories by subject or name, the form may be divided into its areas of use. If this is possible certain of the information may be located in a prominent position on the form. The clerical operations associated with the making of the entries may be simplified by grouping the entry spaces which have a common affinity, or by using similar colour schemes, or by standardizing the form size to economize on the use of equipment, and by selecting the correct paper and materials to allow automatic copying to be used instead of rewriting. Numerous methods of this kind can be used to facilitate the clerical operations and the handling associated with these activities.

A form may be made more comprehensible and easier to use by avoiding a complicated appearance, with too much print and ruling. Simplification will reduce the possibility of errors and the necessity for excessive checking. Various methods can be used in the design to minimize the possibility of fatigue, by employing different ways of segregating the sections of the form into related groups, whether they are groups of columns or horizontal sections. The consideration of the method to be employed in copying the entries can often reduce the incidence of errors. If an attractive form design is obtained this will have an undoubted influence on the quality of the entries made by its users.

The size of the form will be influenced by the availability of the paper sizes and their cost, the filing procedures that it is proposed to operate, and the machine carriages that are used for making the entries, and other considerations of a similar nature. The details of the national standard paper sizes should be obtained, and it should be seen that any proposed form conforms to these sizes, considering at the same time the trimming size the printer is expected to conform to in relation to the paper size selected. If there is a nationally recommended size and layout for a similar type of form such as for commercial envelopes, for instance, this should be given careful thought before any decision is made regarding the size to be used. Standardization of form sizes should never be suggested for its own sake, but the advantages to be obtained from the standardization of a particular form should be appreciated as this may be advantageous for reasons associated with the use of certain kinds of folders, binders, filing cabinets, carbons, or envelope sizes. The variety of form sizes should always be restricted in any given department whenever possible.

Precise captions should be incorporated in the design, and explanations and instructions can be introduced where they are considered necessary. The inclusion of an exact title and an individual reference is necessary only when it will be an aid to the identification of areas of the form. Time spent in considering the means by which a form may be identified can assist the sorting, selecting, arranging, and filing of the form, and as these tasks can often be a lengthy process every effort should be made to reduce this. Often the title and reference can also be made to indicate the use and movement of a form.

The proposed design of the form should also be considered in relation to the use of the form, as the objective of good form design is to see that the design is suitable for the purpose for which it is intended, and that it achieves this purpose with a maximum economy of effort and time.

When considering the design of the form in relation to its production, the clerical costs of using it are the criteria of expense, and not the cost of its production. However, consideration of those factors that will simplify and reduce the production costs of the form should not be overlooked. The draft of the proposed form design should give a visual impression of the completed form, and should consist of a full-size drawing. One style of lettering should be used throughout, the type size being indicated on this draft and not by printers' points. If printing and perforating is to be included in the form, the exact measurements for all punched holes should be specified in the margins of the draft, and their precise position indicated on the drawing. Perforations should be similarly positioned.

It is frequently useful to prepare a form-design data sheet or check list for the analysis of the various aspects of the design to be considered, so that none of these will be overlooked. When every aspect of the design has been considered, and the proposals have been developed into a draft layout, this has to be examined to determine whether it serves the purpose, is complete, whether it calls for all the information needed, or whether it calls for information that is not required. Whether the proposed design indicates to the user what is required, and whether the information can be readily used.

The methods for the production of forms are so easily available in an organization that their indiscriminate and uncritical production can quite easily create numerous problems. As a form is often introduced as the result of an idea by management, its cancellation is usually resisted strongly. In order to eliminate the possibility of situations of this kind, procedures, their forms and number, should be specified and no departure should be allowed from these unless for adequate reasons, and then only as an official amendment, the desirability of which should always be checked by method study. If this procedure is not adhered to, personnel will learn to disregard the official paper-work, and evolve unofficial methods of their own for communicating between one another. These may consist of nothing more than information scribbled on the page of a notebook and passed to a recipient, but at the same time the official form will continue to be filled in by the various clerical staff, with information that will have none other than a historical importance.

The cost of producing each proposed form should be carefully compared with the cost of its use, as the purchase of stationery and special equipment may be out of all proportion to the cost of using the form, and the purpose it sets out to achieve. For this reason the method of reproducing a proposed form should be considered carefully, as it is possible that present resources of the organization can be used instead of an outside printer, particularly if the quantities required are small. The cost of the form and the speed with which it can be supplied are important considerations.

The factors that will affect the production of a form will be numerous, quite apart from the consideration of cost. For instance the quantity to be printed will influence the method by which it is printed, and the size of the paper and its quantity will have a considerable bearing on how the form is produced and used, and how much management will have to pay for it. The other factors such as the complexity of the design, the accuracy of registration demanded in the printing, its general appearance and make up, will all have an influence on the method of production and the subsequent cost.

Colour may be used in the design of the form, but care should be exercised to see that the colours incorporated in a design are not confused with similar colours associated with other forms at present in use. A combination of coloured papers and inks may make a form difficult to read, and if it is to be subsequently reproduced photographically, sufficient contrast between the two should be obtained. The form should, whenever possible, be printed throughout in one colour, unless there is a definite reason for using two or more colours, but it should be realized that if this is done it will increase the printing costs. Procedural studies of forms that are part of a system of paper-work often indicate that copies of an existing form can be eliminated. As forms are a vital part of a system and too much form-filling can waste time and money, it is necessary to review and question their purpose as for any other operation.

Selected References and Suggestions for Further Reading

Organization and Methods, The record of papers read at a conference of the British Productivity Council, London, 1957.

The Techniques of Organization and Methods, Her Majesty's Stationery Office, London.

The Practice of Organization and Methods, Her Majesty's Stationery Office, London.

Churchman, C. W., Ackoff, R. L. and Arnoff, E. L., *Introduction to Operations Research*, John Wiley, London and New York, chapter 4, Analysis of the Organization.

Hall, A. D., *A Methodology for Systems Engineering*, D. Van Nostrand.

Milward, G. E., *Organization and Methods*, Macmillan, London and New York.

Milward, G. E., *Launching and Managing Organization and Methods*, Macmillan, London and New York.

White, K. K., *Understanding the Company Organization*, American Management Association, New York; Bailey Bros and Swinfen, London.

Rowbottom, R. W. and Greenwald, H. A., *Understanding Management*, Whitworth Press, Manchester, 1962, chapter 3, Key to Organization Charts.

Scheele, E. D., *Principles and Design of Production Control Systems*, Prentice-Hall.

Procedures

How to Design a Procedure, Office Management Association, London, 1955.

Procedure Records, Her Majesty's Stationery Office, 1959.

Organization Charts and Lists of Duties, Her Majesty's Stationery Office, 1959.

Carter, L. R., Wells, J., Gupta, T. C. and Syme, A. W., *Processing New Library Books, an Investigation into Procedure*, Industrial Operation Unit, Department of Scientific and Industrial Research, London, 1962.

May, D. H. and Morgan, J. A., *Inventory Control of Type Face Manufacture*, Industrial Operation Unit, Department of Scientific and Industrial Research, London, 1962.

WESTON, M. A. and WHITE, E. M., *Stock Control—A demonstration in the cutlery industry*, Industrial Operation Unit, Department of Scientific and Industrial Research, London, 1962.

LOVIS, F. B., *Computers—Contemporary School Mathematics Second Series*, Edward Arnold, London, chapter 3, Flow Diagrams.

SPLAINE, M., A "Yes–No" Technique for Work Study Practitioners, *Work Study and Management*, vol. 7, No. 12, December 1963, pp. 551–4.

RUDOLPH, H. H., Flow Charting—a system and control technique, *Management Services*, September–October 1966, vol. 3, No. 5, pp. 24–30 (U.S.A.).

Form Design

The Design of Forms, compiled by the Organization and Methods Division of Her Majesty's Treasury, Her Majesty's Stationery Office, London, 1962.

Form Design, Office Management Association, London, 1955.

KNOX, F. M., *Design and Control of Business Forms*, McGraw-Hill, London and New York.

BARNARD, A., A new look at Forms Control, *Systems and Procedures Journal*, vol. 16, Part 3, May–June 1965, pp. 8–16.

Office Methods

BANE, W., *Production Control: The Industrial Dynamics Approach*, Paper No. 10, Science in General Management (SIGMA), London.

LEFFINGWELL, W. H. and ROBINSON, E. M., *Textbook of Office Management*, McGraw-Hill, London and New York.

Manual of Practical Office Short Cuts, National Office Management Association, U.S.A., McGraw-Hill, London and New York.

ODELL, M. K., *Records Management and Filing Operations*, McGraw-Hill, London and New York.

GILMOUR-BROWN, A. and EVANS, R., *Production Planning and Control in the Furniture Industry*, F.D.C. Method Study Report No. 3, Furniture Development Council, Stevenage, Hertfordshire, England.